ARABIAN NATURAL HISTORY

"There is not an animal (that lives) on the earth,
Nor a being that flies on its wings, but (forms part of)
communities like you."

HOLY QURAN – SURA 6 AIYA 38
Translation by Abdullah Yusuf Ali

Arabian Natural History

with

Precious Gold

in Saudi Arabia

Heather Colyer Ross

DEDICATED TO COURTENAY

AND

A TRIBUTE TO

THOSE SPECIAL ANIMALS WE HAVE KNOWN:

GOLD   MAMAPUSS

SAMANTHA   HARVEY

AND MANY OTHERS

Natural History of Arabia
First published in 1990 by
Arabesque Commercial SA
PO Box 9
Clarens-Montreux
Switzerland

© 1990 Heather Colyer Ross

ISBN 2 88373 003 2

Typesetting in Horley Old Style
and production by DP Press, Sevenoaks, England
Printed in the Netherlands by Royal Smeets Offset BV, Weert

Photography Heather Colyer Ross except:
Joyce and George Zaple, p 61, Chipolatta with Silver
Barry W. Ross, p 86, White camel
Jill Silsby, p 126, Desert Dog's nest
Design Neil Adams in collaboration with Arabesque Commercial SA
Illustrations Sharlene McLearon
Cover illustration Sally Michel

Contents

Foreword

"It's a book which involves a talking rabbit!" she said on the telephone.

"A talking rabbit?" I asked incredulously. I hoped I did not sound petulant. "Look lady, I'm a zoologist . . . at least I profess to be. I don't do fantasy, although sometimes I've been accused of it. I think maybe you've got me mixed up with someone else. I'm not into talking rabbits – or talking animals for that matter; mynah birds, maybe." Then with the tone of one about to hang up the telephone I said, "But really it's been nice speaking with you. I've heard a lot about your books."

"Dr. Lawrence," she quickly interrupted, "this book is not *about* talking rabbits. It's a children's natural history book and the talking rabbit is a 'teaching device'."

"Oh", I said, a bit curious but not wishing to show my ignorance of exactly what a 'teaching device' might be in this case. Also I began to feel myself being slowly sucked in.

"It's a book written for children and the rabbit asks questions which the main character answers in story-telling fashion," she added.

"Well, don't get me wrong. I like children. I even have a few of my own. In fact, I have grandkids. And I *can talk* to them. In fact, I think I can *communicate* with kids fairly successfully. Well, I can communicate with *some* kids." I wondered if I was being just a bit too pedantic with that word 'communicate'?

Then she seemed to move in for the kill: "I'll bring the manuscript by the zoo for you to look at. I do need your help in checking the natural history facts for accuracy. I saw you on a television interview and you said it is essential for the public to have proper information about nature, the true facts! Well, that's why I need your help. And by the way, I have a thick skin, like those elephants in your zoo, and if you don't like what you read, then say so, 'MAFI MUSHKILA'."*

"OK," I surrendered. "Bring it by. I'll be glad to help you. And when you do, would you consider bringing me one of those fabulous books which you've written that I've heard so

much about. Maybe the one on Arabian costumes or Bedouin jewellery?"

I thought to myself I might as well get *something* out of this talking rabbit deal. Actually, I was familiar with Heather Ross's work. Her books showed excellent technical scholarship and were aesthetically quite beautiful. But those were *adult* books. A talking rabbit . . .?

Well, Heather Colyer Ross did bring her manuscript to the zoo. Then followed several months of question and answer sessions, friendly (mostly) repartee and challenging (always) conversation with Heather over her book and frustrating (continuously) chess games with Barry.

Her manuscript was good. It was stimulating, well researched, factual and informative. It showed the same careful scholarly research and attention to details as demonstrated by her three published books on ethnic Bedouin jewellery and costumes. But those books were for adults; this talking rabbit book was written for children. In my opinion, however, it is also an ideal book for adults to read to children.

The talking rabbit? Yes, one of the main characters is a talking rabbit. And, after finishing the manuscript, even I began to believe that a talking rabbit named 'Gold' may actually exist. You sort of accept him after a few chapters.

So why am I writing this foreword? Well, because *Precious Gold* [*Arabian Animal Stories?*] is an excellent book about animals for young people. It is the only such book that I know of on Arabian natural history for children. I hope that some day it will be translated into Arabic for youngsters as it is a credit to a remarkable fauna of a remarkable land.

Precious Gold is a survey of the conspicuous aspects of the natural history of the Arabian peninsula. Lower animals are discussed from marine invertebrates through spiders, scorpions and insects on up through fishes and amphibians. Yes, there is a good representative fauna of fresh water life in the Arabian Peninsula – aquatic insects, fishes, frogs, and toads, as well as the fantastic marine creatures of the coral reefs and other habitats in the Red Sea and Arabian Gulf.

The higher vertebrates, reptiles, birds and mammals are covered in some detail. Entire chapters are devoted to major animals, both wild and domesticated species.

This volume is a good sourcebook and introduction for

---

*"MAFI MUSHKILA" is the ubiquituous Arabic phrase which translates as "no problem." It is used whether there is a problem or not; possibly the former more often than the latter.

young people to the ecology (relationships between animals and their environment) and zoogeography (distribution of animal life) of the Arabian Peninsula.

There is another feature of paramount importance in the book, vital for young readers with developing minds. In today's world of environmental destruction and extinction of endangered species the conservation ethic must be communicated. If successful, then the children of today, who will be the leaders of tomorrow, will better understand the issues of natural resource conservation and development, and be in a better position to make intelligent choices between the two. Mrs. Ross has skillfully threaded this element of wildlife conservation as a recurring theme throughout her story. Unfortunately, the future survival of some of the animal species described in this book is in question today.

Enlightened conservation efforts, however, are being vigorously carried out by the following organizations in the Arabian Peninsula: the National Commission for Wildlife Conservation and Development in Saudi Arabia; the Government's Department for Conservation of the Environment, Sultanate of Oman; and the Royal Society for the Conservation of Nature in Jordan. Problems of wildlife conservation are being actively addressed and solutions are already in evidence in many areas.

One outstanding example is the successful reintroduction of the Arabian Oryx to its former wild habitat in all three of the above countries where the Oryx has been extinct in the wild since 1972. This accomplishment represents a living success story of conservation activities in the peninsula.

To the above efforts add the investment and work of the Municipality of Riyadh in building a modern new Zoological Garden, described by Mrs. Ross in her chapter on the endangered desert sand cat. I take personal pride in the captive propagation program developed for this small feline at the Municipality's Riyadh Zoological Gardens. It is another step towards conservation success in the Arabian peninsula.

It is a shame that 'Gold', the talking rabbit, was unable to venture out into the desert and speak with his more venerable wild hare brethren who might have related stories to him of the animals of the desert in earlier times. Perhaps such stories will be a fitting sequel to this volume on Precious Gold's introduction to Arabian natural history. Let's hope so. The children of Arabia will be the beneficiaries of this knowledge.

A suggestion to parents who read to their children: *Precious Gold* is an excellent volume for nightly reading sessions. I tested the manuscript with my own grandchildren and the results were excellent. Except for one night, however, when the kids had all gone to sleep while I was reading to them. I found that I could not put the manuscript away until I finished the chapter myself!

Precious Gold is a natural history treasury to be shared with young people everywhere and in particular with children living in Arabia.

I highly recommend it.

Lawrence Curtis
Director
Riyadh Zoological Gardens
Municipality of Riyadh
Kingdom of Saudi Arabia

Acknowledgements

I am grateful to the following people for their support and assistance. They generously gave me their time and valuable expertise. Joyce Adams, Robert Arndt, *(Editor, Aramco World Magazine)*, Marianne Alireza, Joan Baranski, Malin Basil, Gunnar Bemert, Geraldine Cumberland, Philip Dew, Piera Ferrari, John and Patricia Gasparetti, Pat Gibson, Barbara Goldsmith, Gernot Halfar, Hilary Pahud–Harris, Valerie Hodges, Guy and Bernice Jaumotte, Juanita Kronley, Pat Abercrombie-Little, Jonathan McCalmont, Sharlene McLearon, Thomas Matthew, Fran Meade, Mary Newell, Dr. Rupert F.G. Ormond, Doreen Sharabati, Anne Sheppard, Jill Silsby, Natalie Skeriatine, Elisabeth Svendsen, M.B.E., *(The International Donkey Protection Trust, Devon, England)*, Abdul Hajid Sharif, Andrea Tegstam, Laura Tegstam, Nigel Thomas, Bishop Ambrose Weeks, Peter Whitehead, *(Al Faisal Falcon Centre, Alsoodah, Asir, Saudi Arabia)*, Robyn Williamson, Betty Lipscombe-Vincett, Joyce and George Zaple.

And, I am especially indebted to the following scientists for their good-natured advice and guidance. Realizing the importance of their work, I appreciate that they took the time to read my chapters and give me instruction. Without them, I could not have achieved my goal.

Dr. E. Nicholas Arnold,
Herpetologist, Department of Zoology, British Museum (Natural History), London, England.

Dr. Lawrence Curtis,
Director, Riyadh Zoological Gardens, Owners and Operators: Municipality of Riyadh, Management Contractor: Zied Al Hussein Est.

Mlle. Frances Delany,
Geologist, 1837 Chateau-D'Oex, Switzerland.

Dr. Betsy De Marino,
Unionville Small Animal Associates, Unionville, Pennsylvania, USA.

Dr. Claudia Feh,
Station Biologique, Tour Du Valat, Le Sambuc, Arles, France.

Professor Dr. Ulrich Freudiger,
Director, Klinik für kleine Haustiere, Berne University, Switzerland.

Dr. John Hanks,
Director, Africa Programme, WWF (World Wide Fund for Nature), Gland, Switzerland.

Dr. Andrew J. Higgins,
Director, Animal Health Trust, Newmarket, Suffolk, England.

Professor Dr. Hans Kummer,
Ethology and Wildlife Research, Institute of Zoology, University of Zurich, Zurich, Switzerland.

Dr. Torben B. Larsen,
Entomologist, 29C Snoghoj Alle, 2770 Kastrup, Denmark.

Dr. Angela C. Milner,
Head of Fossil Amphibians, Reptiles and Bird Section, British Museum (Natural History) London, England.

Mr. Anthony R. Pittaway,
Entomologist, CAB International, (Commonwealth Agricultural Bureau), Wallingford, Oxon, England.

Dr. Andrew R.G. Price,
Marine Ecologist, IUCN (The International Union for Conservation of Nature), Tropical Marine Laboratories and Department of Biology, University of York, England.

Dr. Charles Sheppard,
Marine Ecologist, SSOC for MEPA (Meteorological and Environmental Protection Administration), Jiddah, Saudi Arabia.

Dr. Dennis C. Turner,
Head of Pet Ethology Group, Institute of Zoology, University of Zurich, Zurich, Switzerland.

Dr. Ross J.L. Williamson,
International Equine Veterinary Consultant, Newmarket, Suffolk, England.

Also, I would like to acknowledge my especial gratitude to Dr. Fouad Al Farsy, Deputy Minister of Information, Riyadh, Saudi Arabia, for his continued encouragement and direction; to my husband and best friend, Barry, for helping me with this project; and to our son, Courtenay, whose studies in biology enabled him to advise me, and whose dream of his pet rabbit, Gold, talking, resulted in this book.

Thank you.

Heather Colyer Ross

Author's Note

Originally, I intended to write a book only about the animals that shared our life in Arabia. I did not imagine that it would become my largest project and take twelve years to complete. Years ago, when the first manuscript was almost finished, my son, Courtenay, dreamt that his pet rabbit, Gold, could talk, and this was the first addition to the text. As I developed the idea, and researched more, I became deeply fascinated with the Arabian Animal World and conservation. The manuscript grew and grew, and so did the list of people that I needed to consult to broaden my knowledge. I was often discouraged and there were times that I thought I would never see the book in print. Encouragement from many wonderful people led me to the final stages. At this difficult point, I was fortunate to meet Dr. Lawrence Curtis, the Riyadh Zoo Director. He is one of those special people who combines his scientific knowledge with a love for animals and an awareness of their thoughts and feelings. He has taught me so much.

I hope that many young people, and other animal lovers, will enjoy this book.

Best Wishes,

Heather Colyer Ross

1989

Introduction

It was a beautiful day with a sky of clear cloudless blue. Relaxing alone by the swimming pool, I pondered what a wonderful adventure it was to live in the middle of Arabia. The peace I enjoyed was especially rare since our pet rabbit, Gold, had learnt to talk. Yet, I mused, our villa had always been full of animals and people, and there was surprisingly little change, really. It was certainly an astonishing thing to happen, as you might imagine, but our lives had settled down and eventually gone on as usual – well, almost . . .

I clearly remember the day that it happened. Gold first spoke to our son (an only child called Christopher) and I had thought it just one of his pranks. You see, Christopher could best be described as 'busy', and his mischievous deeds sometimes caused havoc. We should not have been surprised by his adventurous character, because we, (John and Susan Blake) are industrious by nature, too, and marvellous experiences have often resulted from our own activities.

We had been living in Riyadh, (pronounced Ree-ard) the capital city of Saudi Arabia, for 10 years when Gold first talked. Up until then, life had been exciting but normal. After it happened, our 'ordinary' days had a habit of turning into a whirlwind of activity.

It had not been at all like that when we first arrived. Riyadh had seemed quiet and slow then, as if it were dozing in the hot desert sun. In those days, before modernization, the dusty roads and buildings were mostly beige-coloured and baked dry – and the sky was almost always blue. At night it was a very deep rich blue, and the moon and stars were brilliant and seemed brighter than I had seen anywhere else in the world. Nights were still and cool, seeming to be especially so when we visited a date palm grove where the orderly rows of trees were tall, straight and disciplined, looking like an army waiting to march.

Our lifestyle might have been less hectic had we not loved animals so much. Animals have been involved in almost every exciting thing that has happened to us. Our pets could easily fill a 48-hour day, should there ever be such a thing, but, not one of us would have it any other way.

All the animals we have had have been interesting, and many have been lovable; but, Gold, our talking rabbit, has been the most wonderful little creature. Surprisingly, his nature remains unaffected and he seems quite unaware of having almost turned our lives upside-down. So many very interesting and clever people visit us now. They come from scientific research establishments and, sometimes, from television and radio stations, and magazines and newspapers. Many are from far away places.

Apparently it is not enough just to see and hear a talking rabbit – he must be recorded and photographed as well. Our inquisitive visitors arrive in groups, carrying lots of equipment, and the clutter and clatter that they make sends our warren rabbits scurrying off down into the burrows until curiosity brings them out again.

Looking back, none of our friends seemed too surprised that it was one of our animals that talked. After seeing that Gold could actually converse, they said it seemed logical that this little wonder belonged to the Blake warren. Hadn't they remarked for years, that our golden cocker spaniel, Samantha, and our Arabian cat, Mamapuss, were as eloquent as some of their children?

Of course, the time was right for something like this to happen. In recent years there had been tremendous progress in people's ability to communicate with animals – especially with chimpanzees and dolphins which are generally considered to be higher life forms than most other creatures. Scientists are no longer ridiculed for revealing their discoveries about animals' thoughts. Yet, it was not so long ago, that they would not dare to speak openly about animals having feelings, for fear of being scorned.

Until Gold spoke to us, it appeared to have been humans who made all the effort to communicate with animals. According to Gold, this might have been expected. He told us that animals can 'talk' to creatures outside their own species but they rarely bother because they have so little in common. Of course, many humans understand their pets perfectly and no language seems necessary. It is just that we would have the chance to enjoy and help our pets more – if we could converse with them; and, because animals are usually so practical, pleasant and well-mannered, humans could learn a lot from them. Dr. Lawrence Curtis, the Director of the Riyadh Zoological Gardens, believes we cannot be certain

that animals have not tried to communicate with humans before this amazing event.

Our son, Christopher, is a serious young man now, but he can still be heard proudly telling people about his friend, Gold, the talking rabbit. The world expected a human to discover what animals think – not someone's 'bunny', (we often use this pet name for a rabbit). No doubt some scientists do feel a trifle humiliated to be beaten by a 'mere rabbit'. At least Gold's achievement will stop people saying, "Silly rabbit!". Hurrah!

Rabbits are generally thought of as a lower form of life than a dog or cat. They have been referred to as cuddly but rather stupid creatures; although, never by people who know them well. Anyone who has had one – and allowed it to live unhutched – knows that this little animal is very clever. Farmers agree that they are smart, but dislike them because they eat crops, and their warrens erode the land. It is just as well that children find rabbits bewitching and most adults see them as charming.

Who can object to a rabbit – besides a farmer? This endearing creature is a vegetarian and has a reputation for being timid and retiring. True, some stories have portrayed it as cheerful, careless, cunning and clever – and always ready to outsmart man and other creatures in order to steal. I can tell you that they are quite like humans – they have individual personalities which can be shaped by their experiences and environment. They are basically very decent and interesting – given a chance. As the great 'Rabbiteer', Ronald Lockley wrote: "Humans are so rabbit!" Mr. Lockley's serious study of the rabbit is a great work, and his comments confirm our family's findings: 'that rabbits are just folk like anybody else'.

Our rabbits have never been restricted to a hutch, or cage for housing small animals. They are free to mingle with humans and other animals within our villa and its surrounding walled garden. The result has surprised many people.

John and I have almost always kept pet hares and rabbits, and our first one came to live with us in Australia, when we were first married. That rabbit's name was Harvey. At the same time, we had a basset hound, Oscar, and an Abyssinian cat called Rama. Harvey, Oscar and Rama were close companions. They had to be respected as individuals because each had the special traits of their own species. They also had totally different personalities. Even so, we expected good behaviour, and we did our best not to spoil them.

In no time at all, Harvey, Oscar and Rama became aware that they belonged to the same family – just as brothers and sisters do. They seemed to develop a genuine consideration for each other – most of the time. They did no harm to each other, but the dog showed no mercy whatsoever to intruders appearing in their territory.

This first animal family caused great interest. People were surprised to see that a hound dog could live with an unhutched rabbit. Hounds are born hunters, and instincts might have made them enemies. Photographers from newspapers and magazines spent hours with them. "Did you see the rabbit and cat asleep together – curled up so tightly that you wondered where cat began and rabbit ended?" And, "Imagine a hound licking a rabbit in friendship," they would say. This cozy relationship had developed so gradually that we were not at all surprised. It had seemed to natural.

Continually, we heard that our trio were 'well-trained'; yet apart from expecting good manners, we have never attempted to teach our animals to do tricks. So, it is clear, anything they have done has been entirely their own invention. Their actions could be considered as having come straight from the heart; or, to be more accurate: from the brain as well as the heart.

Harvey, Oscar and Rama are dead now but they still hold a special place in our hearts. We have had several special rabbits since then, but none have been more loved than Harvey. He was very talented, but he did not talk to us. It just goes to show what a truly precious rabbit Gold is, doesn't it?

1

The Warren

Let me tell you what I have learnt about rabbits, and introduce you to the members of the Blake warren in Arabia, where Gold grew up.

I am sure most people know something about rabbits. They are popular pets and feature in many children's stories and books about pets. Rabbits are supposed to be one of the easiest animals to keep; however, anyone who has tamed one successfully, knows that it must be cared for constantly. It is not good enough to keep a rabbit shut up in a hutch, even with plenty of the best food.

Bunnies do associate gifts of food with kindness, it is true, so it is important to provide fresh water and some new food several times a day – and to see that your pet does not go for long periods without company. Rabbits' tummies have a great capacity, but it is not good to give a mound of food all at once because this can be eaten at one sitting. It is much wiser to feed small amounts several times a day. In a natural environment, herbivorous creatures, such as rabbits and hares, are accustomed to devouring all the food that they find when foraging over an extended period of time. For animals in captivity, it is always best to keep as closely as possible to this natural way. And, to have a truly contented bunny, don't forget the cuddles.

Living in Arabia, where it is very hot most of the time, we cannot store the rabbit's fresh food for long, unless it can be refrigerated. And, we do not like to throw the food away because we cannot always depend on regular supplies. This means that we are constantly seeking suitable food for our rabbits.

Sometimes their greens are given to us and we receive far too much. Occasionally, when produce is scarce, it has been necessary for us to buy expensive 'iceberg' lettuces and the finest carrots. When this happens, we give smaller meals and tell the rabbits that they are to have a 'gourmet' meal. Some of our friends who have come to work in Arabia, and to save money, think that we are mad to keep a warren of ravenous rabbits – especially as we have no intention of eating them.

It is quite a recent idea to keep rabbits as pets. They were originally bred centuries ago for meat and fur.

Records show that the ancient Romans were responsible for introducing rabbits throughout most of their vast Empire. It is almost certain that after the end of the last glaciation, towards the latter part of the great ice age which ended about 10,000 years ago, the wild rabbit was restricted to the Iberian peninsula (Spain and Portugal), and entered recorded history when the Phoenicians reached the Iberian shores about three thousand years ago. It was then that humans began to keep them as a ready source of food.

Rabbits were kept and reared in captivity long before they were domesticated, or bred above ground under the control of humans. Before domestication, a Roman named Varro, who lived about two thousand years ago, had the idea of keeping hares in 'leporaria', or large white-washed, walled gardens containing some shelter. When he added rabbits, the walls had to be made deeper because these animals burrowed, unlike the hares, who made open nests above ground. Strabo and Pliny, of the same era, described the rabbit's establishment on the Balearic Islands: it seems the little beasts multiplied prolifically and the inhabitants had to implore Emperor Augustus to send military aid to relocate the rabbits!

Rabbits were sufficiently important for the Emperor Hadrian (AD 117–138) to have one pictured on some coins of Spain. Of course, leporaria were designed to supply the kitchens, but it appears that rich and influential people were proud to have one of these attractive gardens. Ancient manuscripts show pictures of them, and some were featured in treaties between royalty. Queen Elizabeth I of England had rabbit islands in the sixteenth century. Islands meant that the costly construction of walls was not necessary. King Henry the Fourth of France kept rabbit enclosures at Clichy, now a suburb of Paris.

With domestication of the rabbit, and breeding taking place above ground, selection became possible, which lead to the control of their shape, size and colour. The earliest picture of a white rabbit dates from 1530. By Titian, it is preserved in the Louvre Museum in Paris. In time, some of the white and multi-coloured domesticated rabbits were set free or escaped, and returned to a feral, or wild state.

In recent times, the rabbits' story has been like a rocket to stardom. Their popularity was inevitable, of course. They are gentle and lovable – and the most agreeable of animals. No creature is more attractive and undemanding. Their reputation as a pest did not come about until rabbits posed a serious threat to agriculture, and this was in the countries

where they were introduced by humans. Who can blame the rabbit? We all have to eat.

The Blake family has maintained a warren of approximately 20 rabbits for over 10 years. Replenishment with a new rabbit has been necessary now and again because, sometimes, there were either insufficient males or females. In a happy warren, a healthy buck, or male rabbit takes care of about three does, or females. Occasionally, we have been given a pet rabbit by someone leaving Arabia. Then there were the sad times when a rabbit died of illness or old age – or one was killed by a stray cat that dropped into our garden from the high surrounding wall where it had been spying.

We do give baby rabbits away to friends when one is truly wanted. Children coming to choose one is a happy time. The joy and wonderment on a young face is enough to compensate for parting with the dear little rabbit 'kitten'. 'Leveret' is another name that is sometimes used, but this is correctly the term for a baby hare.

Visitors describe our rabbits as well-trained because they are well-behaved. We prefer our animals to be natural. Only occasionally is a sharp word necessary to remind them of what is forbidden, such as eating the house plants. We sincerely love our animals, and demonstrating this love, and supplying good food is usually sufficient to make them tame.

This method of 'bringing up' is said to 'individualize' an animal. We have found that it does give the pet a chance to show its own special character. Although no restrictions but the most reasonable are ever imposed upon our rabbits, they do have a keen sense of mischief, seeming to enjoy teasing and trespassing. Sometimes a rabbit will appear to be deliberately tantalizing us by defiantly returning to nibble at one particular house plant. It will pause there ready to champ – waiting to catch our attention and receive a rebuke before scampering off. Rabbits love the game of chase and they are very clever. At a word, the little ruffian will hop away. If pursued, it will hop in short spurts, remaining always just out of reach, to return minutes later to repeat the game.

The result of allowing our rabbits to move freely in and out of the house with the minimum of discipline is amazing. These lovable little creatures have shown us the full extent of their intelligence, and each one has developed a distinctly different personality. They constantly surprise our visitors by behaving unlike other rabbits they have known. Unfortunately, rabbits received their reputation for stupidity because it has been the custom to keep them confined in hutches. Keeping them in cages dulls their senses and breaks their spirit. A hutch fetters their intelligence as well as their movements – and it makes them terribly sad.

Science told us years ago that the much-maligned rat is very intelligent and that rats live in societies similar to that of humans. I am quite sure that this is so. Yet, rats are despised as rodents, as we all know. Many people believe that rabbits and hares are also rodents. This is not so. Rabbits and hares are of the mammalian order known as 'Lagomorpha', and they are in quite a different order, or animal group, from rodents. Their separate evolution can be traced back 50 million years.

Lagomorphs have two family groupings: one includes rabbits and hares, and the other, pikas, which are smaller, with no visible tails and short rounded ears. They are the only animals with two pairs of incisors, the teeth normally located in the front part of the upper jaw. These consist of a large, curved pair at the front and a small, reinforcing pair behind. They are very important. They move in a chisel action which is meant to wear down the sharp cutting edge. Should these teeth be broken or damaged and no longer able to meet with the Lagomorph's lower incisors, they will grow outward, like tusks. When this happens the animal becomes unable to eat and it will die from starvation.

Some authors call rabbits a 'burrowing rodent of the hare family', the Leporidae. This description has been especially applied to the common European species, which is usually a brownish-grey colour in the wild. The domesticated variety can be white, black or a mixture of two or three colours.

Rabbits and hares have a short, fluffy tail and divided upper lip, and look very similar to each other. The main differences are: hares are solitary while rabbits are usually gregarious. Also, hares are generally larger than rabbits and usually have much longer ears. Furthermore, hares are born hairy and above ground, whereas rabbits at birth are almost naked, in burrows underground. Domesticated rabbits can survive in the wild but hares usually die in captivity.

Hares and rabbits are quadrupeds with long ears and large, prominent eyes, placed well to the sides of the head. The strong hindlegs are longer than the forelegs and provide the main force in running. The fur is of triple formation: there is a dense, soft, woolly underfur through which longer, stronger, coloured hair projects, and still longer but more sparsely scattered hairs. The coat becomes thicker in winter.

The bucks are slightly larger than the females who have more delicately moulded faces than the males. Under the rabbit's chin, there are glands (larger in the buck) which produce a secretion used for marking territory and each other. The name 'rabbit' derived from French and originally referred to the young. The adults were originally called 'conies', a name that is still sometimes heard today.

Hares (*Lepus*) in general, do not dig or enter burrows, and the females give birth to fully-furred young with eyes opened. The European wild rabbit (*Oryctolagus cuniculus*) lives in communities which are sometimes very large, and they dig and use burrows in the earth. The naked young are born sightless and helpless.

Rabbits are mainly nocturnal, coming out of the burrow in the evening and returning in the early morning. They drink

A snack

Eating 'grins' is a serious matter

Rabby Long Legs sits apart – as usual

An afternoon nap

A peaceful ring of rabbits

Nigel has a habit
of crossing his paws

very little water when greens are abundant, but it should always be available.

Rabbits are sexually mature from 4½ months for small breeds; 5 months for medium breeds; and from 6–9 months for giant breeds.

The doe is an 'induced' ovulator, meaning that she can conceive after being excited by the close proximity of other rabbits.

The gestation period is 31–32 days, and a pregnant doe will make her own nest 3–4 days before giving birth to her young, which should not be touched for 3–4 days. (The doe and her kittens should be left as quiet as possible during this period.) She will suckle her young for about eight weeks, making it possible for her to breed four times per year. The kittens will become independent after 30 days.

When rabbits are left to themselves – usually early in the morning or at night – they re-ingest the soft pellets which have passed through their digestive tract only once. These are rich in vitamins that have been produced within the rabbit's body, and they are necessary for good health. The other pellets are discarded at a special lavatory outside the burrow. A caged rabbit usually selects one corner for its 'toilet'.

The rabbit's natural enemies are weasels, rats, owls, buzzards, ravens, crows, black-backed gulls, certain hawks, badgers, foxes, cats, dogs and people. When disturbed, an alarm signal is made, usually by an old buck thumping the ground with both hindfeet together. All rabbits within earshot respond by dashing towards their burrows. It is not always a leader who gives the alarm, but sometimes another individual high on the social scale, such as a mature female, or matriarch. A terror-stricken rabbit can utter a loud scream, but apart from this, rabbits are normally silent, except for the occasional low growl and grunt; although nursing does have been heard to utter low noises to their young.

When there is rivalry between males over a doe, a fight may ensue after a chase, the two adversaries engaging in a furious joust, leaping high into the air against each other. It is interesting that only a few males gain dominion over a warren and succeed in mating with the females.

There are no wild rabbits native to Arabia, but there is an indigenous hare. It is a small herbivorous mammal, about the size of the European rabbit, and has extremely large ears which can lie flat and act as a protection against the heat. As well as giving shade, the ears radiate the sun away from the body. There are now many rabbits living in Arabia, having been imported. People often call both hares and rabbits 'rabbits', and, in Arabia, they are both called ARNAB in Arabic. Correctly, a hare is ARNAB BURRI.

We have always kept hares and rabbits together in our warren, and although both species live quite happily side by side, we have been told that they do not usually live on friendly terms, and cannot breed successfully together. Science tells us that animals of a different genus do not interbreed, and those of a different species will not normally do so. I am not so sure. In any case, in our warren we refer to them all as rabbits or lagomorphs.

The warren's inhabitants have been all sorts of colours. In the wild, especially out in the arid desert, an Arabian hare's colour usually matches the terrain. This gives them camouflage and helps them hide from predators. We are told that the nomadic people of Arabia like to see a hare, and when a huntsman spies one dashing away, he says: "Thy appearance is a good omen." Probably he says this because the presence of a hare is an indication that there is sufficient vegetation to support herbivores which are food for the carnivores. Plentiful animals means that he can provide for his family.

It is a hard life for a hare in Central Arabia because most of the land is barren. Yet hares do survive and they exist in Arabia's three great sandy deserts too: the Nafud in the north; the Dhana near the centre; and the Rub al Khali in the south. In the waterless places the hare can quench its thirst at dawn, on the dew that collects during the night on the sparse vegetation. And, a certain amount of liquid is obtained from the plant itself, especially at night when the moisture content is higher. It is believed by some that certain desert creatures may be able to manufacture water within their bodies from its component parts, such as forms of hydrogen and oxygen. It is amazing if it is true.

It is recorded that, in certain places in Arabia (known as HAUTAS) no animals were allowed to be killed and no trees cut. Arabian folk tales tell of hunted hares dashing to the safety of HAUTAS. So, you see, no one in traditional Arabia thought lagomorphs were stupid.

Lagomorphs are a source of constant delight in our garden and in our house. We have become accustomed to them hopping in and out of the villa. They do like their own 'rabbitry' or domain outside in the garden, but they have various reasons for wanting to enter the house. Food is their first priority because a rabbit needs a great deal of food to be content, so you can expect to see one or two heading for the kitchen. Some may be there when we first get out of bed in the morning – looking imploringly from the refrigerator to Askalu. When Askalu first came to work for us, she giggled most of the day because of the rabbits. She likes animals but she had never seen them in her homeland, Ethiopia, behaving the way they do in our villa.

Rabbits are very curious, so it is quite normal for them to investigate the house. They sometimes climb the stairs and take a good look around the bedrooms and bathrooms. A rabbit will always check every inch of one area thoroughly before moving on to another. They are extremely cautious animals, and their natural instinct, when startled, is to retreat quickly. It is astonishing to see how exactly a rabbit will retrace his path if it has been in a new area of exploration. I have learned a much-needed lesson from this. Before knowing rabbits, my hopeful 'short-cuts' on expeditions, usually turned out to be dismally unsuccessful and a complete waste of

precious time. How much wiser (and for the rabbit: safer) it is to take a known path, especially if time is scarce.

During the day, there are usually one or two rabbits indoors. Together or singly, they may be found flat on a cool marble floor – or, under furniture, in a dim, carpeted spot where a slight breeze passes. Rabbits like comfort, rabbits do!

Our lagomorphs are very tame and show no fear because we do not permit them to be teased, and we have never intentionally hurt them. They have regular, nutritious meals and, as with all animals, they quickly learn to accept whoever feeds them.

The question we are asked most is: "Where did you get your rabbits?" Some people already know that rabbits are not indigenous to the Arabian Peninsula, but they do not know that rabbits can be bought in a special part of the SOUQ or market place. Various animals are sold there as potential food, and rabbits can be found cheek-to-beak with birds. Arab visitors to our home assume that we are breeding lagomorphs for the dinner table. We explain that we do not eat rabbits, cats, dogs, horses, elephants, rhinoceroses, tigers – and so on – until they laugh and begin to understand how we feel about rabbits.

Those visitors who know that 'live' rabbits are available in the Arabian marketplaces, usually ask if we bought ours there. This question leads to one of Gold's favourite stories, and he is usually hovering close by, hoping to hear it once again.

Let me tell you about it. It so happened that we did not get our first rabbit from the souq. We acquired him years ago in exchange for chickens, and it came about like this: It was winter. Thousands of tiny yellow chicks had arrived in the Dhahran airport and everyone was talking about them, I recall. (We had lived within the small Dhahran airport community for three years, and found that news such as this travelled quickly.) It was not an especially cold winter but it was far too chilly for little chicks to survive for long without artificial heating, so many were dying as they waited to be collected.

A friend rescued six and brought them to us. We were not experienced in handling chicks and three died that night, even though we had put them in the master bedroom, our warmest room. Happily, we were successful with the other three, and very soon, there were three gossipy, yellow balls bouncing in and out of their box and strutting around the villa. We followed with a box of paper tissues.

It was marvellous to see them thriving and so perky. Surprisingly, our amusement and tolerance was shared by our cat, Mamapuss, who went so far as to allow the chicks to tramp up and down her prone body. They would even perch momentarily on the top of her head before sliding off. They were either too young or too wise to dig in their claws.

Boxes and boxes of Kleenex later, we decided that the situation was getting completely out-of-hand. They had begun to reach higher perches. Alternative arrangements would have to be made. The chickens' fluffy yellow down had gradually changed to little white feathers – and one of the three was growing quite tall. We called him 'Big Bird'. Then, almost before you could blink one morning, John had exchanged the three chickens for a baby rabbit.

The Arab family who took the chicks felt that they had the best side of the bargain, but we knew that we had, because our new pet was gorgeous.

We named him 'Smokey' because of his whispy grey colouring. Smokey was very shy and subdued for the first few days, but we knew that each rabbit has its very own personality which takes time to develop. For now, we could not be certain about the sort of character that had come to share our home. Smokey soon began to blossom into a charming rabbit who continually amused us with his antics.

He had a great sense of fun, and surprised people who had never before seen a rabbit with a desire to be inside a house rather than out-of-doors. In fact, he would not walk anywhere unless it was on carpet, expressing an instinctive need for a surface closer to one that was natural for a rabbit. When he reached the edge of our great living-room carpet, he either waited to be lifted to the next carpet or he jumped the distance of the marble floor between. And, it made eyes open wide to see a rabbit choose a chair in preference to the floor. Smokey also appeared to watch television. In the light of Gold's later achievements, perhaps Smokey did like television. Gold tells us that he does not care for it but he said it was possible that Smokey 'saw something in it'.

Smokey's real passion was licking people in return for having his nose stroked. After several licks, he would stop and wait for a return demonstration of affection. Most rabbits do this, I've found, but it could go on forever as far as Smokey was concerned. One night it almost did – and the victim was a guest in our home. This is another of Gold's favourite stories.

It came about one weekend when we had an overnight house guest. It is customary in Arabia to have people stay when they travel about the country on business, or when it is necessary to come to the coast to catch a plane going overseas. Although there are many beautiful hotels in Arabia, private hospitality is still very important, and it is pleasant to stay with friends – even if it means sleeping on the floor.

On this occasion, our friend, Jim, was visiting us from Riyadh. After we had exchanged news and laughed over old times, Jim retired to his bed on the floor of our 'spare' room. This room no longer had a door because we had recently made the area 'open' with an archway through from the living room. Our tropical fish were kept in there.

Yet, if it had not been for Smokey, I believe Jim would have slept soundly. He might have been lulled to sleep by the soothing gloopy sounds coming from the fish tanks. But, this was not to be. Smokey began to lick Jim, moving from an occasional uncovered foot to his neck, face and hands. A rabbit's tongue is nice and soft – not like the rough tongue of a cat – but it can tickle terribly. Jim was woken up many

times until, eventually, he became aware of the gloop, gloop of the aquarium.

We were met next morning by an exhausted, bleary-eyed Jim who said his experience had taken on a semblance of the ancient Oriental water torture. He also said he would have locked the elusive licker in the bathroom, if he could have caught him. Each time Jim grabbed, he clutched air. Smokey had hopped out of reach. It seems that Smokey was being mischievous because he was usually very happy to be picked up.

"Where is Smokey now?" Gold always asks at this point. And, I explain each time that Smokey died not long after Jim's visit. We don't know why he died, but it was sudden. Rabbits have a reputation for having weak hearts, possibly because timid ones have died after being badly frightened. Smokey died the night before we were to have our annual chocolate egg hunt. To save little Christopher's feelings, we told a story about rabbits from all over the world going off to help deliver eggs. The strange thing is that we usually do lose a rabbit every year at about this time.

We've had many rabbits since then and they have all been special in some way or another. We hardly had a chance to know Gold's little sister, Silver, before she caught a cold and died. It was so sad. Even so, Gold likes to hear about her again and again, and always right from the beginning. He will say: "That was the day you went to buy one rabbit and ended up with three, wasn't it, Susan?"

We had gone to the souq to purchase a doe for our buck rabbit, Ginger. The warren had been depleted by several rabbit-world catastrophies which were mostly CATastrophies. It had been a very hot and dry summer so the predatory cats were constantly marauding in our neighbourhood. These were domesticated cats that had reverted to being wild, or 'feral'. They came in from rubbish dumps on the fringes of the desert near the outskirts of the city, looking for water and food. They would pounce, and carry off our young rabbits whenever they could. Many times, our dog, Samantha, saw them and chased them off. Or sometimes, it would be Mamapuss, our gentle cat, who gave us the warning by bristling and hissing. At night, we switched on the garden lights, and occasionally, would see a cat's reflection cast on a wall inside the house. Then we would all run out shouting to frighten it away.

If there were no young ones in the warren, we had no cause for alarm. A fully grown rabbit can usually defend itself against a large cat. A rabbit's powerful hind legs can slash most effectively. Even a rabbit bite can hurt.

Unfortunately, the wounds that cats inflict can result in the death of a rabbit when abscesses form under a fur coat after the visible wound has healed.

That year, our warren suffered from a cold virus which claimed the lives of several grown rabbits. And, suddenly, there was only Ginger left. He had been born in our warren just over three years previously and his survival could be put

down to strength, speed, caution and a robust constitution. He had been Chief Buck of the warren for almost two years, and he was still an alert and handsome bunny, just as his daddy, Bugs, had been. Bugs had died more than a year ago, quite suddenly.

Big strong Bugs had lived a good life and it was a great shock to us to find him dead one morning without any apparent cause. It was a mystery. Beside his lifeless body, there was a hole in the middle of the lawn, yet there was no freshly moved earth around it. This meant that a tunnel had been started somewhere else, because rabbits dig forwards and push the earth backwards though their hind legs.

We assumed that Bugs had died from over-exertion after tunnelling a long way underneath concrete, as the only other hole was 30 feet away. This was a wonderful feat of engineering, if so. It was very strange. It is often said that only the does dig burrows, to house their babies. The bucks are supposed to make use of these sanctuaries, but never, as a rule, dig more than several inches beneath the surface of the ground. These are called 'scrapes' and buck rabbits, like hares, are said to be content with them; yet, I have seen a buck in our warren help a mate dig a burrow.

So, now, Ginger was quite alone. We decided that he should have a new mate and a fresh start. The homecoming of his new doe rabbit was to be a grand occasion. Arrangements were made for a 'tea' of cut-up apples, carrots, wholemeal bread and greens. These are known as 'grins' in our family, derived from the word 'greens'. Our rabbits love bread, too, as long as it is 'wholemeal', and it is our custom to buy batches of excellent bread once a week from a specialist bakery on the other side of town. We freeze the loaves until they are needed. Our friends laugh to see our refrigerator and freezer filled with food for the pets. Still, our rabbits are very particular. This bread is delicious – and they are far too discerning to eat white bread.

Arab friends were responsible for naming Ginger's 'bride'. She was a shy doe with a glossy black coat, and a small dab of white on her nose. They explained that some Arabs consider black things as having come from the Devil, so a suitable name for her would be SHAITANA, meaning the 'female devil'. We agreed, knowing rabbits can be devilishly mischievous.

Shaitana belied her name completely, for she was gentle and serious. You could always find her unobtrusively getting on with the business at hand, whether it be eating, gathering bits and pieces for a nest, or mothering her kittens. She was a placid rabbit which may have accounted for her being the most fertile female in the warren. Each year we could expect about 20 babies from Shaitana.

Despite her original handsome appearance, I carry in my mind a 'tatty' image of Shaitana because her smooth coat was soon constantly ragged. A doe will tug out clumps of her fur whenever it is time to make a nest for the expected babies. Mother rabbits believe there is nothing too good for their children. As soon as we see a doe doing this, we provide a

box of tissues for her to shred – or we supply office waste from the paper shredder.

Gold will tell you that he remembers Shaitana well because she was such a kind and gentle rabbit. He often cuddled up to her side, and she was quite motherly towards him when he was very small. Gold had been far too young to be parted from his natural mother, and Shaitana was very attentive to him, licking him and allowing him to snuggle. He was so tiny when we found him, it was remarkable that he survived.

On that fateful morning, when we had just bought Shaitana, the market-place was in an uproar. It always got like that when we were choosing a rabbit. We had intended to buy only one doe, but John and I always liked to spend time in the animal souq and pat all the rabbits. The vendors seemed convinced that we were mad, especially after restraining an enthusiastic salesman from grabbing a rabbit by the ears and swinging it at us for inspection. Rabbits' ears are not handles, although many people use them as such. Their ears are very sensitive.

The best way to pick up a rabbit is to pat the ears flat first. This has a calming effect. Rabbits never hop away if their ears are lying flat, so this is a good trick to remember if you are trying to catch an elusive rabbit in your living room. Then, you must slip your hand under the ears and take up the skin at the back of the neck firmly, just as you would do for a cat. With the other hand, support the bottom firmly. You must watch out for the hind legs because these are strong and an insecure rabbit may jerk and accidentally scratch you. A rabbit must be held with confidence. Then it can be hugged firmly against the body. Rabbits like to be hugged providing they are not squashed.

When we began 'up-ending' each rabbit in the souq, in order to sort males from females, the vendors began to laugh. What did it matter, they thought, as long as the rabbit was fat? Then we rejected the plumper, juicier rabbits in favour of ones with pretty colours and beautiful faces. They went wild with squeals of laughter. Some had understood that we were telling the rabbits that we would buy them all if we were rich enough and our garden big enough. And, then, when we began saying 'goodbye' to the rabbits that we were leaving behind . . . You have never heard such a hullabaloo.

Right at the point of our leaving, I spied two beautiful little rabbits crouching down in the corner of a box – each one could fit into the palm of a hand; and, they were so small and fluffy . . . One was mostly silver-grey with a little white, and the other was white with some grey on its head and back, and a golden glint in one eye. The other was blue. Yes, each eye was a different colour. "Please may I have them?" I pleaded with John.

We named one FIDDAH and the other DHAHAB, which means 'Silver' and 'Gold' in Arabic. The one with the golden glint in his eye was to become our precious Gold.

Not until we reached home did we realize that they were both too young to eat solid food. The mother must have been sold separately that day, or perhaps she had died. It seemed possible that these baby rabbits were ready to be weaned off milk and we decided to try. Rabbit milk is more than three times as rich in protein as cows milk, so we mixed some cream with water and gave it in an eye-dropper. We also gave the babies some delicate green leaves. Both rabbits began to eat the very next day, turning the household's concern into relief. Fiddah and Dhahab not only survived, they began to thrive.

There is nothing prettier, to my mind, than a baby rabbit – especially when they are full of food and confidence. Our active little bunnies, Silver and Gold, walked, hopped, jumped, leapt, and flipped sideways in mid-air, keeping Christopher entranced with their antics. I have often observed young rabbits walking before hopping. Every now and again they would get tired and drop straight off to sleep wherever they found themselves – even if it were tucked inside John's shirt collar, in that warm place between his neck and his shoulder.

The beginning of this new warren was a pleasure from the start. Outside in the garden, we expected the appearance of Ginger and Shaitana's kittens daily. Gold and Silver, living inside the house, ran free without a serious thought in their fluffy heads. It was impossible to keep them in their box for any length of time because they seemed to have springs on their feet. It was good to see then set out upon their first investigation. They were still far too small to face the perils of the garden without the protection of natural parents.

It is not generally known that rabbits can be successfully house-trained, but they can be. At first, one must always expect that some cleaning up will be necessary until it is achieved. This is normal, whether you are dealing with a puppy, a kitten, a baby rabbit, or a human baby. Askalu, fortunately, was very tolerant with the bunnies.

Our family worked together to locate the first indiscriminate choice of toilet places which were usually hidden in corners, and we soon reduced the places. This can be achieved more easily by limiting the number of rooms open to the rabbit. Cleaning up must be thorough in the less popular spots. Paper can be placed in the most frequently used corners. The rabbit will co-operate by ultimately choosing one favourite spot and this is where the toilet tray must be placed.

Eventually, the tray can be moved successfully from place to place providing the rabbit knows where to find it. Another way is to provide a rabbit hutch with a removable tray. The

door can be kept closed for the first week. Afterwards, encourage your pet to spend some time there, by putting the food inside. You will find that rabbits, like all animals, would rather be clean than otherwise.

When our warren is full – and sometimes overflowing – there is a lot of sweeping up to do in the garden each morning. There were 12 rabbits in our warren at this time last year, and we had 28 a few weeks before that. It meant of a lot of work. Then friends took most of the babies at the same time that dear old Moppet died. Moppet had been a mature, tame rabbit when she was given to us. She was a silver-grey female and, although much larger than Gold, they had liked each other very much and mated. They looked so funny, sitting together like an old married couple, squashed up on the same chair.

We think that Moppet may not have been very well for some time because she had become a bit of a grumpy bully. She was enormous compared with the others in the warren, and she could intimidate the bucks if she wanted to do so. Everyone had supposed that her occasional crabbiness was just part of her natural behaviour in old age.

Despite her lapses, we were fond of Moppet. She was always greedy, and liked to spend time in the kitchen close to the food. On one occasion, she devoured nearly all of the grapes left in a basket on a chair. She obviously enjoyed them very much because she scratched at us when we removed the remainder, tugging at the basket with her strong teeth. It was amusing to see her return to the same spot several times in the following days to see if we had made the same mistake. We miss Moppet very much. She was a great character. Perhaps, if she had been able to talk and tell us what was wrong, we could have helped her.

Keeping a warren provides a mixed basket of emotions. Mostly we are just happy to be among our rabbits. Sometimes we are extremely elated because new babies have emerged from their nest for the first time. And, then, there are the sad times when death strikes. The sadness is occasionally mixed with feelings of guilt, because the dead rabbit had been a treasured pet left with us. Although we have not been to blame, there is still the awful feeling of responsibility.

Both Sandy and Olga came to live in our warren when their owners departed from Arabia for good. Sandy was with us for only six months before she died, and Olga spent her last year in our warren. Olga was a particularly beautiful rabbit with the colouring of a Siamese cat. She had mated with Gold and prepared a nest, yet no babies were ever seen. We found her dead not long afterwards, although she had looked fine. When keeping animals, one has to be prepared to accept their relatively short life expectation.

Shaitana and Moppet's babies were always very beautiful, so most of them were chosen as pets and went to live elsewhere. Shaitana had one baby that I could not bear to part with, and we named it 'Harvey' after our much-loved, identical rabbit that we had in Australia long ago. He had

been named after a famous rabbit character in a play, the basis of a film in which the actor, James Stewart, played opposite the invisible rabbit.

The new Harvey had very short, close fur which was a shiny black and white. He survived in our garden as a young rabbit because he was very, very cautious. At the slightest suspicion of danger, Harvey dashed for cover. We kept another of Shaitana's babies because no one else wanted him. His face was quite plain as a baby, and survival through his dangerous first summer was put down to speed. This rabbit was black and had the oddest appearance. His hair was very long, with grey roots that sprouted for about 2 centimetres.

The long coat draped over the largest, spindly legs. We called him Rabby Long Legs. Rabby could run very fast indeed, and that is how he escaped from predators in infancy.

Placid, slow rabbits don't stand much chance if they are born too close to summer. And, that was the reason for keeping two of Moppet's babies (Flash and Blaze) indoors. Flash and Blaze inherited their dense grey coats from Moppet, but the blush of ginger colouring through the grey, and behind the ears, came from their father, Ginger. Flash has a streak of white on his nose and Blaze has a white star in the same place.

From the start, Flash and Blaze were audacious, bouncy, and very intelligent. They were delightful house rabbits, and we knew they would do well outside as soon as they were big enough to cope. They still go everywhere together despite their personalities being quite different. As kittens, they were always up to mischief. Blaze is the faster of the two and the most playful now, and is elusive when we want to catch him. Flash is affectionate and likes to nuzzle up to us most of the time, but both like to settle contentedly on chairs or laps before television each evening, licking in return for caresses.

When an enormous box of 'grins' arrives from the souq, Flash and Blaze are in the front line, climbing in and out of the box, while Askalu attempts to stuff the leaves into the refrigerator's crisper trays. Warren news travels fast, and the other rabbits are never far behind. Perhaps this is often because an overloaded box leaves a tell-tale trail all the way from the front gate to the villa door. Without any such clue, something similar happens when fresh minced beef arrives from the butcher. Mamapuss somehow knows about it before the shopping is unpacked. Then she will stand on the table greedily eyeing the kilos of beef being 'decanted' into small 'day portion' containers that we freeze until required. At such times, there are more animals in our kitchen than people.

Perhaps the life I am describing seems perfect for animals but, unfortunately, it is not. Sometimes tragic things happen. For instance, our warren rabbits occasionally spurn a newcomer, and this can be heart-breaking. One rejected rabbit was a fully-grown fluffy white albino called Frosty.

Frosty came from a 'broken home', and it must have been hard for him to part with his young master and familiar home when his parents got divorced. To make things worse, the

rabbits in our warren nipped him if he came near the food, and he had to wait until they were finished before he got anything to eat. Sadly, he would sit apart from the groups; and he had to stay outside the burrow at night. We did not want to interfere for a while, because we hoped he would eventually fit in.

We sadly misjudged the situation and one night Frosty was savaged by a stray tomcat. He fought the cat off but he was badly mauled and the wounds festered. Fortunately, he responded to penicillin, and was soon well on the road to recovery. But, still, the warren rabbits did not seem able to accept him, and it was clearly not safe for Frosty to go on living in the open. His pink eyes were not strong enough to help him avoid being attacked. We could see that dear, docile Frosty needed to be a pampered 'only rabbit' once again, so we found a doting family to take care of him.

Buffety Justice was another rabbit that the warren rejected at first. He had also been given to us as a mature rabbit, and Christopher named him after a daring cartoon character that the rabbit brought to mind. His remarkable, independent spirit refused to be daunted by their snubs, and gradually he made his place within our rabbit family. It was obvious from the start that Buffety Justice had great character, and he was wise. He never showed the slightest interest in the does (each of whom had boyfriends at the time, in any case) as if he knew it would be foolhardy to give cause for jealousy. Buck rabbits will take on the most fearful battles if they feel a romance is threatened, and perhaps Buffety Justice had learnt from past experience.

Both Frosty and Buffety Justice had been filthy when we got them. Their feet and under-fur were stained and stinking, which was due to having been confined in dirty hutches. Perhaps the others shunned them because they did not like unclean rabbits. I had given Frosty and Buffety Justice a 'shampoo' immediately after they arrived and was surprised to see that neither objected to being bathed. Buffety Justice seemed to enjoy it. After several bathing session, followed by brushing, they looked smart, and of course, they were more pleasant to be with.

The weather was very hot then and no doubt that was partly why they enjoyed the cool water. I decided to try putting Buffety in the swimming pool to cool him down. We were delighted to see that he was a good swimmer. Then, we tried out some of the other rabbits, and discovered that they all swam naturally, although some liked it more than others. Blaze and Flash were the best. At first, Flash lay rigid in the water, and then he began to tilt sideways while still floating. As we reached out to 'save' him, Flash struck out 'dog paddling' with all of his might until he reached the edge and scrambled out. I keep towels ready to dry the rabbits before setting them down in the sun to dry off. In no time, they look refreshed and fluffy once more.

This has become a regular ritual to cool them down in the middle of summer when the Central Arabian dry heat is intense.

Buffety Justice was the strong and silent type. He was a mixture of grey and ginger, a little like Flash and Blaze. When he finally assimilated into the warren, Buffety became the most aggressive of foragers. As soon as the 'grins' were brought, Buffety was always in the front line to eat it, daringly shouldering aside some rabbits who were of higher rank. Yet, no one gave him more than a passing nip, which he ignored.

Positive and confident, he was a great adventurer. He got along well with visiting cats who seemed to stand in awe of him. I think they gave him the status of 'honorary' cat. When Buffety discovered the passage through to next door's garden, he took to sitting on our high wall, often alongside a big feline marauder. The wall next door has a decorative ramp on it and Buffety Justice would hop along it until he reached the top of our garden wall. Following the wall along, and passing under our enormous overhanging eucalyptus tree, Buffety would reach another ramp leading to the street outside.

He could be seen by moonlight, sitting on the top of this wall for hours, quite often in the company of some of the biggest, baddest tomcats in town. He was even seen sitting in the street with them. The colours of these companions was often comical and very remarkable, so much so, that we sometimes gave them descriptive names. We named Darth Vader and Bat Cat because of their designs. Then, one sad day Buffety Justice was found dead in the street. There were no signs of foul play, so it must have been his time to go.

Mr. Lockley's study of the rabbit tells us that its brain evolved like those of all other creatures, in that it responded to suit the animal's way of life. The life of a rabbit in the wild is one that is beset with many hazards. When danger is sensed, the brain translates the messages immediately. For instance, if there is a fox prowling about, the rabbit will hear and smell it, and automatically dash to safety and hide for as long as it takes for the fox to go away.

Wild rabbits often die in captivity, probably as a result of frustration. It is likely they have a thousand reasons to feel frustrated and frightened in a cage. They might be startled, often, and all of their normal reactions would be futile because there is nowhere to run and hide. Because protected, domesticated rabbits lead a less hazardous life than wild ones, their responses are less nervous and the survival instinct is less strong.

Sometimes, they seem downright careless. Time and again, we have seen our excited dog, Samantha, tear after a cat. She has hurtled her solid body very close to a calm, grazing group of rabbits. Yet, our rabbits have just raised their heads and

Olga

Gold and Olga

"I wonder if Hussein got carrots?"

"I'm coming down, Olga"

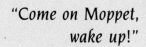

"Come on Moppet, wake up!"

"Hmmm . . . tasty!"

Moppet and Gold dozing
in the spring sunshine

"I'm just pooped"

adjusted the direction of their ears before returning once again to their meal. They obviously trust Samantha completely, and know that she means them no harm. It is good to learn that they feel secure, and this must mean that they have adjusted to the life they now lead. They are free from the dreadful preoccupations of a rabbit living in the wild. Moreover, they are able to take advantage of human comforts such as chairs, carpets, marble floors and refrigerators – all of which they appear to appreciate very much. Our warren is a kind of rabbit Utopia, and it is an ideal place for the emergence of one such as precious Gold.

Many people are curious to know if our rabbits ever try to run away. With the exception of the first Harvey, Ginger and Buffety Justice, none have wandered. Gold has never shown any inclination to go out of the gate or under the wall. Most rabbits remain close to home. Possibly, the world outside is thought of as the 'wild'. Gold told us that his 'world' was around us, and he has no interest in going outside the gate. I know that once Gold's tummy is filled, he does truly enjoy associating with humans. He is an armchair adventurer, enjoying his travel in story form.

Considering this, we fully expected that he would encourage his newest mate, Harvette, to join him in spending more time indoors, and he did. She has become quite tame but has always disliked being picked up. Like most rabbits though, Harvette enjoys the comfort of the house and will tolerate caresses if they are absolutely unavoidable. She puts up with them because she is a stay-at-home rabbit who appreciates nice carpets and comfortable chairs. We have found that sharing a house with rabbits can work out very well, because they are naturally fastidious animals.

I am often reminded of our first rabbit, Harvey, when I look at his namesake Harvette. I had found Harvey in a pet shop many years ago, when he was very tiny. He had similar black and white markings and the same pretty, short-nosed, broad face with widely-spaced eyes. The similarity ends there because their personalities could not be compared.

At the time that I bought Harvey, John and I were engaged to be married and I was living in an apartment. It was my habit to leave the front door open, and I continued to do so when Harvey first came to live there. He could go out into the garden whenever he liked. He had his 'toilet' indoors but he seemed to like to go outside to play, especially to the red gravel tennis courts behind the apartments. At night, when it was time for him to come in, I could see him there very easily in the dark because of his vivid colouring. I had only to call and he would come.

With all this freedom, I should not have been surprised when I learnt he had been to other places as well. One day, a total stranger told me about a black and white rabbit called Harvey who visited people in an apartment close to mine. In time, I discovered he had a wide circle of friends. They all knew where he lived and found out his name from my neighbour. Apparently, he took every opportunity to enter open doors and visit; and he used to accept carrots and apples.

Long before this, I had become aware of his intelligence. After an absence of two weeks from the apartment, Harvey, had displayed his good memory by skipping joyfully in great excitement from one favourite spot to another. His astonishing behaviour clearly said: "There's no place like home."

When John and I married and moved to our new home, Harvey continued wandering, and he again developed a secret side to his life. Friends thought we knew that he had been hopping down and into the street from his favourite spot on our high stone wall. We learned that he would cross the road to play in the park opposite. It was an extremely dangerous thing for a tame rabbit to do because there were often large dogs about. We need not have worried because Harvey eventually showed us that he could take care of himself.

It happened when we got Oscar, a basset hound puppy. Oscar was the biggest of a litter of 13 puppies, yet, at first, he was smaller than Harvey. However, basset hounds grow very quickly indeed, and they are boisterous. We feared that Oscar might kill Harvey accidentally in one of his playful moods, just as he sometimes hurt us. But, Harvey had his own way of coping. He just acted in a superior fashion, showing Oscar by his attitude that he had no intention of being pushed around. Harvey might have been much smaller, but he had been there first and he was clearly the elder.

And then, when we were sure there was no danger, our worst fears appeared to have been realized. Arriving home one night, we found large spots of blood on the floor, and Harvey and Oscar were not there to greet us as usual. In our mind's eye we imagined our fragile bunny slaughtered and our great basset hound hiding for fear of punishment. But, no, there was Harvey, immaculately clean and quite unharmed. Where did the blood come from? Out came a humiliated Oscar from under the table, wearing a 'sheepish' expression on his woeful face. And, he had a long, tell-tale cut on his big black nose. It seemed that Harvey had found some cause to reprimand his giant-sized pal.

Harvey's aplomb, beauty, and tameness eventually led him into the glamour world of modelling. It was a short-lived career because we could not afford the time to take him from one assignment to another. As a tribute to this accomplishment, we did frame Harvey's first pay cheque, his payment for posing with a little girl for a calendar.

He was so appealing, I believe he could have supported us all. That is, if his love of chocolate had not run him into debt. And, if that habit didn't ruin him, his other expensive eating habits might have done. For instance, on many occasions we had to supply a guest with a new pair of shoe laces. Harvey liked to neatly nip off the entire knot and bow from a guest's shoe. He was also partial to straw handbags and once ate his way right through a friend's purse, which she had placed at her feet under the dinner table. Luckily, his nibbling habits

caused laughter and were not too serious. Fortunately, not all rabbits are nibblers.

The most unlikeable rabbit that came out of our warren had neither habit; yet, he had become surly and spoiled. He would probably have bitten his best friend, had his wishes not been met immediately. His name was ARNAB, or 'rabbit' in Arabic. Arnab was adored by his little master who chose him from one of our litters. Michael had hardly been able to wait for the kittens to be old enough to leave their mother. He visited the warren constantly, awaiting the day that he could have Arnab all to himself.

He became so attached to his pet that the rabbit took to bathing with him every evening. The pair would splash about in the bath until the last possible moment, while his mother was getting impatient and cross. Arnab ate the same food as the little boy – even meat. Whatever Arnab wanted, Arnab got, until the whole household revolved around the rabbit's wishes. He grew into an enormous, sulky rabbit that only his master could love. When the little boy went on holidays, we minded Arnab, but we were very glad to send him home.

We usually have happy memories of rabbits, and because of this, so far, we have had two each of Ruperts, Peters, Bugs,

Silvers and Harveys, and each time it has been because we have seen something lovable or similar in looks or character. I doubt that there could ever be two Arnabs.

As I look out of the window now, I can see Askalu carrying a box of parrot seeds and the dry dog food to the rabbits. There will be no 'grins' today, apparently. It will not matter for a day or two. All the rabbits love sunflower seeds – and the meatless protein dog food. They will be cracking and crunching which is good because it wears down their teeth. And, this food is nutritious.

Just look at that. I can see Gold jostling for position among a seething sea of excited fur. He is now munching enthusiastically alongside Silver, Modesty Blaise, Nigel, The Lone Ranger, and Chipolatta. At the moment we have 26 rabbits. Apart from Ginger and Gold, the adult buck rabbits are Peter and The Lone Ranger. The young ones are Flash, Blaze, Rabby Long Legs, Nigel, Nugget, Bugs and Chipolatta. The adults does are Harvette, Silver, Modesty Blaise, Cleopatra, Sheba, Nefertiti, Jacqui, Maggie, Sofia, Marilyn and Liz. The young female rabbits are Tina, Cilla, Koo and Madonna.

2
Precious Gold

There have been several bright personalities in the Blake warren, just as you might expect (considering each buck and doe rabbit is every bit as much an individual as a human). Yet, even looking back to the very beginning of our warren in Arabia, and remembering every special rabbity character, Gold is incomparable.

He is quite the most remarkable rabbit. Against all odds, he has overcome disability, serious illness, and terrible wounds from dreadful battles. Taking into account his small size and deformed front paws, it is an admirable achievement. I have seen large, perfectly normal rabbits succumb from only one of these misfortunes; and just a simple cold can snuff out the life of the average rabbit.

At first glance, Gold's total disregard for danger may be considered stupidity rather than courage. Yet, when anyone becomes properly acquainted with him, it is realized that Gold is very wise as well as courageous; and he is charming. Gold treats everyone, human or creature, as an equal – and he does this without arrogance.

It is amusing to find that he acts in complete innocence. And, whereas such confidence might not seem nice in some-one else, in him, it is wonderful. Remarkably, he is never ill-mannered, despite all the attention he has received as a result of his ability to talk. It has been a valuable lesson for me.

In order to be as confident as Gold, I believe that we must look deep inside ourselves for our own special qualities.

Gold has a strong personality. He may not be in the habit of giving advice, but he does make his point of view very clear by his comments, as you will see. He is asleep right now, in the shade of the lemon tree, so I have a chance to tell you about the time when he first spoke to us. That is one story that I know he would not care to hear again.

It happened some years ago when our son, Christopher, was seven years old. Christopher was at the back of our villa pulling out old car tyre tubes from a small shed. (He intended to inflate them for the swimming pool which we were filling in readiness for summer.) The entrance to our rabbit warren was nearby. As Christopher tugged at the tyre tubes, he heard a bright little voice say "hello". He had hardly time to wonder when he heard the small clear voice again saying: "Hello Christopher."

As Gold was the only one there besides himself, Christopher stared at the rabbit. He began to think that he had imagined the voice, but there was the small voice again: "Well, aren't you going to say 'hello' to me?" Gold now sounded a bit irritable so Christopher quickly replied "Hello" just as Gold continued: "Yes, I am speaking to you, Christopher. Do you know if any carrots came?"

In astonishment, Christopher stared at the perky little rabbit for an instant before scooping him up and running into the villa. By the time Christopher reached me, he was quite incoherent. I asked him to sit down and calm down. I was quite used to his running everywhere – and his excitable nature. My careful questioning eventually brought forth events of the last five minutes. Then, before I could say more, an impatient little voice said: "Yes, I can talk. Do you know if Hussein managed to get any carrots?"

Now it was my turn to be incredulous. I recovered sufficiently to tell Christopher to bring a carrot immediately. He bounded out of the room and bounced back, dropping lettuce leaves and carrots onto the sofa next to Gold; and, he made a grab for his rabbit in almost the same movement. "Christopher, leave Gold!" I cried. But, Gold paid us no attention whatsoever. He had begun to eat. He ignored us completely just as he always did when food was at hand. He had now eaten one carrot and was beginning on another – without a word. We stared at him in amazed silence. When we began to realize that one of our rabbits could actually talk, we looked at each other and then back at Gold. We began to giggle. It was fantastic! We were somewhere between elated and ecstatic.

We all loved Gold very much, but he had been Christopher's special pet. He was such a lovable bunny, and he enjoyed being handled by Christopher whose boisterous ways were not always appreciated by the other rabbits. We were both petting Gold when it suddenly occurred to me that we should share our news. "Get Daddy!" I commanded. "Quickly, Christopher, get Daddy!" and, as an afterthought: "Bring Askalu, too – but don't tell anyone else for the moment. I don't want to frighten Gold."

I need not have worried. Gold nonchalantly munched up everything he had been given before he took any notice of

anyone. He seemed most unconcerned. I said softly to myself over and over again: "I just don't believe it. I wonder if he will ever say anything again. Surely it is not possible."

When we were all assembled and Gold seemed content, I spoke to him. I had quietly explained to everyone what had happened, and suggested that we should let Gold finish eating before speaking to him. Above all, we should remain calm. This was very difficult because our excitement had been mounting. Finally, I spoke to Gold: "Please, Gold, if you can talk, say hello to us." Without the slightest hesitation and with a great deal of confidence, Gold said: "Hello." Then he said: "I can say other words, too. I can speak English and some Arabic, but I don't do so well in Askalu's language." (Askalu came from Ethiopia.)

We were so astonished that we could not reply. We tried to absorb what had just happened. The shock had momentarily subdued us, and we just stood there until Askalu broke our silence by giggling. She giggled and giggled and giggled, until suddenly, she dashed out of the room. Minutes later, she returned with her sister, Segay, who was visiting. Segay hung back at the doorway, and had to be coaxed in to see our talking rabbit. I believe she thought that we had all gone mad. When we recovered from our shock, we took turns to cuddle and pat Gold and to tell him what a clever chap he was.

We hardly knew what to ask Gold first, but that problem was solved when Segay ventured into the room. "Say hello to Segay, Gold!" I suggested. "Hello" he said promptly. "I like Segay because she loves animals, and I love Askalu because she is so good to us and brings us food." That set Askalu off giggling again. Of course, work was forgotten for that day and the next – and the next.

We broke the news of our talking rabbit only to our closest friends, and to the people with whom we worked closely. I brought them to Gold in small groups and asked him to say "hello". The family agreed that his talent need not be kept secret but, to say "hello" would be a sufficient demonstration. Too many complicated conversations could not possibly be good for him.

Gold's personality did not change, but he did use his new skill to get extra food for himself and the other rabbits in the warren. And as he did this in the nicest possible way no one felt like refusing. In fact, everybody went out of their way to spoil him, which is why we were so surprised that he remained pleasant.

He coped with the new event better than we did, and it was Gold who reminded us that it might be nice if he could share some of his extra treats with the other rabbits. In our excitement we would sometimes forget our normal concerns. Then, we realized that since we had Gold inside the house so much more, we were spending less time with the rabbits outside. It was therefore unanimously decided that from then on we should do our 'talking' outside whenever possible.

Whatever were we going to do about this amazing rabbit? Had we the right to keep him all to ourselves? We need not have worried what to do, as events were to carry us along with them. There was no need for any planning at all. News of any kind travels quickly in Arabia – perhaps because with its longer days and a warmer climate people spend a lot of time being sociable. And, because of this, people talked to each other, and it is always difficult to keep a secret. It would probably have been impossible to prevent news such as this from reaching the far corners of the world, as there were people of every nationality working in Arabia. John's company alone had employees from at least ten different countries. Then, there were many men who came to Arabia briefly on business, and they met people who were active in the community. The Western residents in Riyadh are involved in theatre, concert music, school activities, welfare organisations, sports, arts and crafts and lots more.

As we expected, the word was soon out. "The Blakes have a talking rabbit!" Of course most people thought it was a joke, and we were very happy to leave it at that because we wanted our rabbit warren to remain undisturbed. Gold's happiness was especially important.

Although Gold is an astonishing rabbit in many ways, you would not think so to look at him. Without a doubt he is appealing, but he does look rather odd. His front paws are sadly bent because of a vitamin deficiency before or just after his birth. Fortunately, these deformed paws do not hamper him at all, and they have become very strong. He has a hole right through one ear, the result of a bite from another rabbit. And his eyes are two different colours – one blue and one a golden-hazel.

Gold's capacity for life is awesome. He survived a severe cold when he was a weakling baby – a feat rare even for a rabbit in prime condition. Rabbits can die from a common cold.

In Gold's case, without a vet, and in desperation, we gave him a half-filled 'cold-relief' capsule designed for humans. We poked it down his tiny throat, making sure to avoid the sharp front teeth, once a day for three days. It apparently cured the nasty blocked nose and heaving, bubbly chest; and he overcame the cold.

After Gold was better, another catastrophe occurred. Ginger gave Gold a terrible beating. According to rabbit lore, it was to be expected, and Gold apparently deserved to be punished; yet, the fight was so ill-matched, it seemed unfair. Gold was a small rabbit and Ginger was big and tough. The battle was dreadful and it seemed to last forever. Each time that we thought they had stopped, it broke out again. It seemed much worse because it could have been avoided. It was all over a misunderstanding.

You see, Ginger had disappeared about five days before hand and we could find no trace of him. We feared him dead. Gold must have believed he was dead, too, because he took control of the warren, including Ginger's female companions. If Ginger were dead, Gold would have been entitled to 'rule' and to take care of the 'first ladies' of the warren, as he was the oldest and most respected buck. He was next in line to be 'Chief High Buck' of the warren.

As it turned out, Ginger was very much alive. He had found his way to the lush and unkempt garden next door, and had eaten his fill before returning home to set his house in order. And, that meant 'straightening out' Gold. The large hole in Gold's ear was one of Ginger's neater bites.

Other wounds were nasty ragged tears. Gold had cuts everywhere and raw spots where lumps of fur had been torn out. And there were long slashes from Ginger's strong back claws. Gold took his punishment well, really – obviously understanding the justice of it. He seemed quite undaunted next day and although stiff and sore, good humour was restored with the aid of nice things to eat and lots of pampering.

A few short months after that, Gold had another awful fight – this time, with a ferocious tomcat that savaged him dreadfully. The wounds he received from Ginger seemed insignificant compared to the new ones. I expect the cat was wounded, too. Rabbits may be gentle by nature but they can be roused to fury. A healthy, full-grown buck rabbit is quite capable of fighting off a large and aggressive cat.

We were incredulous that Gold could fight this beast off because of his comparative small size and deformed front paws. But then, Gold's character has to be taken into account. He is full of courage, and he has a great will to live. The plucky little chap had an even bigger fight to follow when he struggled to overcome the infection which developed from his injuries. We have not seen any feral cats about lately and the warren is fairly peaceful.

John, Christopher and I have been enjoying just sitting with the rabbits and talking to Gold.

In those early days we used to ask Gold lots of questions, and he would often become a trifle impatient and fall silent. This being so, we decided to prepare a list of questions, asking only one each day. We also began to confine our talks to short periods directly after his meals. Gold was always affable and more relaxed on a full tummy. Rabbits are not very different from humans in this regard. Christopher knew very well when were the best times to approach us for a favour – and, didn't John and I know each other's most favourable moments when something needed discussion?

Eventually, Gold began to initiate the conversations. He told us that he remembered the day when we bought him in the souq. He could remember his sister, Silver, too. He had been very sad when she died, and he felt especially miserable because he had been sick at that time with a bad cold. Gold said he looked upon me as a sort of mother, although he did

not fully understand what it was like to have a real one. He had only vague memories of his natural mother, and the warm nest where he had been born. She had been large and soft.

Now, because he is a buck rabbit, Gold is expected to remain at a distance from nests of newborn rabbits. A doe will not permit even her mate to enter the private chamber in a burrow where the nest is placed. He realizes that a doe takes great care of her babies. We were a substitute, and it was good to hear of his confidence in us, and his belief that we would take great care of him.

Gold loved us very much, and he had made up his mind that we deserved to learn how to communicate with him. He knew that we loved animals, and especially rabbits, so he set about learning our langauge. He began to understand us better just by listening closely. Gold wanted us to learn 'Rabbit' too, although he knew it would be difficult to master because it included something like telepathy which we did not appear to use.

He explained that their language was not like any other, and there were almost no vocal sounds involved. Rabbits mostly communicate with each other by using parts of the body. It is a sort of sign language which includes vibrating their bodies. At least that is how we understand it, from Gold's explanation. He doubted that we could copy this. Ears, he said, were very important. It was an excellent way to pass a message providing the rabbit being 'spoken to' paid attention. He felt that perhaps humans could substitute hand movements.

Apparently, not all rabbits speak the same language, but they can always manage to make themselves understood. And, even though other species of animals have quite different 'languages', Gold said he could communicate with them. Sometimes he spoke to Samanatha and Mamapuss. Usually, he said, dogs, cats and rabbits do not bother to talk to each other because they have so little in common.

These pieces of information were of tremendous interest to the scientists who visited us. Apparently Gold said enough to satisfy researchers, and they felt that it was now possible for humans to begin to communicate with certain other animal species.

Gold's major problem had been to accomplish human sounds. He had known for a long while, he claimed, what our words meant but he could not seem to say them. Rabbit sounds are usually limited to a high-pitched, human-sounding squeal or scream such as a distressed child might make. Bucks and does also make a sort of nasal grunt at each other, a softer sound than their angry low-pitched growl. And, does have been heard 'crooning' softly to their babies.

I understand the problem Gold had in learning to speak our language perfectly. I find the French language presents me with similar difficulties. Furthermore, I am totally unable to sing. It is a sad situation experienced by many people who would love to sing. I have to be content listening to the voices

of others. Apparently this problem has a lot to do with the throat one is born with, and its unique vocal arrangements. Yet it cannot be denied that the 'will to achieve' is very important too. It seems that this is where Gold is to be admired most.

Rabbits do not sing. Nor are they very interested in human music. The wonderful sounds of nature are their music. During the weeks directly after Gold revealed his ability to talk, he usually spoke only when encouraged to do so, or when he was hungry. He seemed unsure, as if he did not know what to say. He still preferred to eat rather than talk.

Then one day Gold told us that rabbits love storytelling, and the most popular rabbits are those who can spin a good tale. Gold has come to love human stories and his interest was born out of curiosity. To satisfy this, and to get each of us involved, he developed a cunning way of asking questions which lead us into storytelling. He likes to be read to, as well, and we began by taking turns to read all of Christopher's fairy tales and adventure stories to him.

Despite his miraculous achievement and the increase in visitors, there was no change at all in Gold's position within the warren community. The attitude of the other rabbits towards him did not alter either. I think, from their point of view, the situation was simple: additional goodies were coming by way of the visitors, so these people were to be tolerated at all cost.

Everybody seemed to bring some rabbity sweetmeat. And, Gold quickly adjusted to his great popularity with visitors. Among the rabbits, Ginger was still the Overlord and he remained firmly in control, though twinges of jealousy occasionally tweaked his whiskers. Fortunately, he was not an overly sensitive sort of chap, and being the Chief made up for everything. Gold and the other buck rabbits respected Ginger as their leader and that was the 'bottom line'. It had nothing to do with what humans thought and did.

Once we were used to our talking rabbit, it seemed to be the most natural thing in the world. After all, we reasoned, my grandfather had a bird that repeated words – and John's family have a 'talking parrot'. It isn't the same thing, of course. Rabbits have more similar values to humans, apart from a lagomorph's very special interest in food; and, make no mistake about Gold, when it comes to meal-time, he is typical of his species. When we have teased him about this, he has assured us that he wanted to talk to us very badly and it had nothing to do with food; but, nevertheless, he has been more than ready to use his talent to acquire tasty extras.

Next to food, rabbits love romance. They spend a lot of time dreaming about each other, and the romantic attachments between bucks and does are a most important aspect of life in a warren. Considering some bucks have several mates, life can be complicated. Their relationships can cause quarrels to occur. Happily, bad feeling seldom lasts much longer than the time it takes to nip or threaten the challenger.

Gold is an incurable romantic who fantasizes every fragment of female attention. With his charming personality and coercing ways, he unwittingly represented a threat to the Chief Buck's sovereignty. During Ginger's early reign, Gold was young. You could say, he was not quite 'in his prime', but the female rabbits noticed him. He has often told us about his ability to charm the does – believing them all to be secretly in love with him. That is his one flaw: vanity – but it is not a serious one. We have to be careful to make sure that he does not see us laugh. It is an amusing quirk in his character because Gold is not otherwise vain or arrogant.

During this period, Gold was often 'put in his place' by Ginger who can be quick-tempered. Sometimes Ginger would hurt him with a quick bite. But, more often, he just rushed threateningly at Gold who got out of the way because Ginger was much larger than he. Then it was only Gold's feelings that were hurt.

The best thing that happened for Gold in a long time was 'Harvey' turning out to be a girl. Previously, no one in the warren had taken much notice of the attractive little black and white bunny. As you know, we named it Harvey because of the striking resemblance to our first rabbit in Australia.

The new rabbit was shy, and it was generally ignored by the other rabbits. When she matured and it was apparent that she was a girl, her fortunes changed. We renamed her Harvette. At the same time, all the bucks in the warren seemed suddenly smitten by her beauty, especially Gold. It was marvellous, therefore, that Harvette had 'eyes' only for him. Surprisingly, Ginger accepted this new partnership without so much as a growl. We do not expect there to be any more trouble between Gold and Ginger for a while – at least over the does. The question of which large rabbit should begin to eat first will always be a matter for settlement. Eventually, of course, when Ginger grows old. Gold will challenge him for leadership. Meanwhile, our precious Gold seems more interested in stories.

3
Animals in Arabia

old looks so comical when he grooms his ears, sitting up squarely on his bottom and fluffy hind legs, attending first to one ear and then the other.

Licking the inside of his front paws, with his head tipped on one side, he places the paws around one ear, close to his head, drawing them towards the tip. He licks them again and repeats the washing of that ear several times before doing the other. He was grooming himself just now out on the terrace, and I was watching through the glass wall of our living room. It is much easier to look out than to peer in, so I have always been able to observe our rabbits without disturbing them.

Rabbits are very clean. In the warren, grooming is a regular affair, and occasionally I have seen a rabbit nipping through the fur before washing; yet whenever I have checked, they have been free of fleas and ticks. In Arabia, I have never found parasites on the animals that we have kept, although I hear it is possible. Fleas and ticks are usually the result of coming into contact with animals that are infested by these parasites, such as camels, cattle and sheep.

"Hello, Gold," I said as I carefully closed the glass door behind me. (I had to be careful to keep in the cool temperature created by the air-conditioners.) "Isn't it hot?"

"Yes, Susan, it is, but this marble floor is cool. In a couple of hours it will become deliciously cold."

Gold stretched out luxuriously on his tummy.

"I can't help feeling a bit sorry for all the Arabian animals that do not have somewhere cool to lie. It has seemed a particularly hot summer this year," I said wearily, as I pulled my chair closer.

"What Arabian animals?" Gold shot the question at me, perking and swivelling his ears in readiness for my answer.

"There are many animals in Arabia, Gold. There are some domesticated ones that no longer have anyone to care for them, and there are wild creatures too, fending for themselves."

"How wild?" he asked in alarm.

"Oh, I don't mean they would do you harm, Gold. Most of the wild animals are very timid. I just mean that they live in the wild. A human may never see these shy creatures."

"Then how do you know they are there?" pursued Gold.

"They are seen from time to time. Once, there were many more than there are now. Ancient pictographs, the pictures carved into the rocks throughout the Arabian Peninsula, show the abundance of wildlife that existed long ago. The oldest illustrations include animals that became extinct at some time in the far distant past. There are scenes showing people hunting and herding animals. These include long-horned cattle that did not survive because so much of the land became arid desert. The harsh countryside was then unable to support animals that required lots of pasture and water each day. There are many pictures of the camel, too. Although some of the drawings and carvings are not very old, it is not always known who made them."

This was just the kind of information that Gold enjoyed. Whenever I began to tell a story, and he was lying on his stomach, he would relax and roll his body slightly sideways to stretch out his back legs – just as he was doing now. And sometimes he shuffled his front paws as a finishing touch. Now, he raised his odd-coloured eyes to mine and fixed me with an expectant look which is my cue to continue.

"The world knew very little about the fauna of the Arabian Peninsula until quite recently, Gold. At this moment, at least 64 different species of mammal are known, and other previously unrecorded species are still being discovered.

"Recent investigations show that Arabia has a surprising variety of creatures. Some live in the seas on the east, west and south of the Arabian Peninsula. But, science has revealed that there were different creatures living in Arabia in ancient times, and when it was connected to Africa and Eurasia millions of years ago. It was once a land of lush forests and vast lakes. Gradually Arabia became isolated and most of it eventually became arid. The animals that survived were adapted to the new conditions.

"As the land slowly dried out and the trees and vegetation decreased, there were not many places left for the creatures to hide. Not only was there less shelter, there was less to eat. Adapting meant a change in diet as well as developing camouflage. You will find today that the colouring of Arabian creatures generally matches their habitat. Many species need to seek refuge in either the white, red and beige sands; the greyish, gravelly lava fields; the vast beige-coloured baked countryside; or among blackish rocks and boulders found in various regions of Saudi Arabia.

"Many animals, living in open country, had to learn to remain perfectly rigid when danger was sensed. It was practical for some to become nocturnal and hunt at night. At night, the desert is alive with snakes, lizards, spiders, gerbils, jerboas and many other nocturnal creatures. The indigenous Arabian hare, and some rabbits (which were domesticated ones returned to the wild, becoming 'feral') prefer to be out in the late evening and early hours of the morning. For many animals, it was best to sleep through the hottest hours of daylight, and hunt for food in the evening and early morning.

"Up until early this century Arabia had plenty of gazelle, oryx, ostrich, leopard, jackal, hyena, wolf and many reptiles."

Gold's eyes had been half closed, but now they widened and he stared dreamily into a place far away, fascinated by some mental picture that I wished I could share. He was probably trying to imagine a time and place where these animals roamed.

"Many Arabian animals once depended on their ability to outrun a pursuer, and they had a fair chance of escaping – even from hunters on horseback. Hunting was once an important part of Arabian family life because the quarry was needed as food. In time, it became a traditional activity known as 'game sport' which men enjoyed.

"Sadly, the speed of wheeled transport and accuracy of modern weapons made hunting a much greater threat to an animal's survival. Quite recently, it became clear that too many have been killed. Certain species have been almost annihilated whilst others have possibly gone forever. Fortunately, the planned preservation of nature and its creatures, known as conservation, has been introduced in Saudi Arabia, and some of the rarest Arabian animals are being re-established in the wild. Today, domesticated animals, as pets, have become part of the modern city lifestyle. It is so good to see animals appreciated and cared for."

"Do other people here keep rabbits for pets, Susan?"

"Yes they do, Gold. There are now pet shops in Arabia. From time to time they also sell parrots and other exotic birds, monkeys, snakes, gazelle, deer, llamas, Shetland ponies, fish and sometimes the large 'cats' such as lions. Peacocks are popular in Arabia, too. Some of the great villas and palaces have beautiful landscaped gardens, where gazelle, deer and peacocks wander free. The zoo in Riyadh is beautifully kept and all sorts of creatures are cared for there, including some of the few Arabian sand cats to be bred in captivity. Zoos are one way to begin the re-establishment of rare creatures for the wild.

"All wild animals have to rely to some extent on their camouflage for survival. Let me tell you about a visit John and I once made to a remote oilfield. We flew to Shaiba in the Rub al Khali, the desert to the south of Saudi Arabia, known as the Empty Quarter. It is called 'empty' because there is almost nothing there – a vast place with insufficient water to sustain much habitation.

"Our small plane landed on one of the natural strips of SABKHA, an incredibly hard and crusty salt flat.

From the sky, these wide strips look like ribbons, alternating with chains of mountainous red sand dunes. The sand continually shifts across the salt floor which was once under water. It was a quiet, desolate place, and I could see no signs of life from the air or on the ground, yet we knew there was at least an oil workers' camp somewhere nearby. All life was hidden from our eyes until the oil men's truck appeared, as if from nowhere, growing out of a small and distant cloud of dust.

"I asked the men if there were any animals about, and an engineer told me that there were lots of creatures in the Empty Quarter. This seemed impossible because we could see nothing for them to eat or drink. He explained that I would learn something if I walked to the point where the salt flat met the dune. It was a long walk and much further than John or I had imagined. As we drew closer, the mammoth dune appeared to rise up before us like a genie emerging from a magic lamp."

Gold's eyes widened in horror. Perhaps he was remembering the story of Aladdin.

"There was nothing to be afraid of, Gold, but I must say we were awed by the size of this great mountain of red sand. Then, on arrival at the foot of the dune, we were astonished to find sparse, coarse vegetation. It had not been visible from a distance. Apparently, these bushes supported the wild life in this vast and formidable desert. Creatures hid and rested for the hottest part of the day; but, even when they did emerge, the engineer said they would be difficult to 'spot' because they were just like me: 'red-haired and scrawny'. My red hair and practical beige-coloured travelling clothes certainly did blend well with the surroundings. We laughed heartily at his faint praise for my slim figure.

"The engineer explained that the herbivorous animals survived by eating from these shrubs, while the carnivorous creatures sustained life by preying on these herbivores; and, both herbivores and carnivores existed on very little water. There was always a certain amount of moisture in the leaves, especially at night, and at dawn, the animals could lap dew that collects on the plants during the night. Some animals, such as gerbils and jerboas, concentrate their urine so as to lose very little moisture as excretion.

"Although many Arabian animals can survive with no more water than those in the Rub al Khali, they do drink when water is available. But wild animals are very wary of humans, and even during the driest times, usually only the feral dog ventures close to human settlements in search of water.

"The creatures know that some moisture lies beneath the sand, and they will scrape a hollow for a cooler bed in which to rest. Even in the barren desert, rain occasionally falls in limited areas, and certain animals can scent it and make their way there, even if it is miles away."

Gold's front paws are sadly bent, but they are strong

Gold raiding the refrigerator

Arabian animals, past and present, can be seen
carved on a rock near Riyadh

"This story is beginning to make me feel very thirsty, Susan."

"Then, Gold, it is time for me to tell you that not all of Arabia is a waterless waste. In some areas there are permanent water courses, lakes, deep waterholes, and mountain forests. And there is food and shelter in abundance for lots of animals in these places. Often in the surrounding countryside, which is sometimes untamed and inaccessible to humans, there are wildcats and wolves. Their lairs are generally hidden in high caves. And lizards dart about while snakes slide and creep among the rocks. On the highest peaks, eagles hide their nests while foxes, porcupines and hares take cover in the scrub and undergrowth. You might say, the region is 'alive' with fauna."

"Tell me about them," demanded Gold. The faraway look vanished from his eyes in his eagerness to hear more about these creatures.

"I would love to, Gold. I shall tell you about them all if you like, but it will take time. There are the traditional domesticated Arabian animals. They are the ones that the people of the Arabian Peninsula have bred and relied upon for their sustenance in the past before the discovery of oil."

"You mean animals were responsible for saving the lives of people?"

"Yes, in a way they were. The Arabian desert people once depended on breeding and herding animals for their livelihood. Their animals had to be able to move with them on foot. You see, it was necessary for them to roam the desert in a relentless search for grazing pasture for their flocks and herds.

It was then every young tribal man's ambition to own at least a dozen camels, 50 sheep, a saluki hunting dog, and, especially, a mare. This horse was his greatest ambition. Naturally, before all of these, he would have to have a DHALUL – the riding camel – and a rifle. In olden times a young man would reckon to double his complement of animals in three years. Women of the desert had similar ambitions. Animals meant wealth. A bride's dowry, the JEHAZ, included clothes, household items, and money. Usually, the money would be invested in a camel or some sheep and, by breeding them, these animals could sustain her should she be divorced or widowed.

"As flocks have always been a source of food for the Bedouin, it was truly a 'walking' bank account. Customarily, male lambs were eaten and the females were kept for milk and for breeding. Young male camels were eaten too. When sufficient adult males were allocated for carrying tents and baggage, the rest would normally be sold. It was only the female camels that were ridden because they were more docile, the trot was softer – and they were kept for milking.

"Horses were much more valuable than camels, and the female horse, or mare, was rarely sold because of her ability to breed. Male foals were usually sent to be sold in the market towns around Arabia. Feeding the foal would drain the mare's strength, and in any case, it might cost too much for the Bedouin to feed as it grew older.

"Mutton (the flesh of mature sheep) and lamb (the flesh of young sheep) are the most popular meat in Arabia. Perhaps this is so because sheep reproduce more quickly than camels. A female sheep is known as NA'AJA and the male is KHARWF or TALY. A male goat is called TAYS and the female is a SHA'A or 'ANZA. Mixed flocks of sheep and goats are called AGHANAM. The single animal is called GHANAM. Otherwise, sheep and goats are usually only referred to separately for their milk. It is interesting to learn that the milk of the female sheep, the ewe, is thicker and is often more appreciated than that of the goat. It is used for cheese and butter; and sometimes made into dried LABAN, a type of yoghurt."

"I don't like milk. I can't imagine how Arnab could drink it," said Gold, pulling a face.

I laughed. "I know several rabbits like Arnab that are partial to milk but it is not usual, I know. Humans are said to be the only mammals to insist upon drinking milk after being weaned from the mother."

"Yuckh!" Gold's comment made his opinion clear.

"Here is an amusing story about AGHANAM, Gold. It is a strange tale. It is said that Arabian sheep and goats interbreed and the offspring are judged by their tails. For instance, if the tail is fat and hangs down like a sheep, then the animal is a 'geep'. But, if the tail is goat-like and held upright, then the creature is a 'shoat'. Yet, I am told, different species do not usually breed. There are strange exceptions, but their offspring cannot reproduce. And true or not, it is an entertaining tale, and no doubt it is the result of the mixed herd having the joint name, AGHANAM.

"It is also comical to see them on the move with the milking females wearing brightly-coloured 'apron' bags over their udders. These are worn to prevent the young animals from suckling all day and taking the milk that the Bedouin need. Aprons made of leftover dress fabrics in floral, stripes and dots add to the charm of the scene. Some aprons glitter in the sunlight with metallic threads. Sometimes, there is a shepherdess wearing pretty colours too."

Gold wriggled his little body and twinkled his eyes at me in a way that I had come to understand as enjoyment.

I continued: "According to the ancient pictographs, or rock pictures, fat-tailed sheep have been living on the Arabian Peninsula for thousands of years. Arabian sheep today, are usually black and white. In central Arabia they have a white head with eyes outlined with black. Most goats are black with some white markings, but sometimes you will see ginger or brown ones. There are wild goats in Arabia too, such as the Ibex and Tahr and there are some wild sheep.

"Sheep, goats and camels once had another and very important value for desert dwellers. The wool of the sheep, and the hair of the camel and goat were needed for weaving. The tent was the most essential item that was woven. You see, nomads had to have a portable house, and since the land has

few trees suitable for building, a house of hair (known as the BAIT AL SHA'AR) was ideal.

"The best tents were woven from goat hair because this was the toughest available animal fibre. This made weaving an essential skill and the most traditional Arabian craft. And, besides woven strips which were joined to make the tent roof and walls, rugs were woven for the floors, as well as many other useful things. There are all sorts of bags and one clever item is a joined pair of camel bags which is thrown over the hump to rest one on each side of the camel. The skins of the animals killed were made into footwear, capes, storage bags, buckets, camel drinking troughs and babies' cradles. Any excess in wool, hair, woven items and leather goods was traded.

"As you might expect, a lifestyle dependent on animals must have been dictated by the creatures' needs. So, man and beast moved almost constantly in search of pasture throughout most of the year. When summer approached, a nomadic tribe moved towards the green shade of date palm groves at an oasis. During the summer months, from June to halfway through October, their tents would be pitched close to the ancient water wells that are found there. These oases are small lakes formed from springs that bubble to the surface in barren deserts. They created the fertile areas where the Bedouin expected to find settled people with whom they could trade their wool and handicrafts for food.

"The date palm is the basis of traditional desert agriculture. It is a remarkable tree that can survive on a little moisture and brackish water. Its fruit is nourishing and keeps well. Summer was the time when the Bedouin rested at the oases, in order to replenish their bodies as well as stock up their saddle bags. When they departed, sufficient dates would be stored to feed themselves and their horses and dogs, too, should it be necessary in the lean months ahead.

"Settled people also kept animals for sustenance and income, and they usually raised pigeons and poultry as well as AGHANAM. Many kept rabbits. When they sold livestock, as a rule, they parted with males only, but for a good price they might have sold a female. They did their best to sell the cockerels first because hens provided them with eggs. I've often thought that it could also be because the Arabian cockerel does not merely herald the dawn after a night of silence. This nuisance crows at any hour, both day and night."

"A very good reason for sending him packing, I'd say, Susan!"

"Absolutely, Gold. We once had a donkey with a similar habit. Donkeys were kept by both the settled and semi-nomadic folk, and only a few had horses. Although traditional life has greatly changed since the discovery of oil, the desert dwellers still enjoy horse racing in some villages. Once, you could expect to see a sandy track surrounding every village. It was part of a lifestyle that endured for thousands of years.

"Settled desert folk live in clay and cement block houses forming QARYA, or villages, and even the smallest has its own mosque, or place of worship known in Arabic as MASJID. Birds and small mammals were sometimes kept inside as well as outside the mud-walled sand gardens attached to the houses. More often, domesticated animals were cared for in an isolated place, well away from the temptation of crops. Fences made of thorns kept their animals in and predators out. The thorny branches of the spreading acacia tree (known as SALAM in Arabic) were cut and laid to make these enclosures. Vegetables were usually grown by settled desert dwellers and these, too, were surrounded by acacia fences.

"The acacia is one of the most widespread wild trees in Arabia. It bears pretty little yellow blossoms in January, but has terrible thorns which hold off wolves, foxes and hyenas. Remarkably, the camel, sheep and goat can skilfully avoid the sharp thorns to eat the tiny leaves. The Bedouin talk of the GEYSUM bush as another source of food shared by AGHANAM and camels, but, strangely, they say that camels never eat it in early spring. And, generally, no Arabian animal will touch the poisonous but luscious-looking evergreen oleander."

"Goodness, it does sound like a difficult life, at least for the animals."

"Yes, it is. Before modern transport, desert life was once one of extreme hardship. Both man and beast became very weary of the heat towards the end of the summer. If rain came at last, everyone was very happy. Grass would shoot up in the desert wherever rain fell, but outside the oases, vegetation usually remained poor, making it necessary for the nomads to follow wadis.

"These dry river beds often had underground water courses feeding those plants with long tap-roots, allowing them to gain maximum nourishment. Plant roots take up moisture and transfer it to the leaves where it is lost in a system called transpiration. Characteristically, perennial desert plants have long roots and little foliage, limiting evaporation and thereby conserving moisture. Further protection comes from hairs, spines and thorns, the modified leaves that create a micro-climate. In some plants there is an absence of leaves, or only very small ones, whilst in others, the leaves are heavy-bodied with a large area for moisture storage. Yet other plants might have a thick-walled, waxy covering – each plant adapted to conserve moisture in its own way.

"In the desert, humans, too, learn to conserve water. When it was time for the great annual migration to commence, the Bedouin packed up their belongings and filled their water bags, knowing they would have to drink sparingly from then on. They set off on a huge grazing circuit, a circular tour which kept them within their traditional tribal ground, or DIRA. It was a pattern of life that was maintained because it dealt with the environment.

"As the Bedouin began their trek, they were aware that henceforth their animals would have to be less and less dependent upon water from wells. They would have to get their moisture from vegetation. This meant that they could not keep sheep and goats unless water was sent for daily. The

camel exists longest without drinking, and, by full spring, and with good pasture, only the herder would require water. Yet, in summer, far from an oasis, a man could live off his camel's milk, even if the beast had gone for days without drinking.

"It was not so long ago that Bedouin tribes owned the desert wells. Many of these are very ancient, their water springing far below the surface. There is a lot of water under Arabia, some of it more than 30 thousand years old. This precious liquid lies at various levels, some wells as much as 50 metres (160 feet) deep. The Bedouin knew that some would flow all year, while others dried up periodically. Drawing water meant that the Bedouin also had to handcraft buckets, ropes and pulleys, using animal hair and hide. Desert folk, have made these utensils and aids to haul water with the assistance of their animals through countless ages.

"Traditionally, some tribal people moved on the perimeter of the great deserts with flocks of sheep and goats. These animals can exist on sparse vegetation provided it is not too far from water. Their daily requirement is sometimes brought to them in buckets by their keepers. By summer, the sheep would have developed enormously fat tails, the camel's hump would have enlarged – and all the animals would have put on extra flesh. They would have to depend on this plumpness during the difficult summertime ahead.

"Desert hardship was shared by humans and animals in a lifestyle that bound them together. Each new day began accompanied by the shuffling of flocks and herds and bleating of lambs. This was the hour of their morning meal. The lambs had to drink well because there would be nothing more for them between dawn and nightfall, when their mothers returned to the camp. The daily counting of sheep is done at dawn, too. Hopefully, none would be missing. Watchdogs should have chased away the wolves. Yet sheep may have been so frightened of the wolves that they were unable to cry out for help. Goats will always bleat when nervous, and wolves, knowing this, do their best to avoid an encounter."

"Perhaps that's why sheep and goats are kept together, Susan."

"That's very likely, Gold. There is usually a very good reason behind Arabian Bedouin traditions and rules.

"There is a Bedouin saying: 'RIJJAL BARRA, NISA JUWA', meaning 'Men outside, women inside'. This was a flexible rule referring to work. It had to be 'elastic' because sometimes fathers, husbands and sons needed to be away from the camp, making it necessary for mothers and daughters to shepherd the AGHANAM and camels in their absence. Young children easily learnt how to help out. They played with the sheep and goats which quickly became tame and fairly obedient. Children helped gather their grass and herbs for fodder too, and it was their responsibility to fetch water to the tent twice a day. Sometimes a boy would ride a donkey on his errand, but for girls, riding donkeys was regarded as AIB, meaning 'demeaning' or 'undignified'; although it was not in bad taste for a girl to ride a camel.

"The various herds were left to graze in fairly close proximity to the tent. At the furthest distance from the camp a shepherd might have needed to deceive his flock into thinking he was standing near them. He did this by planting his staff, the MIKHYAL, in the ground and mounting his cloak, called ABBA, on top. In the evening, the camels were brought into a semi-circle in front of the tents. Because it is cold in the desert at night, and they are not covered, the herder makes them lie down close together for warmth.

"Any AGHANAM were brought to sleep within the space before the tents for fear of wolves. Once returned to the tent, each mother sheep and goat was called by name and her young was brought for her to suckle. As they all look so much the same, it is amazing that she will not accept any lamb but her own.

"It does not amaze me, since to the mothers, they don't look alike at all," explained Gold, a little indignantly.

"I know you are right, Gold. The Bedouin certainly learned to know each of their animals. It was obviously a matter of caring for them constantly and eventually noticing their differences, just as mothers of 'identical' twins do. The shepherds must have learnt so much about each one in his daily round. His last duty was at night, when the kids and lambs were fed. They were then tied up inside the tent or left just outside, usually close to the she-goats and ewes. They did not wander from their mothers. It is no wonder that the animals were tame, when so much was shared.

"And thus, night fell on a Bedouin camp.

"Well, did you enjoy that story, Gold?"

"Oh, yes, Susan. But doesn't it seem sad that this traditional way of life has changed – even though it was difficult for the people and their animals."

"I know what you mean, Gold." I nodded.

And we both fell silent, lost in our romantic dream of how it would be to live the free life of a nomad with his animals in the Arabian desert.

4
Reptiles and Amphibians

old had been asking me questions all morning. He had appeared at my feet wherever I turned. I could see that I would have to pay him some attention soon, so I promised to tell him a story as soon as my work was finished. Even so, he continued to follow me about, trying to satisfy his curiosity with my brief answers. He had seemed pleased to hear that a rabbit of over three years could be considered to be about the same age as a human of 40 years. It made him feel important, I suppose; yet, he was obviously not completely satisfied because questions about age persisted.

"Then, Susan, would you say that Nigel is the same age as Christopher?" (Nigel had been born in the Spring, and was five months old.)

"Well, no, Gold. Nigel is now a sexually mature rabbit. That means kittens can be expected after he has mated with a doe. A human doesn't properly reach that stage until about 14. But, you, Gold – you are almost 'middle-aged' – just like John and me," I teased.

Gold was certainly unhappy to learn that rabbits do not live as long as humans. It had cheered him a little to know that Mr. Lockley believed rabbits to have a very good brain, and that if only they lived longer, there would be a greater chance to learn about their intellectual potential.

"What exactly does that mean, Susan?" Gold had chimed in.

"It means that if rabbits lived longer, then it might be possible to find out just how much they are able to learn. Perhaps all rabbits could talk and maybe they could learn to read."

"Uh-huh," murmured Gold but his troubled gaze had remained, and reached way beyond the living room and out across the swimming pool. I could see that he was not finding it easy to accept a rabbit's short lifespan. I should not have teased him. With my tasks finished, I led Gold to a comfortable spot on the terrace. Samantha, Mamapuss and the warren rabbits were scattered there, resting.

"You know, Gold, in terms of history, our lifespan is very short indeed. The earth has existed for around 4,600 million years – although only the last 600 million can be traced with any accuracy."

I could see by the perk of his ears that I had touched Gold's imagination, and diverted him from further morbid and dreary speculation.

"Were there rabbits in the first stories – 600 million years ago, Susan?"

"No, Gold. There were no stories. And there were no rabbits and no humans. There were no mammals at all! You see, Gold, you and I are mammals. Mammals and birds are called 'warm-blooded' creatures because the food they eat generates body heat. They are believed to be descended from a reptilian ancestor. The major changes that took place in the mammal's evolution include warm blood, hairy skin, increased brain size, live birth of young, and development of mammary glands for supplying milk to the young. The exceptions are the egg-laying mammals of Australia: the platypus and echidna.

"In ancient times there were no such creatures as we are. At first there was only life in the sea, but, eventually some of the ancient sea creatures came to live on land.

"The earth was a very different place then, and it has changed many times since. For instance, Arabia's oil fields were still forest land, awaiting nature's changes which, in time, rotted the trees and eventually converted them into oil."

"Will you tell me about the first land creatures, Susan?"

"All right, Gold. Now, first of all, I should explain how the world has come to know about ancient life. At first, it was a great mystery. Scientists had to gather fragments of information about early life forms from their fossilized remains. A fossil is something found buried in the earth and it is usually obtained by digging. The word 'fossil' describes ancient remains of both animals and plants, or fauna and flora. Well, the scientists put together the facts as if they were pieces of a giant jig-saw puzzle, and they generally agree that reptiles were the first backboned animals to breed on land – about 340 million years ago. And, it is agreed that reptiles descended from amphibians which appeared about 350 milion years ago. They were the first backboned animals partially adapted to life on land which means they had to return to the water to breed. The early amphibians looked very different from the ones now. Today, they include frogs, toads and salamanders."

"What does an amphibian look like?"

"Amphibians are rather small animals that vary greatly in body form. Amphibian means 'double life,' referring to how they live on land when they are adults, yet lay their soft eggs in water. This 'spawn', or batch of eggs hatch into an intermediate life form known as larvae. The amphibian's larval young live and grow in water, and they breathe with gills as fish do. Eventually, they develop air-breathing lungs in order to live on land. One example is the tadpole, the tiny fish-like larva that hatches from the amphibian spawn, and eventually metamorphoses, or develops into the adult form."

"Ultimately, the reptile evolved, a creature that made the break from the water by developing the amniotic egg, whereby the embryo, or unborn young, was surrounded by its own water. This reptilian egg made it possible for animals to live entirely on land.

"The difference between amphibians and reptiles became more apparent with time. Amphibians usually have soft, naked, moist skins and no scales. Many can 'breathe' through their skin's moisture. Most reptiles are covered with thick, dry, scaly skins or horny plates, and nearly all reproduce by means of eggs. Reptile eggs have a shell and they are much larger than amphibian eggs, as the young must be big enough to look after themselves on land immediately after they are hatched. Amphibians and most reptiles do not usually take care of their eggs. One exception is the crocodile. There are exceptions that do not lay eggs at all, and these creatures give birth to miniatures of themselves."

"Are there all sorts of reptiles then?" queried Gold.

"Oh, yes! Reptiles include snakes, lizards, tuatara, crocodiles, turtles and tortoises. All of these, and amphibians, have a backbone, as do fish and mammals. It is often called 'the spine'. Actually, it is a collection of many small bones connected to each other to form the spinal column. The bones are known as 'vertebrae' and all creatures that have them are termed 'vertebrates'. This internal skeleton is a clever arrangement giving the body support and (in most cases) allowing it to be flexible. In the reptile, the spine continues into the tail which is often a long one. For most reptiles, it can play a part in movement and life preservation, as I shall explain." I traced my finger along the length of a lizard that I was drawing and Gold peered at it with interest. "Invertebrates may not have a spine, but many do have an external 'skeleton', or hard structure on the outside.

"Reptiles, unlike amphibians, are creeping, crawling creatures, but they are similar in that neither can make their own body heat. That is why they are called 'cold-blooded', which is not quite accurate.

"Many of them can be happy and active at temperatures higher than would be comfortable for mammals, which are 'endothermic'. 'Endotherm' describes a 'warm-blooded' creature such as a mammal or bird, which manufactures its own body heat. The correct term for reptiles and amphibians is 'ectotherm', referring to a creature that depends totally on its environment for heat. Ectothermic creatures can warm up by the sun or through other warm objects, and it is usual for them to have the same heat as their surroundings.

"Ectotherms need less to eat than mammals and birds because food is not required to manufacture body warmth. And most of them take very little liquid because their thick or scaly skin prevents evaporation and keeps in body moisture. Of course, such a skin also means that they cannot perspire or sweat when they are too hot, so they mainly keep cool by hiding from the sun. So, you see, reptiles can make themselves quite at home in the desert. It is generally warm, and food and water are scarce."

"What do they eat?"

"Adult amphibians eat other creatures but some of their larvae are vegetarians. Most reptiles eat live food and they seize their prey with the jaws and swallow it whole. With the exception of tortoises, terrapins and turtles, reptile teeth are adapted for seizing and holding.

"Their limbs are generally small – when they exist at all – and toes and claws are used for digging and climbing.

"270 million years ago, land creatures were increasing in numbers but they were still predominantly reptilian."

"When did the stories about mammals begin, Susan? Did the reptiles want to eat the mammals when they first came?"

"Sometimes, but it was not quite a matter of mammals arriving, Gold. Do you remember Christopher telling you about dinosaurs? They were the gigantic prehistoric creatures. Dinosaurs existed about 225 million years ago, and, at first, they were quite small: 2–3 metres (6–10 feet) long." I demonstrated the size of the little dinosaur with my arms. "Well, it was about the time that dinosaurs first appeared that the first mammals evolved from the reptile."

"Susan, what do you mean 'evolved'? Do you mean that a mother reptile gave birth to the first baby mammal?"

"Not at all. Evolving means that the changes happen over a very VERY long time. It is a slow process taking millions of years. About 180 million years ago, reptiles began to increase in size. The weather was then very warm and there was plenty of good food for them to eat. They evolved into monsters. In some cases the reptiles' scales, horny plates and shells, adapted and became feathers and the new creatures began to fly.

"Others were able to fly because they had skin stretching between the body and fingers. Even so, they still looked like reptiles. These great creatures dominated land, sea and air for about 135 million years, which is why that period is now known as the Age of Reptiles.

"Living side by side with these enormous reptiles, there were small and primitive mammals, no bigger than rats, and these were evolving too – when they were not being caught and eaten by the flesh-eating, or carnivorous dinosaurs. Some dinosaurs were omnivorous, consuming both flesh and vegetable matter. Others were vegetarians, and defined as the herbivorous species. So despite their large size, not every dinosaur had to be feared – unless he stepped on you. And, while all of this was happening, even the earth was evolving –

revolving and evolving." Gold's eyes followed my rotating hand.

"At that time, when the earth's temperature cooled, the new conditions were unsuitable for some reptiles, so many died. Their habitats were no longer luxuriant, and as the vegetation decreased, the food 'chain' was affected. The herbivores decreased; then, so did the carnivores. Many species died out, while others adapted and survived, but their descendants were very much smaller. By 65 million years ago, the dinosaurs had disappeared completely and many new mammals had evolved.

"By 40 million years ago herbivores were on the increase. The carnivores were growing in number, too, and so were the omnivores – the good creatures that ate both their meat and vegetables. Some animals developed separated toes, and among these were the ancestors of modern cats and dogs. And there was even a primitive ape which is possibly related to humans. You know, Gold, mankind's own history is STILL incomplete, so it is always exciting when someone digs up the fossilized bones of upright-walking creatures."

Gold had nestled into a furry egg-shape with his ears laid back. His small front paws were neatly placed together and sticking out. His body was relaxed but I could tell by his eyes that his mind remained a little perplexed.

"Reptiles sound very odd. They don't seem one bit like any of the other animals you've told me about, Susan. Are there any in Arabia?"

"There certainly are, Gold. You might have seen at least one – a variety of gecko. Various species of gecko dart about our houses and gardens. One lives right here on the terrace. Geckos are appealing fellows – and useful too. I know how you detest insects, Gold, so you will be pleased to hear that these lizards feed on mosquitoes, cockroaches, flies and other insects.

"Geckos are well known for their voices but not quite as you are, Gold. They don't speak human languages. I'm sure that you must, at least, have heard them chattering as they scuttle about, hunting in the cool of the evening. Geckos usually rest during the hottest part of the day. They can run up walls and across ceilings because they have a set of tiny hairs under each toe that grip even the smoothest-looking surfaces. It must be great fun to gallop upside-down, sticking your feet and then releasing them. It seems very clever. Don't you think so?

Gold nodded but did not answer. He did not look so sure. I continued:

"These reptiles are most notable for their great variety. There are at least 30 species in Arabia. And within just one of their genera, or groups of species, some have adapted to living on sand, while other cousins choose hard ground as a habitat. Yet, other relatives inhabit SABKHA, the salt-crusted mud flats which have been left where ancient water once lay. Geckos are various colours and they have different shaped tails which can be dropped and grown again."

"Whatever for?" Gold exclaimed.

"Probably, Gold, they have evolved in this way because it is usually the tail that the enemy catches. The gecko can escape by leaving it in the jaws of its attacker. It is a pity for a lizard to lose his tail, though, because that is where fat can be stored. A supply of fat can keep the lizard alive when there is not enough food about. It takes time to grow a new tail, so it also means the gecko cannot run well-balanced for a while. You see, the life of this reptile can be difficult. You know, Gold, it might be more fun to be one of the large lizards that prowl the sandy-gravelly places of Arabia hunting for food. You could pretend to be a prehistoric monster."

Gecko

"Ugh! I hope I never meet one of those. I don't think reptiles are ANYTHING like the other animals I have heard about." Gold seemed to be a little disturbed by the thought of the harmless little gecko with the detachable tail.

"Maybe so, Gold, but the reptiles have one thing in common with all the other creatures. They have adapted to the hot and harsh desert conditions; so much so that Arabia has been described as an excellent refuge for the modern reptile. Even a few inches of sand can provide a blanket of insulation against heat and cold. The reptile's scales and horny plates help to keep the body water-tight to conserve every drop of moisture that the creature gains from its food. This is especially good for desert reptiles because most of them must go right through life without ever drinking water."

"It doesn't sound like much of a life to me," judged Gold.

"Well, not all creatures have such a cozy life as you do, Gold, but everyone can be happy in their way. Even some rabbits and hares must be content with harsh surroundings; and, remember, Arabia has some lush green woodlands and rich agricultural areas as well as barren deserts. Reptiles of many kinds and sizes live in very different parts of the Arabian Peninsula. Some live most comfortably.

"Lizards are the most common reptile in Arabia, and they are found almost everywhere. The least conspicuous reptiles are the snakes, because they are secretive and generally nocturnal. The most uncommon Arabian reptiles are Chelonians, a group which includes all forms of tortoises.

"Zoologists have now divided tortoises into three separate groups: land-tortoises, terrapins, and marine-tortoises. The marine-tortoises are now commonly called turtles, dwelling in the sea. Terrapins live in fresh or brackish water. In America, the term 'terrapin' is used exclusively for edible forms. In Europe and Asia, 'terrapin' is applied to various other aquatic forms. The term 'tortoise' is now usually kept only for land-dwelling species."

"Tell me about them!" Gold ordered, as he adjusted his position to be more comfortable. Harvette had hopped over to join Gold, plumping down to lean against him. I continued:

"Arabia's Chelonians are all terrapins and turtles. Chelonians are egg-laying creatures with four limbs, and their feet have modified into flippers. The front legs are oar-like paddles and the hind legs serve as rudders. Consequently, they move slowly and laboriously on land. Although water-dwellers, they must come to the surface to breathe every hour or so. And they breed on land, laying eggs in shallow nests close to the water. Around springtime, the female deposits her eggs in a nest she has scraped out, refilling and camouflaging it before returning to the water. It is astonishing to see that the young instinctively head for the water after hatching.

"Chelonians are creatures most notable for living longer than any other animal. Although their average lifespan is about 50 years, many have been known to live for well over 100 years. They have been called 'living fossils'; and not because of their incredible longevity, but because in some features, they are primitive and much less evolved than lizards and snakes."

"So, the tortoise family live longer than humans?" Gold looked up at me enquiringly, and with some surprise.

"Yes, Gold, usually they do. Perhaps their cumbersome, protective armour often has something to do with it. Science tells us that their slow life processes are the cause. Chelonians are unique among back-boned creatures, in having a shell almost completely enclosing the body. The shell resembles two plates." I cupped my hands to demonstrate: "One plate, the 'plastron', is worn underneath like a dish, and the other, the 'carapace', goes on top, like a lid. These plates are covered with horny sections and the whole lot is referred to as the 'shell'.

"The shell can be a fortress against predatory animals. At the slightest disturbance some Chelonians can pull in the head and tail, folding the scaly forelegs to protect the front entrance, and bending the hind feet so the hard soles protect the back end. The shell serves as a perfect armour against humans and many animals.

"Chelonians are not aggressive and they have no teeth. The upper jaw is not moveable, yet the sharp edges of their jaws do very well to cut up grasses, small fish, crabs, frogs, toads, snails, worms and a variety of other yummy things."

"Yuck!" said Gold, pulling a face. "Why do people hunt them, Susan?"

"The flesh and eggs of certain marine-tortoises and terrapins are edible, Gold. There are five species of marine-tortoise in Arabia, and at least two are known to inhabit the Arabian Gulf.

"I am sad to say the Green Turtle is a very popular food. It dines only on grasses and algae, and sometimes exceeds 225 kilos (500 lbs) in weight and 125 centimetres (4 feet) in length. The Hawksbill Turtle is hunted for its shell as well as flesh. All sorts of ornaments such as combs, ladies' hair clips, and handbag frames are made from the shell, and its eggs are a great delicacy. This turtle rarely weighs more than 45 kilos (100 lbs).

"Then there is the Pacific Ridley Turtle, the smallest sea turtle weighing between 90–110 kilos (200–250 lbs) and the shell measuring a maximum of 80 centimetres (31 inches), the Loggerhead Turtle, which can be massive and weigh over 450 kilos (1000 lbs). The flesh of these two creatures is greatly appreciated by some people. The fifth turtle found in Arabian waters is the Leathery Turtle, the largest of all, and reported to attain a weight of 1150 kilos (2,500 lbs) and a length of 3.10 metres (10 feet). It has an almost smooth casing instead of horny plates. In times past, this animal was wanted because it contained large quantities of oil, and its flesh and eggs are desired, too.

"Living in the fresh and brackish waters of north-eastern Arabia, there is the Caspian Pond Turtle, generally referred to as a terrapin."

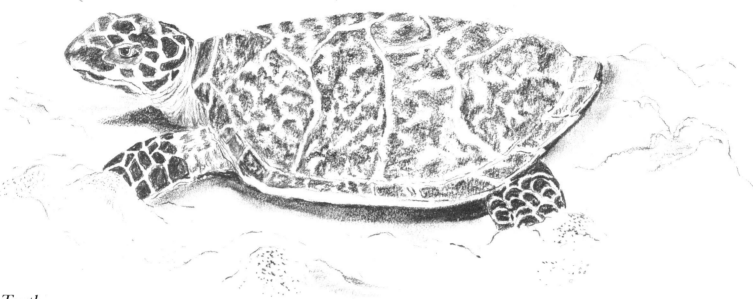

Turtle

"What a shame they move so slowly. It must be difficult to escape," said Gold thoughtfully.

"I think, Gold, the world is now aware of the tragedy of killing these incredible creatures. Turtle soup and frogs' legs are not as popular as they once were."

"Frogs' legs!" Gold screeched in horror.

"Let me tell you about frogs and toads. They are two of Arabia's amphibians, and they are known as Anurans. Anurans are fresh water creatures, found in the same regions as terrapins. They usually dwell in damp places because, as well as breathing with their lungs, they can 'breathe' with their skin, provided it remains moist. Sometimes they live in arid, stony places, and only emerge at night when there is some moisture in the air.

"Frogs and toads look quite similar, both having short bodies, four legs and no tail. The name 'Anuran' is Greek, meaning 'without a tail'. Anurans' hindlegs are longer and more powerful than the forelegs because they are needed for jumping and swimming. The forelegs are used for stuffing food into the mouth. They eat caterpillars, moths, wasps, bees, ants, spiders, and various other insects, catching them with a long sticky tongue that can be shot out quickly." (Gold pulled a face.) "Their eyes are especially adapted to react to moving objects, and they hunt at night, usually watching for food that moves."

"Are there lots of Anurans in Arabia Susan?" Gold questioned.

"There are four species of toad and two ordinary species of frog plus a tree frog. The Arabian Tree Frog is a good climber, and his habitat is the west and southwest where there are forests. The four types of toad and two kinds of frog are found in these areas, and the same species of frogs inhabit the south and as far east as Oman.

"Anurans often like to keep their scooped-out earth or stone houses year after year. You may come across one when it is inactive. If the temperature drops to freezing, frogs and toads can resist the cold by entering the state of deep sleep known as hibernation. If the weather is too hot and dry, they withstand discomfort in the dormant state known as aestivation. At these times, frogs and toads use almost no oxygen and live off their fat.

"In the springtime, Anurans migrate to the water for the breeding season. Those living in dry climates, might breed when rain comes, but not always. The males initiate the breeding by loudly calling the females. Female frogs lay their eggs in masses and toads lay a stream of eggs directly into the water. Some amphibians lay their eggs on land, and others give birth to miniatures of themselves. The eggs of frogs and toads are encased in a jelly-like substance, which the males fertilize by squirting fluid over them. Most amphibian eggs are fertilized outside the female's body in this fashion."

"How peculiar," snorted Gold.

"The hatched larvae, known as tadpoles, swim with the aid of a tail which has a fin above and below. Eventually, this tail shortens and is absorbed. As it disappears, hind legs appear; and not long after, front legs grow. At the same time, the skin of the tadpole thickens in preparation for life on land. The young herbivorous tadpoles continue to live in the water feeding on algae and other small plants until their gills are replaced by lungs. Then they can breathe air on land and live as predators."

"I don't like their choice of food but they ARE interesting, Susan," Gold said grudgingly.

"Most people seem to like frogs but few people are fond of toads. There are lots of ancient tales full of superstitions about toads. They are usually the ugly character in the story. Perhaps this is because many of them produce a toxic fluid which can make you sick. It is best not to touch toads."

"But, Susan, how can you tell which is a toad?"

"It is fairly easy to tell a frog from a toad. Frogs have moist, bright, slimy skin and they jump well. (Frogs have 'jumping' legs while toads have 'hopping' legs.) Toads are dull,

wrinkled, dry-skinned and pimply. Their rough skin is a wonderful camouflage, and they can even change colour gradually to blend with their habitat. Another way to tell, is to wait and watch for a while. Toads have shorter legs than a frog and they seem to 'walk' with great difficulty. To defend itself, a toad will puff itself up, but this does not fool snakes. They know the toad is bluffing and can be swallowed once the air has been squashed out."

"How revolting." Gold pulled a face. "I prefer the lizards to snakes, I think."

"Lizards do very well in Arabia. There are at least 90 species already recorded and new ones are being discovered on an average of one lizard each year. Some appear to be quite rare."

"Tell me more about the lizards!" demanded Gold.

"Most of Arabia's lizards are diurnal, which means that they are active only in the daytime. They are ground-dwellers that climb in search of food, and their prey varies in size according to their own size. Many eat insects, and there are plenty of these in the desert to provide a satisfying meal for a reptile."

"Are there insects as big as rabbits?" Gold's eyes widened and he looked searchingly into mine with growing horror. He detested flies and ants – and cockroaches, in particular. His expression made me laugh.

"Actually, Gold, some large reptiles are herbivorous but others do eat all kinds of creatures, including other reptiles and rodents – and the occasional lagomorph, like you; but, no, there are no 'creepy-crawlies' as large as a rabbit. If you are interested, you must remind me to tell you about Arabia's fascinating insects some time.

"Most of the insects are quite small, so it would take a lot to make a good meal for a lizard. Although, you will remember, reptiles do not need as many insects as birds do because reptiles are ectothermic and do not need food to manufacture body warmth."

Gold seemed comforted, so I continued:

"You can imagine just how quick and clever reptiles must be to catch insects.

"Many Agamid lizards are mostly insect eaters. They sit very still among rocks or shrubs to wait for insects to pass by. Agamids are usually about 20 to 30 centimetres (8–12 inches) long. The Arabian Toad-headed Agamid and the Banded Toad-headed Agamid do not have ear openings, but they can still hear."

"Why are these lizards called 'toad-heads', Susan?"

"It is because their blunt head resembles that of a toad. The Banded Toad-head inhabits gravel plains and salt flats. The Arabian Toad-head is known in Arabia as the TUHAYHI. It lives in sandy terrain and sprints at great speed, but prefers to escape by disappearing into the sand, sinking straight down by vibrating its flat body and shivering so fast that you can hardly see it moving at all. It is out of sight in seconds, leaving only a faint outline on the surface of the sand. His special scaly eyebrows and eyelashes keep the sand out of his eyes. He is a real 'sinking ship' in a 'sea of sand'."

"How peculiar!" commented Gold. He looked up expectantly for me to continue.

Dhubb

"Some Agamid lizards are rock dwellers and it is always a delightful surprise to see a bright blue Yemeneni Agama sitting on top of a rock – especially so, since there are very few blue creatures in the animal kingdom."

Gold looked up at me with great interest but said nothing. We were now surrounded by all the rabbits except Rabby Long Legs who sat among the petrified wood, alone, as usual. Poor Rabby! I continued my reptile story:

"The largest Agamid in Arabia is the Spiny-tailed Lizard. It is known as the DHUBB, and it is one of the heaviest lizards here, growing up to 65 centimetres (25 inches) in length and approximately 20 centimetres (8 inches) wide. There are four species of DHUBB in Arabia and they all look like prehistoric monsters. It is strange that this reptile looks so 'tough' because the adult usually eats only insects and vegetable matter.

"The DHUBB is no different from any other reptile when it comes to shedding its skin. When the creature grows too large, it splits open the old skin and steps right out and walks right off wearing a brand new one. The peculiar thing about the DHUBB is that the old skin usually looks much too large for him – at least it does early in the morning. As the day warms up and the DHUBB begins to warm up too, it fills out its skin. As it gets warmer and warmer the lizards colour also changes – from early-morning grey to beige, then to cream, and finally to bright yellow.

"DHUBBs can stay perfectly still for hours, but watch out! Although they often look languid and ungainly, this lizard can move very quickly indeed and run almost as fast as a rabbit. It may not want to eat you, but, if frightened or angry, it will put up a ferocious display.

"The DHUBB looks quite fearful because of its long, sharp, powerful claws and broad tail, all ringed with sharp spikes. And it can use the tail to inflict painful injuries. But, first of all, it gives a warning by puffing and hissing fiercely – and inflating itself like a balloon. Then it will thrash the tail at the enemy and prepare to bite. DHUBBs never fight with their claws; these are just for climbing and digging long tunnels in hard, gravelly ground, although some do inhabit other kinds of terrain. In summertime, it is nice and cool down in a DHUBB's deep tunnel; and it is warm underground in the cold months.

"Family groups of these lizards live in arid, waterless country mostly, and can go for long periods without anything to eat. Their eyesight is excellent, and helps them watch out for large birds of prey which are their enemy. The Bedouin hunted them. Some say the flesh of the DHUBB is like chicken. Others say it is more like tough lamb. In any case, everyone agrees that the tail is the best part."

"Poor chap!" said Gold. "It doesn't seem fair. He doesn't eat anyone but everybody wants to eat him."

"True!" I agreed. "Most of the other lizards are hunters. Lacertids are diurnal hunting lizards, usually about 20 centimetres (8 inches) long. There are over 20 species of Lacertid in Arabia. They are 'ordinary-looking' lizards with cone-shaped heads and long tails. They change colour less obviously than most other lizards do, but they are still very interesting.

"Then there is the Spinyfoot Lacertid which is a real speedster. He moves swiftly with the aid of fingers and toes fringed with rows of outward-pointing scales. They work like boat oars in soft terrain. In Arabic he is known as the SA'WADDAH. The Desert Lacertid prefers harder ground, and the third main kind, the Lacerta, inhabits the moist highlands of northern Oman in southeastern Arabia. Lacertids can shed their tails just as geckos and skinks do."

"Skinks! What are skinks? What a funny name!"

"Skinks are another kind of usually diurnal hunting lizard, often about 15 centimetres (6 inches) long. The Arabian DAMMUSAH is a skink known as the 'Sandfish' because it can dive in and out of sand almost as if it were water. Its world is a 'sea' of sand. When pursued, the sandfish plunges beneath the surface to cruise under the steep slip faces of moving sand dunes. Its round, smooth, shiny body with a short, plump tail and tiny rounded limbs are as streamlined as any submarine. The scales overlap completely and tightly, and the ear, nose and mouth openings are so well designed that they keep out sand when 'swimming' along. The toes are fringed with flattened scales that help the lizard on its way."

"Goodness! Sinking ships; feet that work like boat oars; sandfish swimming and diving in and out of a sea of sand. Do Arabian reptiles think that they are still amphibians?" said Gold with glee. He was enjoying himself very much. He half got up and shuffled his feet before settling again.

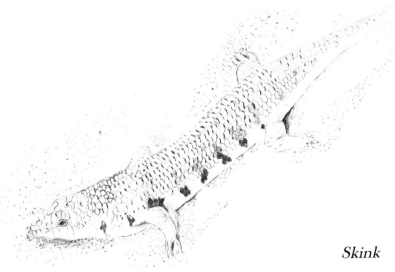

Skink

"There are several species of skink in Arabia, Gold, and some inhabit green coastal regions and leafy hiding places; others live where they can climb rocks and trees. Most give birth to miniatures of themselves. Although these animals are usually active by day, Hemprich's Sand Skink is an exception. It prefers to hunt by night and spend the day in the burrow. When the diurnal creatures return to their hiding places for the evening, this species of skink emerges to hunt, as do geckos and the other nocturnal animals. Both of these lizards

Nigel often sits
on the diving board

Nigel's first
swim

Gold floating

Shaitana, so gentle and placid, was always a wonderful mother

have eyes that resemble a cat's eye. Unlike a cat, however, the vertical slit eye of a gecko has notched edges, which can be brought together to form a series of tiny pinholes. Their separate images are then superimposed on the back of the eyeball.

"The eyes of reptiles show an extremely wide range of adaptations and modifications. Those with little need of vision have only dots in the skin, while others requiring keen vision in order to survive, have amazing and unique eyes."

"I think lizards are fascinating. It's funny, Susan, how some can change colour. I would like to do that. I wouldn't mind being blue sometimes – but on second thoughts, I would hate to turn yellow. Bleaah!"

"I wish I could show you a chameleon, Gold. Chameleons are lizards that can change colour right before your eyes. They do this to hide among their surroundings, but quite apart from camouflage, the chameleon changes colour when it is afraid or excited, just as certain other lizards do."

"Tell me about him," Gold ordered.

"The chameleon is a peculiar chap to look at. His eyes can swivel about independent of one another. One eye might be looking upwards, watching out for the enemy while the other eye might be checking somewhere else – perhaps looking below for some insects to eat. When hunting, it means that there is no need for him to move until the last moment. These lizards inhabit Arabian woodlands and gardens in the west and southwest. When climbing trees, the special claws grip well and the tail gives additional support. The tail is 'prehensile', which means that it can curl around and hold a branch. Attached to the tree and hidden, a chameleon waits for dinner to come by. It is caught with the sticky end of a very long tongue that shoots out like an arrow.

"Now, the Great Monitor Lizard, the WARAL, has a forked tongue as snakes do. This tongue catches particles of scent as it is flicked quickly in and out, taking them to a special 'smelling' organ in the roof of the mouth, known as Jacobson's organ. In this way the WARAL learns when prey or the enemy are about. WARALs can change colour, too. They begin by being grey in the early morning, and they warm up to a light beige during the day.

"The WARAL is the largest Arabian lizard and some are about 150 centimetres (5 feet) long. This carnivorous reptile can enlarge its jaws and throat to eat animals rather like snakes do. Rodents, snakes and other lizards are swallowed whole. WARALS have been said to have an aggressive nature, and there are stories about them attacking and killing the DHUBB, even when they are not hungry. Some Bedouin believe the WARAL is a dangerous lizard and they will have nothing to do with it – they won't even eat its eggs.

"Dangerous or not, the WARAL certainly looks ferocious. The markings on the snake-like head give it an angry, scowling appearance, and the unusual 'eagle' eyes and frightening hooked claws add up to a fierce-looking lizard. The claws are used only for climbing, but it will lash the long,

thin, whip-like tail if cornered. It is wise to keep in mind that the WARAL can run very fast and it does bite.

"Now, the Amphisbaenian lizard of the Eastern Arabian Gulf region is completely different. Its name in Arabic is NADUS. This creature is shy and rarely seen because it lives under the sand and seldom comes out. The NADUS is legless and is often mistaken for a snake. And, because it lives in darkness, the eyes have become almost sightless dots. The NADUS remains buried in order to survive. Any reptile will die if it gets too hot but the NADUS expires especially quickly if exposed to the sun."

"Well, you could hardly say he evolved in the right place," said Gold.

"But, Gold, you must agree that he has adapted well and found the perfect way to survive. Sand is a wonderful insulator against heat and cold."

"Hmmmm! So, what is a snake?"

"A snake is a reptile without legs and eyelids. It is covered with scales that can be very beautiful. But to describe it better, a snake looks like a small, pointed head attached to a long tail. In reality, this animal has an especially long, thin body and a long thin tail. Another name for it is 'serpent' and poets sometimes refer to them as 'slender serpents' because they are so long and slim.

"Snakes eat live prey and can unhinge their jaws to open the mouth wider, allowing them to swallow prey whole. Snakes can also stare without blinking, having a transparent skin which covers and protects the eye instead of a closing lid.

"Serpents have been on earth for about 70 million years and some of the oldest stories and poems are about them. Snakes are associated with evil and fear in many parts of the world. In Australia, the aboriginal people believe in a Rainbow Snake god. An ancient Greek legend tells of winged serpents in Arabia. And, the Arabian Bedouin recount a story about a snake that can fly through the air like an arrow to strike a human on the forehead. It is supposed to be the deadly Black YAYM – an extremely rare Arabian cobra. Some Bedouin say that to dream of killing a snake is to triumph over the enemy; and they recount that some tribal people would eat the flesh of long serpents but the flesh of short ones was given as medicine to camels."

"Is there really a flying snake, Susan?"

"Certain snakes exist that glide from trees, and though there are none here, there are some dangerous snakes on the Arabian Peninsula. Since it is difficult for most people to know which ones to avoid, it is safest to move away from any snake as calmly, quietly and as quickly as you can. Snakes are seldom seen because they are shy – they can hear or smell us coming, and usually depart as we approach.

"In any case, snakes are nocturnal as a rule. It is just that warmth attracts them because they are ectothermic, and they like to bask in warm sun. That is how you might come across one. Snakes usually give a hissing warning sound if startled, normally attacking only when cornered.

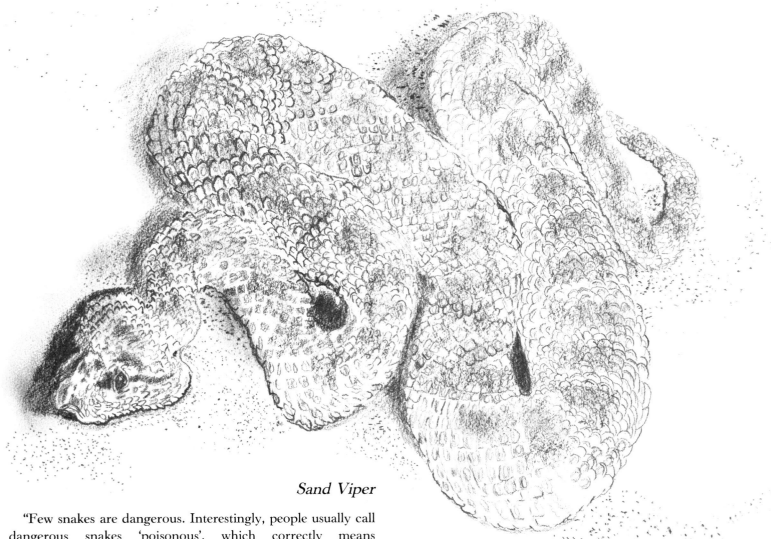

Sand Viper

"Few snakes are dangerous. Interestingly, people usually call dangerous snakes 'poisonous', which correctly means something dangerous if eaten or drunk. A herpetologist (that is someone who has studied reptiles and amphibians) will tell you that the correct word is 'venomous'. Venom is a toxic saliva that some reptiles produce to drug and help digest their prey. Of course, venom can help the snake to defend itself, too.

"It is dangerous to be bitten because the snake's fangs send venom deep into the wound. Fangs are the twin teeth – sharp as hypodermic needles – that are usually found in the front of the upper jaw. In some snakes these special teeth are at the back of the upper jaw which usually makes the snake's bite less dangerous for a creature as large as a human. The fangs are either hollow or they have a groove running down them. Venom is squirted through this channel and into the victim at the moment the fangs strike and bite."

"Eek!" squealed Gold. "Are there lots of dangerous snakes in Arabia?" Gold looked wide-eyes and terrified.

"There are eight really venomous land snakes, Gold, and ten venomous sea snakes."

"Sea snakes!" screamed Gold. "But you swim in the sea. Are they amphibians?"

"Oh, no, Gold. They live in the water, but it is necessary for them to come to the surface now and again to breathe air.

The end of the tail on a sea snake is vertically flat and this helps them to swim because they use it as a rudder. There are at least 10 species of sea snakes in the Arabian Gulf and Gulf of Oman – and, one is known to live in the southern Arabian seas. None have been discovered in the Red Sea on the western side. Sea snake venom is very potent. They are related to the dangerous cobra but they are not generally aggressive, and usually swim away from humans. Even if they wanted to bite, sea snakes have a small head and their fangs slope backwards, so it would be difficult to bite a human although, they do at times, and the result can be devastating.

"Most of the venomous land snakes in Arabia are vipers. Vipers have two large, sharp, hollow, fold-away fangs to inject venom into a victim. The Sand Viper inhabits dry places and eats lizards and rodents. It is often found in sand dune areas. This viper has a thickish body and is commonly called the 'Horned Viper' because some have horn-like scales above each eye; yet, less than half of the species have these features and, sometimes, they are only scaly bumps. In certain cases, the viper has two long, pointed 'horns'.

"Arabia also has two carpet vipers inhabiting the cultivated

Southern Arabian plains. As you have probably guessed, they were named because their patterns are similar to Oriental rugs. When carpet vipers are alarmed or angry, they make a hissing sound by curling into an 'S' shape and rubbing their body scales against each other. The Common Carpet Viper is a bad-tempered snake, and it has bitten many people.

"Burton's Carpet Viper is another, and is found in the moist wadis of Oman and in some mountainous places in Western Arabia. It is one of the most dangerous vipers.

"Don't look so worried, Gold. It lives far away and it prefers to eat toads. Another snake that is best avoided is the Puff Adder, a thick-bodied serpent found in southwestern Arabia. It has been known to be aggressive and its bite is dangerous.

"Some snakes kill by coiling their body around and around their prey before tightening and squeezing until it is suffocated. That is the python's way. There is a snake in Arabia related to the python and it kills in this way too. It is Jayakar's Sand Boa which the Bedouin call BETHIN. The BETHIN is smooth and can slip easily through sand. The Bedouin believe it buries itself below the sand and waggles its tongue to attract unsuspecting birds who think it is a worm; yet, experts say it does not eat birds. Lizards are its main source of food. This snake submerges itself in sand, up to the peculiar protruding eyes that are set on the top of its head. In this way, it can peer out without being seen.

"Some snakes have just enough venom to subdue their small prey. The Moila Snake is one of these. It likes to play at being a deadly cobra. Rearing up the forepart of its body, it forms a small hood on its head by spreading and flattening each side of its face. The moila has often frightened people very badly by doing this." I raised my arm and tilted my cupped hand to illustrate a cobra for Gold. He looked at it with interest but was not at all frightened. Only his imagination could do that.

"The Sand Snake and the Cat Snake also have just enough poison to drug their prey. Their grooved fangs are at the back of the upper jaw – in the same place as the moila. Moila snakes live in rocky country, usually, whilst the Sand Snake is found in many different types of terrain. They often have attractive stripes and colours which help to camouflage them as they slither up trees and through bushes looking for birds and lizards. The Cat Snake is found mostly in the mountains of southern Arabia. It creeps about at night, hunting. The Awl-headed Snake is also nocturnal, and often hunts among the dunes.

"Arabia's farms attract the Diadem Snake – a creature with a reputation for being aggressive. It lives on rodents which are plentiful in such places. The Diadem Snake is not at all venomous, and there are others that are quite harmless. Some have exciting names like 'Whip Snake' and 'Racer'. Both of these snakes are just as active as they sound and some have beautiful markings. The Cliff Racer got its name for being so good at climbing rock faces in southern Arabia. The Elegant Racer of the North has dramatic bands of black and yellow.

"Then there are very small snakes. One of the tiniest Arabian serpents is called the Flower Pot Snake because it likes to live in places like garden pots. It is peculiar because there is only one sex – and that is female. It can reproduce itself without a member of the opposite sex, unlike most creatures that must mate in order to create young. The ability to produce young as a single sex is known as 'parthenogenesis'. Thread Snakes are tiny, too, and you might find these in old gardens and damp places on the perimeter of Arabia.

"Now, Gold, you have exhausted me AND my information for today. Did you enjoy that?" I asked wearily.

It was enough for Gold, too, I could see. His ears had suddenly begun to look quite droopy. He said "thank you" very nicely, though, but could not resist 'tut-tutting' and adding: "It's no wonder snakes have a bad reputation, Susan. They all seem so full of tricks!"

5
Aquatic Creatures

One morning, Hussein arrived and called loudly at the kitchen window for Askalu to open up. He was apparently very pleased with himself. It was not every day that he succeeded in getting a carton of free 'salad' for the rabbits. Hussein's achievement was the result of his having arrived at the souq early enough to see the produce picked over and smartened up for the day's sales. At least for today, our family joke about rabbits 'eating us out of house and home' would not come true.

As the warren had not had greens for days, I hurried to tell Gold, while Askalu plucked out the bad pieces.

"Hello, Gold. You might like to announce that there will be a feast of beautiful 'grins' today. Hussein has brought a big box, brim-full; and, after you've eaten, I'll tell you a story."

Gold's eyes and ears puckered and perked with delight. He could never resist a story, especially when it followed a large lunch. All his lunches were large, one way or another, I mused; although, today, we DID have an especially exciting tray to offer. It included a few misshapen carrots complete with their feathery tops – and some imperfect apples.

Some time later, Gold appeared in the kitchen and hopped up onto a stool. He looked up, fixing me with his 'important' look.

"Susan, I was telling the rabbits about how Life began in the sea, and they were very interested. They do love stories. Well, perhaps they prefer tales about rabbits," he added thoughtfully, and continued: "But I think they will try to understand – if you tell us about the creatures that live in the sea. Perhaps they will begin to understand 'Human'," he reasoned.

This had been a long speech for Gold, and before it was finished, we found ourselves at our favourite cool spot on the shady marble terrace. To my surprise, some of the rabbits were assembled there, apparently waiting.

Gold really must have generated interest because the others quickly came to join us. I wondered if they would understand anything.

Gold nestled down between Nigel, Modesty Blaise and Nugget, the other bunnies scattered about in an assortment of positions. Mamapuss, sat apart, as usual, and I could see Samantha over by her kennel, fast asleep. It would be the first time that I had told a story to the entire warren, and I felt a bit self-conscious.

I began somewhat nervously:

"By popular request, the story today is about animals that live in water. The ones that live in the sea are described as 'marine' creatures, and the word 'aquatic' refers to all fauna, or faunae that inhabit sea or fresh water."

Gold must have sensed my embarrassment because he shot me a comforting glance. Encouraged, I continued:

"As Gold has correctly told you, the animals on earth are descended from creatures that once lived in the sea. But, even before these ancestors, the sea was the habitat of primitive life forms with no spinal column, known as invertebrates. No one knows exactly when Life began, but it is believed to have happened about 3,800 million years ago. And, no one knows how the sea's first vertebrates evolved from the primitive invertebrates, but certainly it came about very gradually.

"From a study of the oldest vertebrate fossils, 450 million years old, it is known that the early sea creatures were jawless fish. A small number of such animals exist today as lampreys and hagfish. But, let us return to the ancient sea story where life evolved in a fascinating way.

"Science has traced two main lines descending from the early jawless fish: ones with skeletons made of cartilage, or hard gristle, such as sharks, skates, ratfish, and rays; and ones with real bone skeletons, known as bony fish. Cartilaginous fish are mostly flesh-eaters and give birth to living young, or they lay a few large-yolked eggs. Bony fish produce large numbers of very tiny eggs.

"Fish with jaws evolved about 400 million years ago, and they consist of vastly different groups. Today, out of all the types, it is the bony fish that are by far the most numerous; and they combine a remarkable range of sizes with great diversity of colour – although there are similarities. For example, the limbs of a fish do not vary in number. There are always two pairs. The forelimbs, or front pair, near the head, are called pectoral fins, and the hind limbs or back pair (below and usually behind) are called pelvic fins. The other fins do vary. The one running down the back is the dorsal fin; and some fish have two instead of one, which is also the case for the fin along the underside of the fish: the anal fin; then

there is the caudal fin, or tail fin. Bony fish are mostly bony-finned, and sometimes described as ray-fins. A small group are called lobe-fins as they have fleshy lobes instead of fins.

"Lobe-fins were notable for having been the first creatures to emerge onto land. Eventually they developed feet. Those first land and water creatures were amphibians, and the gigantic land reptiles, or dinosaurs, descended from them. Some time later, beginning about 54 million years ago, certain land mammals returned to live in the sea. Most probably they did so because there was a greater abundance of food in the water. As a result of their changed habitat, the feet of these creatures ultimately modified into flippers. It is known that whales and seacows lived in the sea at this time. And, although, no one knows how whales evolved, it is believed that their ancestors walked on land."

I glanced at the rabbits and wondered what they were making of all this. They appeared to be dozing, with the exception of Gold who was gazing at me with steady concentration. For him, I continued: "Around that time, most species of ocean creatures evolved into the shapes and forms that we know today. Then, in the following fifteen million-year period, the first crabs, mussels and snails appeared. Science learnt of these creatures from their fossils.

"Fossils show that the first sharks were over six metres (about 20 feet) in length, and their teeth about fifteen centimetres (6 inches) long. These big sharks and certain other creatures began to disappear about eleven million years ago. Fossils tell us that for the last million years, sea life has remained much as it is today.

"Arabia is special for those interested in ancient marine life because some of it was under water 170 million years ago, and fossilized seashells are still to be found in the desert."

"What sort of sea creatures are there today?"

"Before I tell you about the animals, perhaps I should explain that when most people think of aquatic creatures, they think of fish first. And, this is not surprising, when you consider that more than half of the world's vertebrates are fish."

"I suppose so. But, what exactly is a fish?" Gold looked as though he were ready to ask a dozen questions, so I proceeded as thoroughly as I could:

"A fish is a cold-blooded vertebrate that lives in water, breathing with gills throughout its life. Gills are the lungs of a fish, usually located each side of the head near the body. These organs of respiration for water-breathing creatures, are capable of absorbing oxygen from the water, and using it to aerate the blood to keep the animal alive.

"In addition, most bony fish have an 'air', or 'swim' bladder, a gas-filled sac that regulates buoyancy, so that the animal can remain where it is without the effort of swimming."

"But, what does it look like?" persisted Gold.

I sketched a simple fish in the sand beside the terrace. Gold peered at it beneath the stick I drew with, while Samantha, full of doggy nosiness, came briefly to sniff the disturbed sand. Mamapuss, who might have shown some 'curiosity of the cat' remained haughty and unmoved – although she observed everything through sleepy slit eyes. The rabbits, with the exception of Gold, seemed quite uninterested in my drawing. Were they listening? I continued my instruction, at least, for Gold.

"In the open sea, animals have become adapted to chase prey, or to evade pursuit. Various animals have evolved in different ways to cope with the problems they encounter: such as eating and keeping from being eaten. For example, most bony fish have a protective armour of overlapping scales set in the skin. And, to answer your question, the fishiest-looking creature is long, sleek and streamlined, and there is no real neck between the head and body. The greatest width is towards the middle – and the body tapers to a two-vaned tail which propels the fish. It is a practical body, designed for speed and manoeuvrability; although, not all speedy sea creatures are this shape. The ray, for instance, resembles a giant pancake with a long thin tail. Another exception is the little darting sea horse, named for its head and arched neck which resemble the horse.

"Certain clumsily-built sea creatures survive by the aid of armour, deceptive colouring, poisonous discharges and venomous stings. Some depend on others for protection: The tiny shepherd-fish lives amongst the dangerous tentacles of giant jellyfish, and little coral-fish move in squadrons, relying on their bright hues as camouflage against colourful coral reefs. They are ever alert to danger, and keep to a well-defined territory, feeding off small organisms scraped off coral and rocks.

"The filefish pretends to be a reed, waving its long thin body while hovering suspended upside-down among eel grass. The spiny-globefish, or puffer fish, inflates its body with water and resembles a balloon. It knows that a predator will have difficulty swallowing or biting a blown-up body; especially as it is covered with spikes that stick out when inflated. Once the danger is passed, the puffer can quickly deflate. The several species of spiny-finned fish that do this, are known as Tetradontiformes.

"It usually surprises people to learn that true fish are only a small section of the sea's community – and, to discover that almost every main kind of land creature also exists in the sea – including mammals. Moreover, not everyone knows that the brains of certain sea animals are among the most complicated of all living creatures. For most people, the sea and its creatures are mysterious."

"Living in central Arabia, makes it especially difficult to believe that water is the most common, most abundant substance on earth – and that sea water covers a great deal of the earth's surface. The oceans and seas are vast. Even so, harmful effects caused by some human activities, can still do serious damage. For instance, humans have plundered the seas for centuries. And pollution has increased with progress. Consequently, certain species have become extinct and others are in grave danger. The alteration of natural coastlines has been greatly responsible for destroying habitats and breeding grounds, and this can be more serious than water pollution.

"Fortunately, mankind is aware of his mistakes, and care is now being taken to preserve life in the sea. In Saudi Arabia, important conservation work is being undertaken by organizations such as MEPA, the Meteorological and Environmental Protection Administration, and the NCWCD, the National Commission for Wildlife Conservation and Development. The NCWCD's future plans include the establishment of marine biological research centres on the Arabian Gulf and Red Sea. Dr. Rupert Ormond, the head of the Tropical Marine Research Unit, and as a consultant for

The International Union for Conservation of Nature, IUCN, lists the potential threats to the marine environment as:

'industrial discharges; effects of shipping; oil pollution; effects of increased habitation along the coasts; recreation spearfishing; commercial over-fishing and shell-collecting. IUCN has carried out surveys and identified many areas as deserving to be set aside as marine conservation sites.'"

"Are there lots of sea creatures, still?" Gold asked.

"Worldwide, there are about 25,000 known species of sea-fish and about 80,000 species of mollusc, which are invertebrates. In the Red Sea alone, over 1,000 species of mollusc are recorded and around 200 corals. Other groups are equally well represented. This may seem remarkable, unless you consider that it is perhaps easier to live in the sea than on land. At least, it seems reasonable to assume that it is so. The water is buoyant and there is not the burden of gravity that land animals have to cope with; nor are there the same harsh seasonal and regional contrasts. Generally, the surface water temperature, in any one place, does not vary as much as temperatures do on land.

Globefish

A friendly stray
cat pays a visit
to the warren

Wuzzo shares bird seed with the rabbits while Mamapuss rests nearby

The hole in Gold's ear
was one of Ginger's neater bites

Wuzzo at the
kitchen window

Gold goes upstairs

"The majority of sea creatures inhabit a zone, or a place that is most suitable for their species. Being sensitive to change, the animals live where the water pressure, light, temperature, and quantity of salt are more or less constant. But, sharks, whales, and some other fish, are less bothered by these variations. They can swim freely up and down the seas and oceans – providing the water is deep enough.

"Life in the sea depends on plants, just as it does on land. Sea plants are just as productive as land plants – and they need sunlight for their survival too. Consequently, they grow fairly close to the water's surface – where the light can reach. This is why most sea life occurs nearer the surface than the seabed. In the sea, the ocean is the farmer, and his plough is the ocean current. Thus, the sea is continually refertilized by the recycling of matter that is partially the result of dead and decaying marine life.

"Professor Doctor Hans Hass, the famous marine biologist and explorer, described the code of the sea as 'merciless', because any organism that is less than perfectly healthy – and tough – is devoured by sea creatures. He explains that every second, thousands of animals die in the breakers, or they are eaten; and tens of thousands fight over the fragments that are left. This cycle is an ecological marvel. Ecology is the scientific study of the relationship of living things to one another and to the environment.

"The basic sea pastures are free-floating microscopic plants called phytoplankton (pronounced: fie-toe-plankton) which sometimes floats in a thick 'broth', letting in very little sunlight – similar to a cloudy day on land. The tiny plants are food for minute floating animals called zooplanton, a variety of tiny animals mostly invisible to the naked eye. Certain zooplankton can sting; but, nevertheless, they are devoured by some sea creatures. Plankton refers to both plants and animals. Alga (plural: algae) is the simplest of these plant forms, having neither roots, stems nor leaves. Algae ranges in size from microscopic to large seaweeds that reach 30 metres (100 feet) or more in length.

"In order to grow, plants require the visible wavelengths of the sun which do not penetrate beneath 100 metres (330 feet). Indeed, most light is lost at 10 metres (33 feet), so below 100 metres, there is much less life. The animals that live in the depths have had to develop special ways to survive. Nutrients do 'rain' from above, but meeting up with someone to eat, or to mate with, can be a problem in the deep. Down there, it is very dark, and very cold; and there are less flora and fauna. Because there is no light many of them have evolved their own form of bioluminescence. This is the production of light by a living organism through internal chemical reaction. A wide range of marine animals can do this.

"Angler fish inhabit deep water. And, because they do not find food regularly, a meal must last them for a long time. Their huge mouths and expanding stomachs allow them to swallow fish much larger than themselves. Some deep water fish have sensitive telescopic eyes for seeing in near darkness.

Breeding down there depends on meeting another of the same species. Certain deep-sea denizens cope with this problem by remaining together forever, once they have met. One example is a certain species of angler fish. The male is much smaller than the female, and it attaches itself permanently to her."

Gold's sudden burst of laughter gave me a start – and it woke up the dozing rabbits.

"What a marvellous idea. I could go for a free ride if I could find a doe who would do that. I love a dip when I'm really hot, but I find swimming exhausting. Wouldn't it be marvellous to sit on the back of a large doe while she does all the swimming."

Gold was obviously delighted with the idea because he giggled and chortled until I found myself laughing along with him. Then, we had to wait for the startled and somewhat indignant rabbits to calm down before I could continue. I decided to tell Gold next about the seas surrounding Arabia, and began:

"The creatures living in Arabian waters today, are descended from ones that have adapted to suit vastly changed habitats. The Arabian Gulf of today, for instance, has been both much shallower and much deeper in the past. It was sometimes a lake, believed to have dried up from time to time; its salinity also varied. It is now an almost completely enclosed sea, lying northwest-southeast forming the eastern coast of the Arabian Peninsula. Kuwait, Saudi Arabia, the United Arab Emirates, and Oman are the countries situated on the western side of the Gulf with Iran on the eastern side. The only opening is the narrow Strait of Hormuz, only 50 kilometres (31 miles) wide in the south, restricting the flow of waters between the Arabian Sea and the Gulf.

"The Arabian Gulf is extremely shallow, with an average depth of only 35 metres (100 feet), and in many places it is much shallower. The water temperature varies greatly and rapidly, both daily and seasonally, and it is very salty. The salinity differs, too, from place to place, caused by heat, restricted water flow, and the high surface evaporation which exceeds any input of water from the surrounding arid land. (High salinity and extreme temperatures – both high and low – are among the most important environmental factors that control marine life.) In addition, there are tidal currents, causing the marine life some physical stress, as well as bringing benefits. Creatures must cope with all of this to survive.

"Islands and sandbars are numerous in the Gulf, and coral reefs are quite common in the shallower parts to the north; but, generally, the low winter temperatures, high salinities, and often turbid waters, create conditions that are unsuitable for the development of coral.

"Sealife in the Gulf on the eastern side of the Peninsula and Red Sea on the western side is generally similar. They have many species in common. However, the diversity of animals inhabiting the Gulf's coral reefs, is far lower than that occurring on those in the Red Sea. Yet, there is a recorded

71 species from 25 families in the Gulf's shallow-water reefs, and seven of these are 'endemic' (the technical term used to describe a species that is believed to occur nowhere else).

"Close to the east coast of Saudi Arabia, lies the State of Bahrain, made up of thirteen islands and twenty small islets, all of which are situated in the shallow Gulf of Salwa. These islands provide varied marine habitats, or 'biotopes', for an assortment of creatures. There are inter-tidal areas including mud flats, sand flats and tidal creeks; soft, sub-tidal sea-bed; and sea grass beds, as well as coral reefs in offshore banks and in deeper water. In this area, Tarut Bay, with its abundance of seagrass, has an especial wealth of sea-life. Research programmes there are helping to discover the full range of marine habitats. Unfortunately, pressures from oil pollution, and particularly heavy siltation (caused by landfill and dredging) has upset the 'ecosystem', or Balance of Nature. The Gulf reefs have also suffered from silt accumulation, and they have been broken by fishing boat anchors. Such places have been the subject of recent scientific study, and information has been gathered using the most modern methods, including satellite imagery.

"Individual biological and ecological discoveries can be very exciting, but scientists are cautious and aware of their responsibility to observe, record, and carefully question the findings. After one serious oil spill, which was at first linked to the death of various sea creatures, MEPA began a programme to protect the populations of animals that remained, as well as marine life in general. And ROPME, the Kuwait-based Regional Organization for the Protection of Marine Environment (comprising Saudi Arabia, Bahrain and other countries) agreed to take measures towards a safer system for human activities in the Gulf. Yet despite modern development and its threat to nature, there are still plenty of fish in the Arabian Gulf. It has always been a highly productive sea, and remains a rich natural resource, where a range of marine habitats continue to exist. Indeed, in some cases, certain species have been seen to flourish.

"Further south, and linked to the Arabian Gulf, lies the Gulf of Oman and the Indian Ocean. It is there that the Sultanate of Oman enjoys a 2,000 kilometre (1,250 miles) coastline. As a result of research programmes within the last decade, knowledge has increased dramatically about Arabian 'benthic' life – or life on the seabed. Research centres, linked to national universities and fisheries' ministries, in surrounding countries, assist in the education of marine scientists. In this way, they develop an understanding of marine life. Scientists study what lives where, how much of it there is, and why.

"The surveys in Oman revealed an unusually high variety of marine habitats. And it was discovered that the coral reefs of the relatively small Omani Capital Area are the most developed in the region, despite being in their early stages. The few thousand years that they have been growing, is considered to be a brief span, in terms of reef life. Yet they have become one of the most important components of marine life in the area.

"The Red Sea on the opposite side of the Arabian Peninsula, provides different conditions to the Gulf, and consequently it supports some other life forms. This strip of water on the western side is not a very old sea. Twenty to thirty million years ago, it was merely an inland lake – the result of an earlier rift on a central line where Arabia joined northeast Africa. The rifting was completed about five million years ago, when the Red Sea opened out to the Arabian Sea at the southern end. This narrow southern entrance, 28.9 kilometres (17.9 miles) wide, is called BAB AL MANDAB, or 'Gate of Tears'. At the northern end, lie the shallow Gulf of Suez and the deep Gulf of Aqaba.

"The Red Sea has many islands and wonderful coral reefs, which make splendid habitats for numerous forms of life. The warm and salty water does not suit some fauna, resulting in fewer kinds than in the neighbouring seas, but despite this, there is great variety among the groups that have thrived."

"Susan, why is it called the RED Sea?"

"No one is certain, Gold. Several reasons have been suggested. A popular belief is that it is due to outbreaks of large patches of microscopic red plants which appear on the surface for a week or two every few years. In fact, this sea-way has had many names in history. Sunsets sometimes cast a red reflection, and this possibility is supported by the fact that, in ancient times, the Mediterranean was known as the 'white sea' because of reflected light. It was a marine corridor between the civilizations of Egypt, Greece, Rome and the rest of Europe, linking them with the productive lands of the Far East.

"The endemic sea-life in this busy water way is a result of a most unusual environment. It has caused certain species to be changed over time – each was adapted uniquely because conditions were different to those which they were accustomed to previously. The ancestors of these creatures originally came from the Arabian Sea and Indian Ocean entering when Arabia and Africa separated.

"Since then, the Red Sea has remained closed to certain deep-sea animals because the entrance is especially shallow – just 100 metres (300 feet). This, and its narrowness has kept it comparatively isolated. And, like the Arabian Gulf, it is especially salty, due to the hot climate causing evaporation; and there being no rivers in the surrounding lands that flow in and dilute the water.

"Hans Hass, described it as 'amazingly warm; the warmest and saltiest sea in the world'. It is a very special environment that has caused certain species to develop, whereas similar creatures are almost extinct in other seas. Above all, and despite humans having endangered some of the animals, it remains a sea exceptionally rich in marine life."

"In times past, a life at sea was one full of excitement and adventure. For the purposes of trade and fishing, men braved seas that were often treacherous. One of the most feared regions was the southern tip of the Sinai Peninsula where the winds of the Gulf of Suez met those of the Gulf of Aqaba. Ancient ship wrecks, recently discovered, confirm the danger of this area.

"It is recorded that Arabs were among the earliest navigators in the world, and, since remote times, they have been great fishermen. Early explorers in Arabia noted that the inhabitants of the eastern coastline were especially sturdy and industrious fishermen, carrying out their occupation with 'great expertness'. They would go to sea fearlessly and relentlessly for sharks, while poorer fishermen, who did not have even a share in a boat, worked with casting nets. This was severe and arduous labour. They would also have had a 3 metre long (9 feet) barbed spear, with a hand-operated rig to catch porpoises and rays. In addition, they used a GARGOOR, or large circular basket trap.

"The fish were caught in the open sea, near the shore, at the surface, and on the bottom of the sea. They were sold by auction or direct to regular customers. The best seasons for fishing were spring and late autumn. Mr S.B. Miles, who was an early authority on the Gulf, noted that the number of fish there was 'truly astonishing'. He also writes that fins of sharks and rays were sent to China, the rest of these creatures used for food and oil.

"The people living around the coasts of Arabia are known to eat a lot of fish. The population of Jeddah, alone consumes about 15 tonnes of seafood daily, but the fishermen catch much more than that because they also supply other Saudi Arabian cities and neighbouring countries.

"At the moment, the Red Sea and Arabian Gulf continue to have an abundance of edible fish, despite the increased coastal pressures coming from burgeoning seaside populations, and the growing traffic to and from modern ports. As occasional oil spills can seriously contaminate the water, it has been feared that the balance of nature might be threatened in the waters that hem all three sides of the Arabian Peninsula. Sea water has become a vital source of drinking water for Arabia, too, and massive desalinization plants now supply entire cities.

"Fortunately, not all waste is toxic and poisonous to fish. Discharged waste contains some nutrients which are essential for the growth of algae and other marine plants, but very large quantities can be harmful to both flora and fauna – particularly to forms better suited to low-nutrient conditions.

"When an ecosystem is upset, certain life forms can die from insufficient suitable food, or because others are better adapted to the changing conditions. You see, the creatures depend on one another; and should a species die off, another often suffers. For instance, coral does best in low-nutrient seas, and marine animals that are tenants of reefs, can be threatened, if the coral dies.

"Reefs teem with life and the various types of coral are important to fish, as well as to a large number of invertebrates. Some deep-sea varieties of sponge, or *Porifera*, are enormous and throng with life, too, as they also provide homes for many animals. A sponge is a fascinating invertebrate found near coral reefs. It is an inactive sea animal, whose fibrous skeleton often ends up in bathrooms. There is a fantastic range of patterns in sponges. Thankfully most are not suitable for humans to exploit.

"The newest threat to the animal life has come as a result of the Red Sea revealing its great secret. Valuable minerals are apparently lying in deep pools within the central trough. These include gold and silver, as well as zinc, tin, manganese, lead, iron, copper, cobalt and cadmium. The bad news is: in order to extract this treasure, pollutants may be released that are known to be dangerous to marine life."

"Do you think they will do it?" asked Gold in alarm.

"Perhaps, Gold. But, it would be a very difficult operation – and very expensive, so it is not imminent. You see, the Red Sea is a narrow body of water running north and south: 1,932 kilometres (1200 miles) long and 306 kilometres (190 miles) at its widest part. The maximum depth is 2,359 metres (8000 feet). A coastal shelf with a maximum depth of 500 metres (1600 feet), drops to the main central trough, 1,000 metres (3,300 feet) deep in the middle. And, within this trough lie the pools which are 2,000 metres (6,600 feet) deep or more. The best-known pools are 'Atlantis 2' and 'Discovery Deep'. It would be a tremendous feat of engineering, coping with such an unusual sea floor as well as seasonal currents." I sketched the Red Sea as I spoke, and showed it to Gold.

"Tell us about the animals that live in the coral, Susan."

"Firstly, I must tell you a little about corals, because they are animals, too. It is only in the last century that biologists discovered that corals were not plants. They are living organisms that must feed and breathe. And they are sensitive, and dislike very cold water and sediment.

"Coral reefs form in fairly warm and salty tropical seas, rather than in sandy places, where rivers rush in to dilute the water and stir up silt. That would clog up their mouths and tentacles. Corals depends on the clarity of the water. It requires a minimum depth of 50–100 metres (150–300 feet) in order to receive the maximum of oxygen which increases near the surface, plus light, and plankton to eat.

"Hard corals are made up of colonies of tiny creatures, resembling the sea anemone, to which they are closely related. Colour is an indication of live coral, and a bleached white appearance is a sign that it is dead. The living part of a coral formation consists of a thin layer of these minute anemone-like individuals, linked together, covering the surface of the coral 'skeleton'. Each member of the colony is called a polyp, and the skeleton on which it lives becomes larger and grows outwards as each polyp secretes a white limey calcareous substance beneath itself. This is the common building material among sea organisms, including corals and shelled molluscs.

"The corals' reproduction is curious. They can be either sterile, male, or female. Some produce free-swimming larvae, while others release eggs into water like fish; most multiply by asexual budding, the polyp dividing into two or more polyps. 'Asexual' is the term for reproductive processes which do not involve mating. This allows the colonies to grow in size, not just multiply.

"There are many different species of coral making up a reef. For instance, as well as hard corals, there are soft corals, stinging corals, black corals, and the gorgonians, which look like feathered fans. And they have an amazing range of shades in beige, blue, brown, green, mauve and pink. Some hues are strong and vibrant, while others are subtle and delicate. The forms are incredible. One resembles fine fur, and a certain spherical coral looks very like the human brain.

"The Red Sea reefs are amongst the greatest natural wonders of the world. Reefs have been described as valuable laboratories where mankind can learn more about life on earth, so that makes them useful. They also provide a source of great beauty and pleasure for people who swim underwater. Many enthusiasts are content to observe or take photographs of the coral, and seashells, but there are those who remove these treasures for souvenirs. This is a great pity because coral takes many years to grow, and the seashell species associated with coral reefs cannot be replaced quickly either.

"Fortunately some shellfish are so big that it would be difficult to move them. Certain corals can also protect themselves: the 'fire' variety, which belong to the jelly-fish family, will 'burn' with its 'stings' if touched. Divers have described how some huge mussels, bedded among corals, defend themselves by slowly closing when approached. Such shells are extremely sensitive to water vibration and a slight movement, as much as 10 metres (30 feet) away, will cause them to close."

I used my hands to demonstrate.

"If a diver remains perfectly still, the mussel will open, once again. Mussels are a close relation of the giant South Sea clams. Story books tell how they have closed to trap divers but this seems impossible because these molluscs move so slowly.

"Left alone and in place, the shapes and colours around a reef are infinitely more pleasing – like a splendid garden. There are bouquets of bluish-violet pen coral; bright bunches of star-coral; peach-coloured bushy growths of cup-star-coral; rose-coloured, pointed, bristling branches of crown-coral; brownish-yellow catkin-coral; prickly sprigs of lilac to reddish alcyonia-coral; and greyish-blue xenia in beds of orange-tinted and deep black dermoid alcyonia enlivened with tiny violet and reddish-purple star polyps.

"It is a garden that flourishes, seemingly unattended – the sea silently lending a hand. In the case of mushroom-shaped coral, perpetuation depends on the currents. Their polyps are different, in that they are part of the coral beneath them only during the first stage of their growth. Thereafter, they develop a widening head on a delicate stem base, until eventually, the sea's movement snaps the head off. Currents toss it about the sea bed while it continues to grow. Meanwhile, the stem goes on to grow a new head.

"The coral reef formations in the Red Sea are different from anywhere else in the world. Divers have described seeing fish there, fluttering like birds in what looks like sunken ruins. One part of the reef resembles an oriental city full of temples. In another place, there are 'castles', with majestic battlements and fine turrets that tower to 12 metres (40 feet) in height. And, a rich growth of feather-corals, spreads like a primitive forest among luxuriant 'vegetation'; their eight-feathered tentacles opening like thousands of little stars that pulsate with the movement of the water – unless they are disturbed and close up.

"These reefs have also been described as a kaleidoscope world, where breath-taking, coloured patterns constantly change. Hundreds of microscopically small fish apparently glitter like rubies, rocking up and down to the rhythm of the waves. Silver streaks of slanting sunlight shoot among them like arrows. Perhaps a sturdy spiny-rayed perch will be swinging back and forth before its hole, round eyes glaring at a shoal of small fluttering fish that burst onto the scene, darting out of one crevice and disappearing into another. There is hardly time to be sure of their colour, I am told. Then, another fish might swim into view and pause, motionless, while every scale on its rainbow-hued body sparkles.

"The inhabitants in and around a coral reef are of many shapes, and are very colourful. Tropical fish are usually brilliant, and many of them are able to change colour to give them camouflage when predators are about. It is also a useful disguise when waiting for prey. In the early morning and late afternoon, many of the more active creatures emerge from hiding to nibble plants and hunt.

"A coral reef is a sort of apartment building – and a kind of pantry as well, because it provides homes and hiding places for all sorts. Each one preys upon the tenants that are smaller than themselves, or they consume plants on and around the reef.

"As you have probably guessed, there is great competition for space on the reefs. Life there has been likened to a human city where every inhabitant goes about his daily business in his own special way. One citizen prospers while another is ruined, and the one with advantages becomes very important. Those who do not adapt, disappear, and their vacant places are taken over.

"Once, when Hans Hass smashed a pen-coral, he described the scene as resembling 'an hotel on fire'. Little creatures came out from their hiding places and dashed off in all directions. The 'residents' included grotesquely-patterned trapeze-crabs, which raced past green grasshopper-crayfish, while a tiny spotted fish floundered its way out of the wreckage. A poor date-mussel lay helpless, because it had lost

its mooring, and a scale-star wriggled to get under an irridescent annelid worm which fled.

"In the sea, predators always have a 'heaped plate' of smaller creatures to eat. There are tiny animals with their vastly different lifestyles and habitats all around them, seemingly doing their utmost to outsmart their enemies. Yet, clever as they often appear, these invertebrates are the so-called 'lower animals' because they are somewhat senseless. Many are crustaceans, characterized by jointed legs, segmented bodies and a hard, external skeleton – such as crabs, shrimps and lobsters. Others are molluscs, a large group usually characterized by a soft un-segmented body, protected by a calcareous shell.

"Many depend on camouflage for defence, or brilliant colour to advertise that they are poisonous; or they have spikes with venom; or tough, rough and hard exteriors to make them difficult to digest. Certain shellfish, such as the cowrie (which can secrete acid) is just too hard for all – except the wrasse. The wrasse is a fish that feeds on shrimp, crab and shellfish, breaking them with its pointed jaw teeth before crushing with strong, broad teeth further back in the pharynx, the cavity at the back of the throat, connecting the nose, mouth and larynx.

"The lower invertebrates that are commonly hunted, include anemones, clams, jellyfish, mussels, oysters and other shellfish, sea-snails, sponges, worms, and the nudibranch – a stunningly colourful marine slug with lungs that are exposed directly to the water – hence its name, meaning 'naked lung'. Oh, and there is a small octopus that makes a tasty meal for some."

"Octopus! Is it something like our Mamapuss?" queried Gold, looking up suddenly, in surprise.

"No, Gold, octopuses have short, rounded bodies with eight, long webbed arms called tentacles. The word 'octopus' means 'eight feet'. The mouth is a parrot-like, horny beak and ideal for seizing crabs. To escape predators, this creature can squirt a cloud of 'ink', and swim off backwards, while opening and closing the webbed tentacles like an umbrella. When swimming rapidly, the octopus uses jet propulsion, squirting water from an organ called a hyphonoma, located at the side of the body.

"The octopus belongs to a group of animals known as Cephalopods which includes squid and cuttlefish – and noted for having well-developed brains, and eyes that look remarkably like those of vertebrates. They also have the ability to change colour to match any background. This is a great aid to survival. The squid has the ability to change instantly through an amazing range of glowing colours, and it has been called a 'quick change artist'.

"The shape of each sea creature is the result of adapting to suit its environment and specific needs; yet, why fish have so many fantastic colours and designs is still not completely understood. One theory is that colour might be a guide to their zones. At the very least, having a special colour can help a fish locate another member of the same species at mating time.

"The slow-moving lower invertebrates are easy targets for swift predators. That is probably why many hide during the daytime. Yet, some of these nocturnal animals remain noticeable, such as the spiny-skins, or echinoderms, which include starfish and sea-urchins. Sea-cucumbers, a variety of echinoderm, remain in view, too; perhaps because they are generally larger than most of their kind. I wonder if their size gives them confidence. It is an amusing thought.

"The mouth of the starfish is on the underside, and it feeds off coral, tiny sponges, and other animals, while moving about with the aid of little suction pads. Sea-urchins also have their mouth on the underside. They scrape algae from rocky surfaces with their five large teeth. They travel from place to place, stilt-walking on stubby spines and tubular feet. Sea-cucumbers are less active, lying about on rock, sand and mud in shallow places. The mouth is at one end, surrounded by tentacles that trap food, or shovel in sand, out of which organic matter is extracted for digestion.

"The crustaceans, or animals with horny external skeletons belong to a group called Arthropoda, represented on land by insects and spiders. In the sea, they are crabs, shrimps, crayfish and similar creatures. Divers describe big crayfish in the Red Sea as looking like pale and hideous phantoms, stalking along on long, spidery legs, waving their great feelers, as they search for suitable food.

"Crabs have five pairs of legs with large claws on the front pair, as do many shrimps. There are crabs of all sorts, shapes and colours – both in the water and at the sea's edge, lurking, crawling, swimming, or scuttling about their business while constantly on the lookout. Shrimps are less obvious because they are mostly very small and, often, remarkably well-camouflaged. Despite this, the many species of shrimp are regular and important nutrition for the larger inhabitants of the sea."

"I would hate to be thought of as nutrition," said Gold, pulling his little face tight down into fur, as if it were a safer place to be.

"It is Nature's way of keeping the Balance, Gold. Occasionally, little invertebrates have increased disproportionately for one reason or another, and they have become pests. For instance, a certain kind of starfish has, from time to time, increased to plague proportions, destroying vast stretches of beautiful coral that was once a habitat for tens of thousands of creatures.

"The vertebrates of the Red Sea are quite different from each other, in shape, colour and habits, Gold; and their names are descriptive and often illustrate the appearance of the creature. There are angelfish, batfish, barracuda, blenny, butterflyfish, clownfish, goatfish, parrotfish, and wrasse. These are commonly seen by divers, and they all belong to the perchlike fish order known as Perciforms. Of all fish orders, it is the largest and most varied in body forms, containing more

species than any other vertebrate order. Perchlike fish are fascinating because of their diverse and unusual habits.

"All of the angelfish species, with their various shapes and colours, seem to be friendly and inquisitive. They have become favourites of fish watchers and photographers. The batfish, with its deep, laterally flat body, large dorsal and anal fins, is so named because it swims on its side, flapping like a bat. The predatory barracuda is notable for being fast, powerful and aggressive, with fearsome fangs. These are displayed while swimming in shallow 'drop-offs' close to the reef.

"In contrast, the blenny seems shy and secretive – feeding on small invertebrates close to the seabed. It commonly dwells in the small holes of brain coral, and will jealously guard its home. Butterflyfish are plentiful and very colourful, with patterns all over their blue, red, gold, yellow, copper or silver bodies. They are 'disc-thin' laterally, which is convenient for slipping in and out of coral 'forests'. They are among the prettiest fish on the reef. They can be frequently seen grazing and exploring in pairs or small groups, sometimes feeding on certain soft-bodied invertebrates or coral polyps. Although seldom tolerating a close approach, and more usually darting suddenly away in alarm to hide in a crevice, butterflyfish have been known to be curious, and glide up to examine a diver.

"There are many varieties and colours of clownfish (sometimes called 'damselfish'). Some are boldly-coloured, wearing bands of orange and white with dark-rimmed fins. They belong to a group called Pomacentrids, notable for forming friendships with giant anemones which have deadly stinging tentacles. Fortunately, clownfish are immune to the venom. Colonies of this attractive fish inhabit reeftops, feeding upon shoals of minute drifting animals. Sometimes they will swarm fearlessly towards human visitors and harmlessly nibble.

"If startled, a clownfish may even take refuge within the anemone's maw where other fish are digested. It is believed that this little fish attracts food for its host. Anemones shelter such guests from predators in return for cleaning services. Clownfish are known to eat up their host's tiny parasites. They will also 'dine out', making a quick dash from their haven, to grab a bite somewhere on the reef. It is also necessary for them to adventure forth to lay eggs on beds of coral or rock. At this time, both parents take turns to stand guard.

"As you might expect, goatfish have what looks like a beard, made up of two sensory barbels which trail the sandy seabed. While swiftly skimming, or foraging the reef, these detectors help to locate small edible animals. Many fish are totally herbivorous and feed on all sorts of plantlife. Angelfish feed off algae, but they also eat sponges. Parrotfish have strong beak-like jaws for scraping edible algae and coral polyps off rocks and reefs. Farther back in the throat, the parrotfish has large 'grinding' teeth which crush hard food. These gaudily-coloured fish have been likened to a flock of

flying parrots, because of their up-and-down pectoral-fin movements. Furthermore, they 'perch' at night in branches of coral.

"The carnivorous wrasse belongs to the most common family on the reef. They are 'cleanerfish', often called 'doctors of the deep' because they pick parasites and diseased tissue off other fish. Certain species of wrasse choose specific places to set up practice. Their patients float motionless, flaring out their fins and gills in preparation for a good 'spring-clean'. Divers have been amused to see fish waiting in line to take their proper turn.

"Certain kinds of shrimp do similar work, making them a valuable asset on a reef, too. Some tiny fish act as 'dentists', entering the mouths of bigger fish to pick out parasites and decaying matter. The surgeon fish does not help out, despite his name. This beautiful blue and brown creature is decorated with yellow designs on the head; and it got its name because it wears two little daggers at the root of the tail. This armour can be snapped open and shut in defence.

"The pipefish is a close relation of the seahorse, and does not look like a fish at all, but rather like a straightened-out seahorse. Small black eyes glitter from a narrow head that has a long tubular snout and a small mouth. The long, thin, segmented body is encased in bony armour, the whip-like tail (a dorsal-fin resembling a comb) its main means of propulsion.

"There are many species of filefish in the Red Sea. Their name is derived from the small spines on each scale, giving a rough texture similar to a file. They are a sub-species belonging to the triggerfish family. Apparently, it can be frightening to see filefish pass by, patrolling in fearful-looking squadrons, all spindly and thin, with wicked-looking crocodile-like jaws. Experienced divers know this appearance to be false because these fish are timid and harmless – dashing away in long leaps, if startled.

"Frogfish are irregular-shaped, motley-coloured, slow-moving, unappealing fish that crawl the seabed, aided by their pectoral fins. They feed on small fish and crustaceans. I think 'toadfish' would be a more apt name. Stonefish are even less attractive, but their appearance is a very clever disguise. Resembling algae-covered rock, weathered coral or a bunch of seaweed, all of this species are difficult to spot, as they lie camouflaged amongst rubble. Man must beware, for stonefish are ever ready to roll back the skin from their dorsal prickles and deliver an extremely painful and often fatal sting if stepped on. All twenty varieties of stonefish (which belong to the scorpion fish order) have thirteen 'needle-like' dorsal-fin spines, equipped with venom glands that produce the most deadly of all fish venoms.

"The lionfish also belongs to the scorpionfish order. In contrast, it is astonishingly beautiful, resembling a lovely flower. Yet, concealed in a gorgeous comb which bristles down the back (matching the broad feathery and fan-like, long pectoral-fins which extend all around the body) there are

"Isn't it time to build a nest?"

Modesty Blaise gathers paper for her nest

Dashing down the burrow with another mouthful

A rest between digging

Silver collecting for her nest

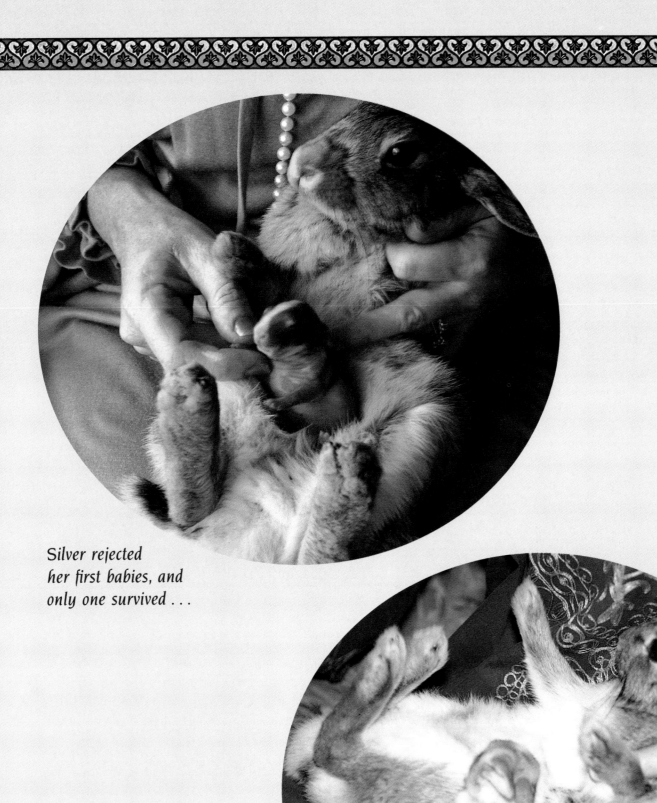

Silver rejected
her first babies, and
only one survived . . .

. . . We named him Chipolatta,
and he grew very quickly
into a big rabbit

spines as sharp as hypodermic needles. They can inflict a potent, toxic venom which can prove fatal to humans. They have been seen in the shallow waters of the reef where humans frequent, and they are a great danger.

"Lizardfish are long and sleek, with large heads and wide jaws that are set with long, sharp teeth. The motley-coloured scales and reddish tail help it to blend with the background, when lying partially buried on the seabed. This aggressive carnivore catches prey by darting swiftly upwards.

"Groupers belong to the great sea bass family. They are generally large, feeding on smaller fish and crustaceans. As their flesh is edible, groupers have become popular sportfish that are also caught commercially. It seems small wonder that divers interpret this greyish-brownish, silvery fish's look as gloomy: they say, goggle eyes stare morbidly at them from underwater nooks, where it habitually lurks.

"Crevices and crannies in coral reefs, and rocky-bottomed areas, are the habitat of the nocturnal squirrelfish. This brightly-coloured red fish with bluish fins, emerges at night to dine on crustaceans. It is notable for making territorial and breeding sounds.

"The rocks in the shallows are also full of life. Rock tops provide seating accommodation for sea-squirts, moss-like creatures, and little sponges. The narrowest cracks and channels are embedded with little worms, but some choose to build their tiny houses from sand and fragments of shell.

"Sea-urchins live tucked between the rocks. Small sea-crabs burrow their claws into sand-filled cavities. Soft, scaleless sea-jumpers glide high up on to the rocks, and spring like underwater grasshoppers. Brick-red scale-worms adhere to rocks, snail-fashion – and will sting if touched. For other creatures, the rocks are merely a refuge until nightfall when they emerge to hunt.

"Man is the greatest hunter in the sea. And, each year, he returns to fish, even though he sets out with the knowledge that there is danger. For the most part, ocean currents and bad weather are all that he has to fear. According to one early authority on the Arabian Gulf, however, the most formidable foe in these waters was the sawfish. It was said to attack whales and large fish with its sharp-toothed snout. This 'saw' is often almost two metres (six feet) long. Yet some modern marine biologists declare that the sawfish is not aggressive, and its blade-like snout is used for raking molluscs from the sea bed.

"The early reports add that fishermen, 'who cared nothing for sharks' dreaded this 'brute', whose assault was 'certain death'. They described the eyes as 'peculiar'. Its snout was considered an effective good luck charm in olden times – if they could land the fish and kill it. There have been reports of the sawfish inflicting serious wounds to both fish and fishermen, when accidentally caught in a net. One record from olden times confirms the power of this animal, which caused a catastrophe in the Sea of Oman by striking a ship.

"Many people fear sea snakes because they are so much more venomous than land snakes; yet, I am told, they are docile, inoffensive, and not aggressive; and, a swimmer rarely meets one. Even so, the short, venomous, grooved fangs near the front of the upper jaw, are capable of inflicting a dangerous bite despite their small gape. Their extremely toxic venom is an adaptation used to subdue the fish upon which they prey.

"The yellow and brown banded sea snake is one of the ten recorded as swimming in the coastal waters of the Arabian Gulf. There are none recorded in the Red Sea and no one knows why. Some grow to two metres (6 feet) in length. These creatures have rather slender bodies and depend on a vertical paddle-shaped tail to propel them along. Sea snakes never venture on to land. Despite this, they are air-breathing, so it is remarkable that they can remain submerged for up to eight hours, closing off the nostrils to keep out water.

"Of all the dangerous sea creatures, Gold, humans mostly fear the shark – the fish that is sometimes called 'tiger of the sea'. It is a fear resulting from the seemingly savage and unpredictable nature of certain sharks – and the deaths and dreadful injuries caused by the powerful jaws that are set with large, triangular, serrated teeth."

"Oooh! They don't sound very nice," shuddered Gold.

"Divers are usually cautious when sharks are about; although some marine explorers are convinced that they can cope with this creature. To scare the fish off, they either yell as loudly as they can, or hit it on the nose with a camera or hammer.

"All sharks have skeletons of cartilage. They are sleek, stream-lined, and supple – and swift swimmers. So far as is known, there are seven shark families and 199 species in the world. Almost all have two dorsal fins, one anal fin, and five gill slits.

"The Red Sea reefs are frequented by three types of shark, each just over a metre (3 feet) long. They are the reef whitetip, the blacktip and the grey reef shark. The larger silvertip and oceanic whitetip are often seen in deeper water; the tiger shark and long-finned shark are sighted sometimes. Also present is the white shark, often called the 'great white shark'; although, it is only white underneath – it can be any colour from grey to brown on top. This shark is aggressive and has a reputation for being a 'man-eater'.

"Other sharks known to be in Arabian waters are the blue shark, the shortfin mako, and the smooth hammerhead, plus the whale shark – the largest living fish, which can grow up to eighteen metres (60 feet) in length. This seems peculiar because certain of their species feed only on small fish and plankton, filtering a huge intake of gulped water."

"I can't imagine anyone wanting to swim among sharks, Susan. If you ask me, that white shark would be lucky to have a friend."

"Nevertheless, Gold, sharks are both fabulous and fascinating, and science would like to know more about them. And, however fearsome they might seem, it is a curiosity that

sharks permit small pilot fish to accompany them everywhere.

"These fish are said to guide sharks to their prey, receiving scraps in reward.

"It is known that sharks track and take prey using their senses of smell, taste, vision, and hearing, plus a vibratory sense which informs them of disturbances in the water – even over long distances. The struggles of an injured fish, or the splashing of swimmers, can attract a shark sufficiently for it to come and investigate. Fortunately, unless provoked, it usually goes away, preferring to keep to itself, going about its daily business of eating and breeding. I have heard, that some underwater adventurers in Arabia, armed with cameras, have complained that they have never seen a shark.

"Another cartilaginous fish with a bad reputation is the ray. Several of their species are referred to as 'stingrays'. This is because of one or more very sharp, large spines set above and towards the root of long whip-like tail. If the fish is disturbed or startled, its lashing tail helps drive the venomous spine deep into a wound. Many Arabian fishermen fear and hate the ray, believing it to be dangerous. Yet, it is not aggressive, and feeds on tiny floating organisms, minute shrimps, and sea-snails dug from the sea bed.

"Rays can be colossal in size. With their flat, diamond-shaped body and huge pectoral fin flippers, they resemble giant prehistoric birds or outsize bats. To swim, a ray flaps its flippers up and down, giving the appearance of flying. Although clumsy in comparison with most fish, rays can travel at incredible speeds. They often behave as though they are gloriously happy – heaving the tremendous flippers upwards until the tips break the surface of the water. Arabian fishermen have reported hearing them splash about in the night.

"The blue-spotted lagoon ray is a close relative of the stingray, and is the most common of its kind in the Red Sea. It is a peculiar-looking creature, resembling an enormous diamond-shaped pancake with a long kite-like tail – and an absurdly small dorsal fin. Its large yellow eyes are set on top of its blue-splodged body, protruding from twin humps like headlamps. The gills and mouth are on the underside of the fish.

"The spotted eagle ray, also seen from time to time in the Red Sea, has its eyes at the front of its body. It is known for being a more graceful swimmer. The torpedo ray is not at all graceful, but is notable for being able to deliver electric shocks of between 70 and 220 volts. This can kill prey or stun a man.

"Everyone's favourite is the mammoth manta ray, described as 'superbly graceful' by many. Dr. Rupert Ormond, a noted marine biologist, said: 'They seem to fly through the sea, with slow but elegant beats and effortless beauty.' At mating time, they have been seen leaping high out of the water, to return with a thunderous splash. The manta can measure over six and a half metres (20 feet) wide, and more than five metres (16 feet) long, and weigh about two tonnes. Their two thick lobes, resembling horns (positioned either side of the great jaws) are used for directing food into the mouth. They have caused the manta to be called 'the Devil'.

"Beneath the manta's smooth white belly, big suction fish can be seen swimming. Amazingly, they keep in the same position, imitating every movement even when not attached by the suction discs on the top of their heads. It would seem that many large sea fish permit pilot fish and suckerfish to remain unharmed in return for cleaning duties."

"The manta sounds like a big softy, doesn't he, Susan?" Gold now wriggled with enjoyment. Previously his eyes had been wide with a mixture of fright and fascination.

"Let me see what you think about the moray eel, with its peculiar face, snake-like body, and unpredictable nature.

"There are about one hundred species of morays, but, it is the brown moray that is the most common in the Red Sea. It can grow to a metre (3 feet) or more. It has a scaleless, boldly-patterned, long, flattish body, taller than it is wide. There are no pectoral fins, but long dorsal and anal fins – and a large mouth full of strong, sharp teeth.

"The moray is an aggressive predator with the disturbing habit of opening and closing its mouth, while wending its way through dense coral forests, or lurking in rock crevices. From such a vantage point, it will peer out, waiting for fish, squid and cuttlefish to pass by. Morays can be vicious and savage if disturbed, so divers keep clear of a likely lair, knowing its hold is difficult to break."

"Sounds like a most unpleasant creature, Susan. Isn't there anyone in the sea like us?" queried Gold.

"That depends on what you mean when you say 'like us'. There are several mammals living in Arabian waters. One is especially romantic, and many tales have been told concerning it. The Arabs know it as AROUSA EL BAHAR or the 'bride of the sea'."

"What on earth is it?" Gold sat up smartly, jostling the bunnies about him. The puzzle had set his imagination running riot.

"It is the dugong, or sea-cow – a slow, shy, docile and elusive herbivore – quite harmless and, just like a cow, it wears a contented look. Its colour is reddish-brown to olive-grey with lighter under parts. The scientific name is *Dugong dugon*. It is a member of the family Dugongidae."

Gold was visibly deflated, and replied witheringly:

"It doesn't sound like much. What makes it so special?" He seemed quite 'let down'.

"The dugong belongs to an order of rare creatures known as Sirenia, of which there is only one other living member, the manatee. Dugongs and manatees are unique, because they are the only completely aquatic mammals to live almost entirely on plants. Dugongs are the only marine sea cows while manatees inhabit rivers and estuaries which vary from fresh to marine water, depending on the weather.

"A dugong's main food is seaweeds and sea grasses, but other organisms are occasionally eaten. They feed at night, coming close to shore at dusk to graze at the grass beds in

shallow waters. Their existence depends almost entirely on healthy meadows of marine angiosperms, or sea grasses which are in limited supply. Heavy siltation, caused by landfill and dredging, as well as pollution, is harmful to the fragile angiosperms. These inhabitats have been greatly disturbed in recent years, so this rare mammal's future is precarious.

"There was once one other species of sea cow (the Steller's Sea Cow) but it was exterminated in the latter half of the eighteenth century when hunters sought its flesh, hide and tusks. The meat was said to taste like very tender beef. Weighing half a ton, a single individual yielded humans a great deal of protein.

"Many dugongs died quite recently about the same time that oil had been spilled into the Arabian Gulf. Pollution was thought to have been responsible for their extermination. Fortunately, studies have revealed that these animals still number several thousand. Even so, the International Union for Conservation of Nature (IUCN) lists the dugong as 'vulnerable to extinction'. Efforts, therefore, are being made to protect the dugongs, as well as sea turtles and other marine animals, and to learn more about their populations. Previously, very little scientific information had been gathered. It is now considered imperative to protect their habitats and the seagrass beds on which the dugong depends.

The four basic conditions necessary for sea cow habitats are: warm temperatures, shelter from strong wind and heavy seas, an abundant food source and shallow marine water, although they spend their days in deep water.

"The dugong's normal life span is estimated to be about 50 years, but, as it has a low reproduction rate, it cannot recover from over-exploitation. The gestation period is about 12 months, and it is believed that the female gives birth to a single calf (or twins) only once in about every five years. The mother takes care of the infant for almost two years."

"That's not very romantic."

"But, MERMAIDS are romantic, Gold. Do you remember Christopher telling you about the beautiful mermaid – with long golden hair and the tail of a fish? And, do you recall a story about the sirens of ancient Greek mythology? Sirens were said to be part woman and part bird, and they lured sailors to destruction by their enchanting singing?"

"Does a dugong look like one of those?" Gold's eyes now widened, and he gave me his 'sideways incredulous' look. His raised voice again startled the rabbits, but they soon shuffled down to doze once more. Their 'attention span', if it existed, had long since come to an end.

"I thought Christopher said mermaids were make-believe," Gold added.

Dugong

"They are, Gold; a dugong is nothing like that to look at. And the 'heartless siren' image is quite unlike the dugong's gentle nature. It is just that sea cows were said to be responsible, in olden days, for luring desperate sailors and their ships to destruction onto rocks. You see, stories tell us that dugongs were mistaken for mermaids.

"Furthermore, they have an eerie and plaintive cry with a human sound to it. One can easily imagine a ship in trouble on a stormy night, with dugongs wailing like sirens on the rocky shore. Seen through the raging sea's spray and the mist; the captain and his crew must have been convinced that help was at hand."

"You made me go all shivery," shuddered Gold.

"The dugong is docile and has no intention of harming anyone, which is another reason why I think humans should help them. This creature leads a slow-paced, peaceful life. Nothing could look less like a mermaid, though. A dugong resembles a giant garden slug, similar to a big fat seal, except for its elephant-like face set with small eyes; and a short, broad snout for digging up sea grass roots.

"It is a distant relative to the elephant, growing to a length of between two and three metres (6–10 feet), and weighing between 300–500 kilos (600–1100 lbs). People have described the dugong as 'ugly', 'mishapen', 'torpedo-like' and 'sluggish', but I think it is an appealing animal. It is almost hairless, but with a whiskery face, and kind, bright button eyes. Its body is quite streamlined, allowing it to be surprisingly graceful. Yet, the calves have been seen playing in the shallows like 'slow, clumsy puppies'."

"I think I could recognize a dugong,' said Gold confidently.

"The dugong and manatee are very similar, Gold, but their flat tails are different: a dugong tail ends with a crescent-shaped fin, known as a fluke, while the manatee has a paddle-shaped tail. The dugong's fleshy snout and partially-divided upper lip, usually hides the male's two tusks, or huge incisor teeth set in the upper jaw. That would help you to tell the males from the females.

"Just like other mammals, sea-cows breathe air, have hair, and a back-bone; and the female suckles her young just as humans do, holding the baby up, clear of the water while it is feeding. Perhaps some short-sighted sailor imagined he was seeing a mermaid nursing her child.

"On the western side of Arabia, herds of these placid mammals live in the Red Sea where there are many islands. They also inhabit the Indian Ocean to the south. Eastwards Arabian Gulf dugongs cluster for most of the year around the islands of Bahrain. It is believed that these mammals migrate in the summer to cooler, deeper waters. Groups from between twelve to almost seven hundred have been spotted. It is believed, that as many as 4,000 to 8,000 may live in the Gulf, but there seem to be far fewer in the Red Sea.

"Dugongs enjoy the warm shallows where they graze on sea grasses. Their large paddle-like flippers are too small to permit them to leave the water, but they are useful for swishing plants towards the mouth when feeding, and as an aid to moving about and swimming. Sea-cows spend time lying on the seabed, too, but they must rise to the surface to breathe every couple of minutes. With nostrils on the upper surface of the muzzle, they are able to breathe while remaining almost submerged. They sleep afloat in this way.

"Dolphins are another mammal found in Arabian waters. Six kinds are recorded as inhabiting the Red Sea. They belong to the Cetacean order which includes all those mammals that spend their entire lives in water, such as whales and porpoises.

"The dolphin's front limbs have modified into flippers whilst no hind legs are visible. There are twin tail fins, horizontally set, called flukes and a vertical dorsal fin." I used my hands to illustrate what was vertical and horizontal – and Gold laughed when I flapped my arms to demonstrate the flippers in use. I felt a little foolish but decided to ignore his reaction.

"A dolphin is a type of small whale, notable for being a speedy swimmer. With skin that is smooth and silky to touch, it uses a sleek, slender and streamlined body to advantage. Its shape allows it to be as fast or faster than any other sea creatures. It is the most accomplished of all swiming mammals, sharing with the porpoise, the greatest ability for long-distance travel, navigation and acrobatics. Dolphins love to play, sometimes becoming so excited that they leap right out of the water, completing a graceful arc as they dive back in. Even a very small one can follow its mother high into the sky, copying her every movement exactly. In groups, families can be identified because the males are larger than the females.

"A comical appearance will tend to make any animal popular as a rule, and this is the case with the dolphin. It has a mouth that is curved upwards, and it always seems to be smiling. The lower jaw projects beyond the upper one, the forehead bulges, and, most species have a pointed beaked snout. As gregarious creatures, they form well-ordered social groups, which continually communicate and co-operate with each other. And, once a friendship is formed with humans, dolphins are known to be affectionate, and as playful as great big puppies. The eyes have been described as looking wise, understanding and intelligent. Some humans have been so captivated as to wear dolphin suits – and learn to swim dolphin-fashion in order to get better acquainted with these lovable animals. The shared inter-species experiences has been named 'interlock'.

"Since man discovered that several species of dolphin have brains larger than that of humans, attempts have been made to communicate with them. At first, it was thought best that these mammals should be taught a human language, but then, researchers began to study 'dolphinese'. Sadly, very little progress has been made, although this work has been going on for over thirty years. Some researchers claim that the dolphins' understanding of the world about them is much

Dolphins

broader than that of humans. They cite this as a major stumbling block with regard to communication. Furthermore, difficulties arise because the values of humans and these animals are unalike. Certainly, the sensory organs are completely different.

"Science has established that the dolphin is a creature with good vision, but this method of 'seeing' is secondary to sound for the animal. It learns about its surroundings by bouncing sounds, such as shrill whistles, while swimming along – a method, known as echo location. Sounds reflected off the environment, send returning sound waves to the animal for assessment.

"Some researchers surmise that dolphins can 'see', 'read' and 'hear', even into each other's hearts and brains, because sound waves can pass through skin and muscle. If this is true, they can have no secrets from each other. Marine biologists assume the large brain is very active; otherwise, it would have grown smaller over time from disuse. As this mammal does not read

or make anything, its brain must be fully occupied as a complicated transmitter operating within the world of dolphins."

"No wonder they look wise and understanding," said Gold in a small awed voice.

"Stories often tell how dolphins treat each other kindly, and how they show compassion. There are even tales about them helping humans in distress. It is wonderful to think that such a gifted animal will use its fantastic powers beyond the survival of its own species.

"It is difficult for humans to comprehend the possible values of any species outside their own, and this, apparently, is another obstacle to be overcome in the efforts to communicate. Dolphins certainly appear to be willing to try. Some of them have formed firm friendships with humans. They learn well, or at least, they have proven to be good mimics. Even if we never know more about them, I would settle for friendship with a dolphin. Wouldn't you Gold?"

It had been a long story and I suspected that Gold had suddenly dozed off. Some of the rabbits had hopped away, and others were now either scratching or washing themselves. But, no, Gold was still listening, even though his eyes had been closed. Suddenly, they opened wide.

"Oh, yes! I wish I could meet a dolphin," he said with enthusiasm. "I'll bet I could find out a thing or two," he boasted.

"Perhaps one day, you will see an aquatic animal. In Arabia, even inland, there are creatures living in water. Many irrigation channels have tiny fish. And, the most astonishing creatures spring to life in pools after the briefest of rainstorms in the barren desert – even in places where rain has not fallen for years. Shallow pools form after heavy rain and in no time at all, there is life in the water. One can find all kinds of little animals including a type of shrimp, known as a 'triops'. It is a crustacean similar to a tiny crab, about two centimetres (1 inch) long."

"How can that be possible, Susan," said Gold, in doubt. "Are you sure?"

"According to the evidence of fossils, the triops is a descendant of an animal that existed 180 million years ago, and notable for reproducing itself parthenogenetically. Do you remember, from our story about reptiles and amphibians, such creatures reproduce without mating?

"When a desert pool dries up, triops' eggs develop a hard shell and lie dormant among grains of sand, close to the surface – until the next rainstorm. Then, once submerged in water, the egg swiftly sheds its shell and the little triops rapidly grows to full size and lays eggs. Thus, the lifecycle of a triops has been repeated down through countless ages. Isn't that incredible?"

"As you know, Susan, I've never liked creepy-crawlies, but I

do like the sound of some of these teensy-weensy water animals. They are so clever!"

"There are many more astonishing aquatic creatures, Gold. There are water beetles, and even a water scorpion; and, there is a mollusc living in the Red Sea called a 'seahare': It is a greenish-brownish sea-slug, with a pair of upright tentacles on the top of the head which look like rabbit's ears; but it is not at all pleasant like the hare. It cleverly defends itself by secreting slime."

"Yeough!" Gold exclaimed in disgust. "Now you must tell me about a NICE aquatic animal."

"Anemones are nice marine creatures – if you mean that they must be pleasing to look at. Many people call them 'plant animals', because they look just like flowers; yet, they do have sense-organs, and the ability to move about and eat solid food. Sea anemones are best-known for their beauty. They have a wide range of colours which seem to be purely decorative, serving none of the usual functions of camouflage, warning, advertisement and recognition for territory, or mating.

"There are many kinds and sizes, but basically they are all cylindrical, bag-like creatures with tentacles, formed in a ring on the upper edge around the mouth. Each of these is armed with a stinging cell to paralyze and hold a victim, while stuffing it into the mouth. The other end is a sucker foot like a supporting stem.

"Jelly fish can be pretty, too, and they are often colourful. They are close relatives of corals and anemones. The typical, free-swimming species is umbrella-shaped, with a rounded or conical body with four, eight, or many tentacles that are armed with stinging cells. The mouth is underneath.

"The jellyfish swims along, slowly and rhythmically, opening and closing like an umbrella. It is carnivorous – dining on the fish, shrimps and other small creatures that are

captured in its trailing tentacles, paralysed, and pushed into the mouth.

"Around the Red Sea coral reefs, it is possible to see some big and beautiful jellyfish species, drifting along. In tones of opalescent blue, they trail long thread-like tentacles and side tufts of bright yellow."

"I really don't like the sound of that one, no matter how pretty. I would hate to be a shrimp when he came by," said Gold.

"But that is the Law of the Sea. It is worthwhile to remember that sea creatures only take as much as they need. Animals seem much wiser than humans in this respect.

"Crustaceans, such as shrimps, crabs and lobsters are specialties in restaurants worldwide, and consequently, they are 'big business' commodities. One marine biologist and author, Dr. Peter Vine, says that Bahraini shrimps are among the most delicious to be found anywhere in the world. Unfortunately, this appreciation has helped to put them and some other species in danger. Apart from overfishing, shrimp populations are also threatened by pollution, and the destruction of their natural nurseries where the foreshores are being developed. Complicating the problem, in these areas, shrimp trawl nets have proved to be a major hazard to the survival of the green turtle and other creatures.

"The life cycle of a popular commercial species of shrimp begins in early spring, when spawning females discharge thousands of already-fertilized eggs into the sea – generally under the cover of darkness. This spawn drifts amongst the plankton for about a day before hatching into pear-shaped 'nauplii' larvae. Nauplius is the first larval stage of many crustaceans, characterized by three pairs of appendages and a single eye. They are active swimmers, and develop through a series of moults into 'protozoea' larvae that feed on phytoplankton. After another series of moults, they become carnivorous 'mysis' larvae, feeding on zooplankton. Eventually, with a further three moults, which takes a total of three weeks, they settle to the seabed to become juvenile shrimps."

"And that's what you put into shrimp cocktails," nodded Gold, having 'put two and two together'. "What about John's favourite: oysters?"

"Ah! The oyster! This is another commercially-fished invertebrate. You have heard how maritime traditions have been carefully preserved in Arabia, and how the seafood industry is so vital, but I have not told you about the part played by shellfish. Certain ones are of great commercial value. These delicacies are clams, scallops, mussels and oysters – known as bi-valved molluscs. Bi-valve means that the creature possesses a two-part hinged shell. Bi-valves are the second largest class of mollusc. The most common species are snails and slugs.

"Shells are the homes made and inhabited by molluscs, or soft-bodied invertebrate animals. Certain species of these faunae live on land, but most inhabit fresh or salt water.

Marine molluscs are vital, serving as an important food for fish, as well as a nutritious source of protein for humans. Their shells have been gathered down through the ages to provide tools, and articles of adornment, too.

"There are approximately 47,000 species of mollusc, their sizes ranging from a few millimetres (less than a quarter of an inch) to more than 20 metres (65 feet) in length: the largest is a giant squid, a form of mollusc. Although greatly varied in body form, molluscs have many common features: the body has two basic parts, a visceral hump which remains inside the shell (if there is one) and the head area, which extends from the shell. It has a sensory and feeding apparatus, and an organ of locomotion.

"Two other features are unique to the mollusc. One is the mantle, a fleshy fold of membrane that operates as a cape for the soft body. It usually secretes a protective shell into which the body can retract. The other is the radula, present in many species. It is a kind of toothed tongue with microscopic hook-like teeth, used as a flexible rasp for filing off pieces of food, similar to the action of a cat's tongue.

"Amongst the bi-valve molluscs, the oyster stands alone. It has been of especial importance in the Arabian Gulf, because certain species produce pearls, prized by humans since earliest times. Pearls have been the cause of great adventures and have brought fabulous riches for some. These precious gems are either found in their natural state by divers or farmed in man-made beds under strict control.

"The waters of Bahrain have been a treasure chest of the finest pearls, and have provided considerable wealth for some of the inhabitants in times past, as well as establishing trade links to distant lands. Shell middens, or mounds of broken shells indicate that the pearl oyster has been fished around Bahrain for at least four thousand years.

"Bahrain has two species of pearl oyster of commercial importance. Pearl reproduction takes place by synchronous spawning. This is a process whereby some triggering factor results in eggs and sperm being ejected into the water at the same time so fertilization takes place. The eggs become larvae, or immature animals whose form differs from the adult. They live on plankton, and attach themselves to something that is hopefully safe from uprooting by storms. Bahraini oyster young, or spat, mostly adhere to sea-grass. The main period of their settlement is between March and April. They are greenish in colour at this stage, and grow rapidly during the summer months to a size of around 5mm (¼ inch).

"By October, when the grass withers, the spat have changed to a brown colour. Releasing their grip, they gradually move to deeper water. Once there, they secrete byssal threads to attach themselves to hard substrata near the base of the sea-grass slopes. Adult pearl oysters generally live out their lives attached to some hard object, but it is possible for them to move and reattach by secreting new byssal threads. They eat by trapping food particles of plankton, larvae and fish eggs in their gill filaments.

"Of the Bahraini annual catch of seafood (now over 7 million kilos or 7,000 tons) a good proportion comprises crustaceans and bi-valved molluscs. Apart from these there are the fish: barracuda, garfish, goat fish, grouper and grunt; leather jackets, mackerel and mullet; parrotfish and perch; sea bream, sergeant fish, silver biddies and snapper; tuna and trevally; but the most landed fish, beside the trevallies, are the siganids, better known as rabbit fish."

"I think you are teasing me, Susan."

"Oh, no, Gold, that is truly what they are called. But, it is time to prepare dinner. I know what Askalu has for you, and I know that we are having fish: either SHAREE, HAMOUR or SAFFEE – they are the Arabic words for lethrinid snapper, a species of popular grouper – and the rabbit fish."

Having added the SAFFEE for effect, I jumped up and all the animals scattered, except for Gold, who just sat there. He was obviously wishing he could think of something clever to say to me, to repay me for my teasing.

6
Predators and Scavengers

ne very hot day, when everyone seemed tired and irritable, I went to snatch a quick rest on the terrace. Suddenly, the peace was shattered as Gold 'pounced' upon me with an urgent question.

"What exactly is a predator, Susan? I heard John telling Mrs. Henderson that our new baby rabbits were taken by a predator."

I had been preoccupied, and he gave me a start. The poor little rabbit looked very upset, and he seemed anxious to get to the bottom of the sad affair.

"You, Gold, are a predator!" I snapped, before I could stop myself.

Gold had hopped up to me without so much as a SALAM ALAYKUM, despite practising his Arabic greetings constantly for the past week. Concern had apparently made him forget his manners completely. Now, he looked taken aback, so I hurried to reassure him. I tried to take his mind off the tragedy.

"Of course rabbits are not predators, Gold, but what sort of a greeting is that? A true predator is one that preys and pounces upon creatures in order to nourish itself. It is any animal that lives by eating others. In short, it is someone who will come over the wall and eat you if you don't remember your manners."

"Sorry, Susan," he said contritely.

"That's all right, Gold. I was just teasing. Your manners are fine. I do that, too, time and again, when there is something preying on my mind. We are all upset about losing the baby rabbits. The guilty predator was a cat. It was just a 'stray' and not a wildcat. It is quite natural for cats to hunt, you know, because they have inherited predatory instincts from their wild ancestors.

"This cat was probably starving and thirsty. Domestic cats usually only prey upon mice, rats and other small creatures when they are very hungry. The street cats must be getting desperate again – they always do when the weather begins to warm up. You can see them drinking from the swimming pool sometimes. Some look quite dreadful – especially the tomcats. We must keep a watch out now, because they will be on the prowl constantly until summer is over.

"The strays are pitiful creatures to look at, which is very sad. If only they had someone to care for them, then they would not be taking our rabbit kittens."

Gold still looked glum.

"Would you like me to tell you about some real predators in Arabia, Gold?"

"Yes, please, Susan," said Gold with exquisite politeness.

"If you asked the Bedouin to tell you what is the worst predator in Arabia, he would probably tell you that it is the wolf. You see, wolves repeatedly attack their flocks, and they have been known to attack humans. Consequently, the Bedouin usually kill these animals whenever they can.

"The shepherds feel so strongly about wolves that they have often hung them by their hind legs in trees, and left a notice. This might read that the predator was put to death by humans because it killed sheep; and the number of slain may be mentioned.

"Sometimes a wolf has been tied up and kept prisoner by the Bedouin. This is much worse than being killed. Such punishment is a terrible fate for wild animals because they are naturally timid."

"Do the Bedouin tie them up because they hate them?"

"No, Gold. Some desert folk believe that the wolf has magical powers. There are many Arabian folk tales about this animal and some stories tell of its power to drive out sickness, and also to promote fertility. In the past, you might have seen a wolf chained up close to a tent where there was sickness, or where the family did not have children. Even the eye of a dead wolf was once considered to be a powerful amulet, or a thing worn as a charm against evil. It was believed that the eye could protect the family from danger and aid the owner in his daily life. Some tribes ate the flesh of a wolf, to cure certain ailments. The skin was useful, too, but in a more practical way. It could be made into musical instruments."

"Ooo! I think I would rather be tied up than be made into a musical instrument," Gold said as he pulled a face.

"I do agree. If wolves understood this, it would be no wonder that they hold a grudge against the Bedouin, as the folk tales tell us."

"Oh, please tell me about it, Susan." Gold had cheered up and was ready for a story. He nestled into his furry 'egg-shape', and looked at me expectantly. I began:

Fennec Fox

"The wolf is called DHIB in Arabic. In the myth, he was supposed to have been a human being, long ago, when his name was SERHAN. They say that he still understands human speech, and who are we to doubt that, Gold?

"The story goes that when the wolf was human, all the sheep and goats belonged to him; but then, because of some great sin, the flocks were taken away and given to humans. However, the wolf still felt that the sheep and goats were his, and he has borne a grievance against shepherds and their dogs ever since.

"What does the wolf look like, Susan – now that he is no longer human?"

"The Arabian wolf looks just like a medium-sized bushy-tailed dog, somewhat similar to an alsatian – but smaller. The wolf belongs to the dog family, and is believed to be the ancestor of the domestic dog. They can be many colours because they have adapted to their surroundings. Their camouflage, and clever ways, help them to stay hidden. They are fairly common in Arabia, with habitats that are quite widespread; yet, they are seldom seen. Wolves are not generally found in the great deserts because caves and crevices are preferred as dwellings. Occasionally, there are reports of them in the southwest, where the mountains provide very good hiding places.

"Wolves have sometimes made use of deserted hyena dens at whelping time, when the she-wolf gives birth to her pups. Although dog-like, the hyena family is more related to cats. The Bedouin have a myth about wolves mating with female hyenas, and producing puppies they call SIB. These animals have a reputation for attacking humans, without provocation.

"True or false, wolves cope well with life in Arabia. The wolf is a creature that cannot go too long without drinking, so some choose to live near a well. When hungry, an oasis is an especially good place to be, as the water will attract birds which the wolf might catch.

"The tracks of a male wolf are larger than those of the female, and this spoor has helped humans to learn something about their habits. For instance, it can be seen that the Arabian wolf usually hunts alone or with its mate, but not with a pack, as wolves do in some parts of the world.

"Wolf pups have been raised successfully in captivity after the she-wolf has been killed or lost, and some pups have been born in captivity.

"Mature wolves have been kept successfully, too, becoming somewhat tame – and responding to kindness."

"Are there many kinds of predators in Arabia, Susan?"

"Oh yes. Carnivorous animals living in the wild have to prey on other animals in order to survive. Some birds are predators, too; and, many creatures that are predominantly herbivorous, such as certain kinds of lizards, will also snap up tiny creatures, if they pass by.

"Another predator is the Arabian Fox. In Arabic, it is known as AB AL-HSEJN, TA'LEB or ROREJRI. It is another member of the dog family, although as agile as a cat and much more inquisitive. This animal is very good at jumping, and it will even climb trees to catch birds. Its chief food is rodents, especially rats and mice in agricultural areas – those creatures that infest, and in some cases, destroy crops. Foxes will also eat birds, eggs, insects, camel spiders, scorpions, cockroaches, frogs, snails and snakes.

"The fox rarely barks, but it will make a variety of other sounds that are not at all 'doggy'. It can also scream."

"What does the fox look like, Susan? Does it look like a dog or a cat?"

"It looks something like a dog. A fox is a very pretty creature with a long, bushy tail, a long, sharp pointed muzzle, and very large, erect ears that lie back flat if it is annoyed. The big ears are generally upright and alert, and move constantly to catch any sound. Quick eye movements make the fox seem suspicious and give it a cunning look. The eyes are similar to the cat's, so a fox can see well in poor light.

"Foxes are mostly nocturnal creatures, and hunt stealthily at night. They lead solitary lives, except in the mating season. When the cubs are about to be born, the vixen often digs a shallow cavity in the ground, in a place hidden by bushes. Sometimes she uses the deserted den of another animal. The vixen habitually remains hidden with her cubs during the day while her mate, the dog fox, stands guard close by, catching small animals to bring for his family to eat.

"There are several species of fox in Arabia. The most common is the Arabian Red Fox, but it is a sandy-beige colour, not red. It is the same species found in Europe and America, however. This fox will venture quite close to man in search of water, and is often seen on the outskirts of villages and towns. Another species is known as Ruppell's Sand Fox. Its habitat is widespread, but it is rare and seldom seen. It is believed that this species can go without drinking for long periods, and will run great distances over the desert to find water. The foxes that live in the barren parts of Arabia are smaller and lighter-built than those that inhabit the mountains of the west and south-west.

"The fennec is a very small fox said to inhabit sand dunes. Although it has not yet been recorded in Saudi Arabia, it has been found nearby. It is a rare fox throughout its range in neighbouring countries.

"Foxes are appealing animals, naturally playful. They can catch small creatures by an enticing method known as 'charming'. Rolling playfully on the ground, its legs waving in the air, the fox can, in this way, trick curious birds or rabbits into coming close enough to be caught."

"What a rotten trick!" said Gold indignantly. "Is the fox always so crafty, Susan?"

"Fables do portray the fox as cunning and unlikeable. And, there are several Bedouin stories which describe this animal as clever. But, none of them give it a good character. One Bedouin story claims that the fox has a grudge against humans, just as the wolf has.

The story goes that a fox once helped rid mankind of his old enemy, the serpent. Afterwards, humans forgot their debt to the fox, so they are resented for this ingratitude.

"In Arabia, long ago, the fox had every reason to live in fear because it was hunted as food. With the aid of a hunting dog, the victim was run to ground. The fur between the pads of the fox's feet helped the animal to dash quickly across the shifting sand, and sometimes to safety.

"Humans should be grateful to the fox for eating pests that would otherwise spread disease. Of course, it is very annoying when a fox breaks in at a farm and kills chickens. Yet, people who wish to protect the fox, will tell you that this animal rarely kills poultry. If only foxes kept to a diet of pests, people would like them more. In the desert, away from farms, foxes will scavenge. too. In the wild, there are some very special animals that are scavengers."

"What's a scavenger?"

"A scavenger is a creature that does the cleaning up. It feeds on decaying animals and carrion."

"What's carrion?"

"Carrion is rotting meat or vegetable matter."

"Disgusting!" said Gold, wrinkling his nose in distaste.

"Perhaps, but isn't it a good idea to leave the countryside in a clean state?

"Whenever there are predators in the wild, Gold, you will find the remains of their kill and scavengers. In Arabia there is the hyena, known as SAB'A in Arabic."

"The hyena is the mother of the SIB, isn't it?"

Hyena

"That is what the folk tales tell us, Gold, but the SIB is quite likely a mythical animal. Sometimes, the hyena is a predator, too, preying upon small animals, but it is more often a scavenger."

"No wonder it has naughty children," judged Gold, no doubt thinking that he might make a good meal for a hyena. "What does it look like?"

"Hyena pups are quite attractive but the mature animal is most unusual.

"The Arabian species is known as the Striped Hyena, because it has stripes on its hairy body and legs. It looks quite doggy, although is not of the dog family. The hyena has its own family, the Hyaenidae, which is only very distantly related to the dog. It is a strange-looking creature, with forelegs longer than the back legs. The hind-quarters seem quite poorly developed in comparison with the powerful shoulders and neck. The heavy head has strong jaws, designed to crack open bones to get to the marrow.

"Hyenas were once widespread in Arabia, but now they are scarce.

"As naturally nocturnal creatures, living in caves and earth dens in mountainous places, they are rarely seen. Just occasionally, they descend to the foothills or come out during the day.

"Unfortunately, story books have given the hyena a dreadful reputation. 'Cowardly', 'greedy', 'cruel', and 'treacherous' are the adjectives that have been used to describe this animal; and its howl has been likened to someone laughing fiendishly. And, because its woolly coat is often shaggy and untidy-looking, the hyena has been called 'ugly' in appearance as well as behaviour.

"Surprisingly, although the hyena looks quite ferocious, it is not aggressive at all. It is classed as 'extremely timid'. Its coat has a peculiar dorsal ridge of long hair that runs straight down the length of its back, and when this creature is frightened, this mane of hair will stand straight up. In captivity, the hyena has tamed well, and with proper care, it becomes a handsome animal.

"Old records show that hyenas once dwelt in northern Arabia in large numbers. The Bedouin speak of great dens in which these animals hid by day. By night, they claim, their packs 'infested' the whole territory, opening graves, devouring corpses, and attacking wounded and ailing camels. Terrible tales claim that this creature even hunted crying babies, but it seems unlikely behaviour for a timid animal.

"In olden day folklore, if the Bedouin found fresh hyena spoor, or tracks, they would surround the den while one man was appointed to crawl inside, holding a long rope with a noose on one end, over his left arm. Crawling on his stomach, dragging the other end of the rope behind him, the man would grope cautiously on all sides, searching for the hyena.

"When he found the animal, he would grab it, and slip the noose over its neck, shouting at once, 'It isn't here! This isn't it! I have found a piece of old sheepskin!' Perhaps he said this to give himself courage, yet warning his friends of the capture; and, with a sign from this brave man, his comrades would drag out the animal, to kill and eat. Certain Bedouin considered very young hyenas to be especially delicious.

"The teeth of the hyena were worn as amulets, long ago, and it was believed that these would protect children against various diseases. To lower a fever, a drink could be made by mixing water with gall, a bitter, greenish liquid from the animal's liver!'

"Poor creature, and after cleaning up the desert. Are there any other scavengers in Arabia, Susan?"

"Yes, Gold, there are several kinds of wild dogs that are called jackals. They are mostly found around the great Hofuf oasis in eastern Arabia. Similar to the wolf, the jackal is also a member of the dog family. Jackals live alone, in pairs, or in packs that prowl in the late evening and through the night. These scavengers also inhabit open country, but during the day, they conceal themselves amongst brush or thickets. Most wild dogs 'sing' in the evening, and the jackal is known for its especially depressing and dreary howl – a much more dismaying sound than that of the hyena.

"The jackal does hunt and kill. To some, it seems cowardly because it preys on tiny creatures. Others see this as a clever example of survival. It usually eats what is left over from a predator's kill, and survives on whatever is available.

"Yet, when it is starving, the jackal has been known to make night raids into cultivated areas to eat delicious watermelons growing on the vines.

"Folklore tells of a time when the lion expected the jackal to work for him by finding suitable animals to kill. In return, the jackal was permitted to wait for the lion to finish eating, and then clean up. Of course, there are no lions in Arabia today, so the jackal must take whatever he can get, I suppose. It is true that jackals in other lands habitually follow large cats and wait to finish off the carcass of the 'kill'. But, when hunting in packs, jackals can bring down prey as large as a sheep or small antelope.

"A jackal's den is recognizable as an odiferous place with the peculiar odour of the animal which is caused by a glandular secretion at the base of its tail. The female gives birth to the young in burrows near the den."

"It is strange to think that these dog-like creatures are distant relatives to Samantha," commented Gold

"Samantha is not so different when we are clearing the table after a meal. She always hopes to receive titbits. As for true scavengers, they are an essential part of nature and the biological process."

"I can see that now, Susan. Thank you, or, should I say SHUKRAN, for my story today," he said politely; and as he hopped happily away to join the other rabbits, he called MASALAMA, in farewell. His new Arabic words, manners, and good humour appeared to be restored.

7
Small Mammals

ut, OUT, you little rascals!" I cried, as I shooed rabbits from the living room. "Just look at my plants – and there is dirt all over the carpet."

I could have cried. It had been ages since any of the rabbits had nibbled at my house plants, and I had forgotten that they might do this. Gold never touched them any more, since I explained how much the plants meant to me – and, how difficult it was to grow them in the dry central Arabian climate. None of the older rabbits even looked at the indoor plants, now. Perhaps Gold had told them; or, maybe, they had grown accustomed to waiting for mealtimes and preferred the food we provided. The marauders had been a band of youthful rabbits. I had clearly recognized Nigel as he dashed away, and I think the others were Chipolatta, Jacqui, Maggie and Sofia. "They will get a piece of my mind when I catch up with them," I muttered to myself.

"Oh, Oops! Poor Susan. I'm, sorry about your plants. Perhaps they are not too bad. I am sure you can make them look alright again," said Gold, sympathetically, as he hopped in and surveyed the scene.

"You're right, Gold. It's silly of me to be quite so upset. It is natural for rabbits to be herbivores."

"Oh, Susan, they really are quite young, and they meant no harm. I don't think there is any need for you to call them such a name."

Gold seemed puzzled when I began to laugh. I laughed and laughed until I saw that he was looking uncomfortable. "Remember, Gold, a 'herbivore' is not a bad thing. It simply means that the creature's natural diet is plants. We usually call you rabbits 'vegetarians' because we feed you fruit and vegetables. It is almost the same thing."

"Oh yes. And, I'm glad you feel a little better, Susan. I shall speak with the young rabbits, though, and ask them not to do it again."

"Thank you, Gold. You are very kind. Would you like me to tell you a story about some of Arabia's other small mammals that are herbivores? Perhaps you would also like to hear something of the small omnivores, insectivores – and the little carnivores, too. Insectivores eat insects. The omnivorous creatures eat meat and vegetables. And, as you will recall, the carnivorous ones eat flesh, so they have sharp teeth and especially big canine teeth to help them tear up raw meat and crunch bones."

Gold loved exciting stories usually, but this time he gave a little shudder. "I'd love a story about herbivores, Susan, but I'm not sure about the others. Carnivores sound a bit grim for the mood I'm in."

"Alright, let's begin with the herbivores, omnivores and insectivores. Askalu wants to clean up here, so let's sit in our favourite spot on the terrace, and I'll try to forget about this mess.

"Most people think of Arabia as a totally arid land which it is not, although the barren deserts are extensive. Nevertheless, Arabia plays host to many creatures that eat only plant life; and during seasons with adequate rainfall, there is usually sufficient herbage to feed these animals – even in a dried up river bed, known as a WADI. Many herbivores are small, and live in burrows near wadis where there are rocks and shrubbery in which to hide.

"Most small herbivorous animals are timid, and the Arabian Peninsula provides many ideal hiding places. There are rocky, rugged, green areas in the southwest that are too difficult for humans. And, all the mountain ranges in Arabia are 'alive' with these creatures, too. They usually have sufficient succulent plants upon which to feed, even in central Arabia, where the climate is dry, as well as hot, for most of the year.

"One of the most appealing herbivorous animals is the rock hyrax. It is one of Arabia's smaller mammals. It is called WABR in Arabic, which is the same name for a guinea-pig. Although the hyrax looks a bit like a large guinea-pig, it is in no way closely related to them. The distant relatives of the hyrax are the elephant, and rhinoceros – and sirenians, which we talked about in Aquatic Creatures.

"The hyrax has a 'koala-bear' face with large, bright eyes, a black, shiny nose, and little round ears. Its furry body is fat, and it has a very short tail, and nice little feet. The toes are unusual, and resemble tiny hooves. The short brownish coat of the hyrax has some long hairs here and there over the back, and these respond to touch, just as cat's whiskers do. They are known as tactile hairs.

"Hyrax are quick and agile, and very good at climbing

rocks. Their habitats are the mountains in western, south-western and central Arabia, where they make homes in deep rocky crevices. As gregarious creatures, they live in groups which act as marmots do. A few, appointed as sentinels, stand guard to warn the group when danger is close by. They can be seen in the early morning and at dusk, feeding on leaves, berries, seeds, roots and bulbs. Their cry may be heard at night. Although the hyrax is a cautious animal, it is not afraid of humans. Catching it is quite easy, and when tamed, the hyrax can become a most affectionate pet.

Hyrax

"And, let me tell you about the hare in the wild. The hare, commonly called ARNAB in Arabic, is given additional names by some tribal people. The male hare is called HAZAZ, the female is EDENE, and the young are known as HURNEZ. Hares can be many colours in Arabia, as they are adapted to be camouflaged among their surroundings. Local stories tell how the hare can hide behind a stone or some brushwood, or by crouching close to the ground. It will not move, even if a herdsman walks right past; but, if the hare notices the man returning, it will dash madly away.

"In Arabian folk tales, the wild hare is said to be boastful about his abilities, and says: 'I am the one who hides beneath a tiny shrub, whose fur gives pleasant warmth, and who is not seen except by the camel herdsmen.' And, he likens himself to the gazelle and the antelope who must sometimes quench their thirst with dew only. Says the hare: 'I am he with the white lip, living in the plain with the dried-up plants, who satisfies two and makes the mouth of the third one water.' This must mean that there is only enough meat on his bones for two people."

"This folk tale hare is fond of talking about himself. What a show-off!" said Gold – with a hint of jealousy, I thought.

"Rodents are plentiful in Arabia, Gold, because desert life suits them very well. They can survive without water, and cope with extreme temperatures. Rodents arrived in Arabia millions of years ago, long before it became arid, and at a time when the land had flourishing forests practically everywhere. The desert dormouse is said to have been one of the first – arriving during the great ice age, which began two and a half million years ago, and ended about ten thousand years ago. Many parts of the world were completely covered in ice, at a time when Arabia enjoyed a more temperate climate. There were forests and meadowland everywhere. When the ice receded from the other parts of the globe, and the world grew warmer, the Arabian rodents had to adapt once more because the land became increasingly barren. Animals such as the dormouse adapted very well.

"What exactly is a rodent, Susan? You told me once that many people call rabbits and hares 'rodents', and we are not, but you didn't explain what they are."

"Rodents are all those animals that have only one pair of strong incisors, or sharp cutting teeth in the front of each jaw, and they have no canine teeth, (those are the four sharp, pointed teeth most mammals have, one each side of the incisors). In Arabia, rodents include various kinds of rats and mice, porcupines, voles, jerboas, gerbils and molerats.

"Now, the mouse, known as FAR in Arabic, and the rat, called JURATH, and FAR also, are found everywhere in Arabia. Rats and mice have survived and thrived wherever they have been transferred. Many species travelled to Arabia by trading ships that sailed between distant ports. There is never any real danger of these rodents becoming extinct because female rats and mice produce at least four or five babies several times a year.

"As you know, the chief enemy of the mouse is the cat. In the desert, where there are few cats, the mouse goes into the tents of nomads and carries away food. It will even gnaw at sleeping people. The Bedouin have many folk tales about the mouse. In one story, a tribesman, sleeping with his provisions beside him, awoke to find a mouse stealing from them. He wished only to frighten the mouse, but he accidentally killed it. Thereafter, he lived in fear of the revenge of the mice.

"In another story, the mice were living in dread of the cat, so they agreed that every cat must wear a little bell around its neck to give them warning. The mice bought many little bells, and their chief, CEBIR AL-FAR, called on the bravest to come forward and undertake to hang the bells around the cats' necks. No mouse ever came forward and the bells are still lying in the storeroom of the mice – and, cats continue to torment the poor creatures for their timidity.

"Rats and mice have often been called the world's most successful mammals because they thrive everywhere. They will eat almost anything, including insects, (so they are really omnivorous). They even eat paper. There are several species of these rodents throughout Arabia. They are adapted particularly well to arid terrain.

"The rock rat is a soft-furred little mammal that is found in many places on the Arabian Peninsula. And, there is a bandicoot rat living in eastern Arabia, which originated in India. Sand rats are plentiful, too. They are known as jirds, and they especially love to climb rocks. A jird does not look

like the average rat because of its very long bushy tail. Colour differs in various Arabian habitats.

"There are dormice in Arabia, too, and there is an attractive little creature known as the spiny mouse. Spiny mice live throughout Arabia."

"They sound peculiar!" Gold shot me a quizzical glance.

"It just looks like a very pretty mouse but its coat is not smooth. There are longer hairs among the short hairs all over the back, so this mouse is often called the 'spiny-backed mouse'. Spiny mice live side by side with the gerbil, which is another common desert rodent.

Gerbil

Spiny mouse

"Arabia has many species of gerbil – an appealing little mouse-like creature. It can be recognized by its long tail which has a tuft on the end – and it has large ears, big bright eyes, and long whiskers. The colouring matches the surroundings so some are greyish and others are golden-brownish. They make nice pets.

"Gerbils are herbivorous and can do without water. In the wild, they live in rocky terrain, hiding in deep burrows by day, and tending to remain at home on cold nights. This little creature is plentiful because they have as many or more babies than the mouse.

"There are several extremely interesting rodents, on the Arabian Peninsula. Unfortunately, most of them are not easy to observe because they hide in the daytime, coming out only at twilight and in the cool of night. This is the best way for them to avoid predators.

"At night, the sands of the desert become moist with dew, making the surface firm enough to register the tracks of nocturnal animals. So, for a short time, in the morning, the tracks reveal something of their activities. Then, as the day warms up and the surface of the desert dries out, the sand shifts, and at times you can watch it sliding, making it seem almost liquid.

"Many creatures make their homes in the dunes beneath this moving surface. It is necessary for them to spend most of the daylight hours out of the hot sun because they have no

water to drink, and they must retain their body moisture. Small mammals rely on the roots of plants to provide a firm anchorage for their burrows. It is fortunate that most perennial desert plants have root systems far greater than the vegetation they produce above ground – the roots growing long as they search for water.

"The jerboa is a small rodent that copes astonishingly well with living beneath ground in the arid desert. It plugs the entrance of its cool underground home in order to keep in the moisture. And, whatever vapour the jerboa breathes out, is absorbed by the seeds that it has stored in the walls. As it rests, this small mammal keeps its nostrils close to the seeds, to take the benefit of their moisture. In this way, the existing humidity is recycled. It is a very efficient life-sustaining system, making the most of whatever liquid is available."

"How clever" approved Gold.

"Yes! The jerboa is also talented. It is a GREAT jumper. You see, it has strong hind legs and hairy feet, so it can spring away in long leaps, wending a zig-zag path. Jumping desert animals, such as jerboas, have hairy feet to help them get a more secure grip on sand. It must be helpful as insulation against the hot surfaces, too, and it might prevent the paws from drying out and cracking."

"Is the jerboa something like a rabbit?"

"Not really, Gold. There are several kinds of jerboa in Arabia, and they look similar to each other. There are the small species, known as GARBU in Arabia, and the larger ones, known as GERDI. The small one, the Lesser Jerboa, is a very pretty rodent, resembling a tiny kangaroo in many ways, except that it has a very long tail with a tassel on the end. It has a face quite like the gerbil, but the legs are different. The forelegs are very tiny in comparison with the large hind legs. These propel the jerboa as high as 60 to 90 centimetres (2–3 feet) into the air. It is not easy to find the tracks of the jerboa because it leaps for distances up to seven metres (23 feet), leaving few tracks in the sand.

Jerboa

"All rodents need to run fast, or leap, especially if they come out in the daytime, because then, apart from being more exposed to danger, the sand can be very very hot. At night, they have to be quick to get away from nocturnal predators such as the owl and fox.

"In the past, the desert dwellers hunted the jerboa, too. The lesser jerboa makes its passages directly beneath the surface in sandy soil and the soft plains, walling its burrow's entrance up. Stories tell of riders being thrown because their horses stumbled in collapsed burrows. The Bedouin say the GARBU closes the entrance for fear of snakes, and that a closed door is a sure sign that the animal is at home. The desert folk used to stamp on a burrow in several spots to frighten the GARBU out into the open. Once caught, the little rodents were roasted whole, and only the legs were not eaten.

"The larger jerboa excavates deep passages in the uplands and stony deserts, especially in northern Arabia. Their burrows are formed in such a way that water does not penetrate even during the heaviest rains.

"Jerboas have been kept as pets, but sometimes they will resent captivity and refuse to eat. They can do without water, yet drink when it is available. This little creature loves to bathe in sand, so it is rather cruel to keep them in cages. And, they do have lots of babies, so they are not an ideal pet.

"Molerats and voles are small mammals that are found almost everywhere on the Arabian Peninsula. Both are rodents, too. Molerats have a very unusual social set-up that is similar to bees. Apparently, only the 'Queen' rats breed, and there are 'worker' molerats.

"The Arabian porcupine is yet another omnivorous mammal, eating ants as well as vegetation. It is known as NIS in Arabic. The porcupine is Arabia's largest rodent and can measure almost a metre long (about 3 feet). It has a blunt face, bright round eyes, and a large body, weighing about 15 kilos (about 33 lbs).

"The porcupine is best known for its coat of sharp quills that look like knitting needles. This handsome black, brown and white coat is also made up of coarse hair, as well as the quills which are modified hairs. The head and front part of the body are covered in coarse black hair, too, which has a long tuft on top that sweeps backwards, resembling a lady's upswept hairdo.

"The quills on the back are of different lengths, and the ones on the tail are short, white, hollow, and open on the end. When the creature is frightened or annoyed, it will first turn its back and bristle. An excited porcupine then huffs its warning and noisily rattles the tail quills. It has been said that porcupines shoot quills at the enemy, but this is not true. The quills are loosely fixed, and they sometimes fall out when the animal shakes its body.

"The Arabian species of porcupine may not have barbs on the end of its quills, as some other species do, but the quills are sharp weapons and they do help to protect the animal. To avoid predators, this rodent depends on its keen sense of smell and acute hearing, because its eyesight is poor. It does have strong claws, but these are for digging holes in which to hide. Porcupines also take refuge in caves and among rocks in inaccessible mountainous places.

Small enough to
fit into boots

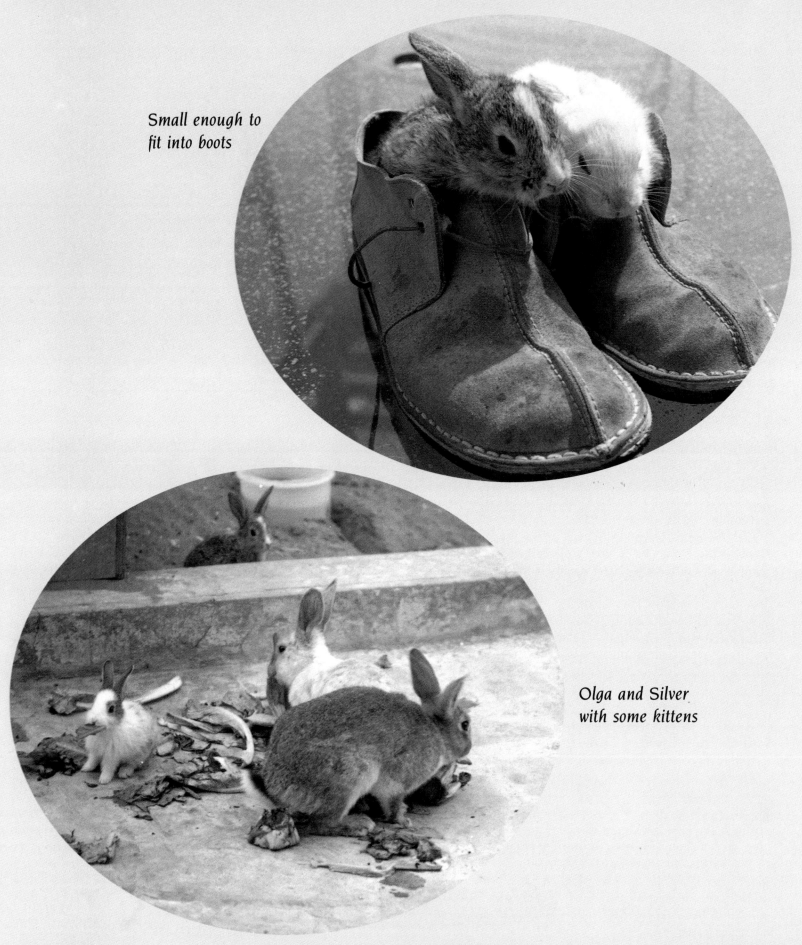

Olga and Silver
with some kittens

A basketful of
rabbit kittens . . .

Gold as a baby

. . . Not much bigger
than eggs

79

"The porcupine was once hunted, and there are reports of it scratching and biting. Its quills were once added to traditional Arabian silver jewellery, and the flesh is supposed to be delicious. Although this animal now appears to be scarce, there might be many of them still in existence. Their numbers are difficult to assess because they are nocturnal, timid and rarely seen."

"Poor chap. That's enough to turn a herbivore or omnivore into a carnivore."

Gold sounded exasperated.

"Oh, I must tell you about the hedgehog. In Arabic, it is called a KUMFOD. The hedgehog looks something like a tiny porcupine because it has a spikey coat, too. Despite a resemblance, the hedgehog and porcupine are totally unrelated. In fact, hedgehogs are a family all on their own, having evolved separately for millions of years. They existed before such extinct creatures as sabre-toothed tigers and woolly mammoths. It is a rodent with a tiny tail and front legs shorter than the back ones. The hedgehog has a long, pointed, pig-like snout and small beady eyes. The eyes are almost sightless, so this creature relies upon acute senses of smell and hearing to avoid predators. Furthermore, when frightened, it can roll up into a tight ball of sharp spines that keeps most enemies at bay. Although the hedgehog has many hunters, there are just as many wild animals that live happily side-by-side with this dear little creature.

"Hedgehogs are gentle. If you treat them nicely, taking care not to startle them, they become quite friendly. These small creatures may not be cuddlesome, but they are entertaining – especially as they love to dash about in the open, with a habit of sometimes running in circles, resembling clockwork toys. They are most active in the late afternoon and early in the morning. The hedgehog rarely makes an appearance in the middle of the day, unless it is to hunt beetles that emerge after rain. In winter, they hibernate away in some secret, sheltered spot."

"Is a hedgehog a carnivore, Susan?"

"No, Gold, but it has been known to eat its own young, and it will eat almost anything. It is classified as an insectivore. Its favourite pastime seems to be eating, and a hedgehog will return to your doorstep if you leave food out – especially, milk. Yet, this animal can survive without any liquid at all, because it can get sufficient moisture from its food. A normal diet consists of all sorts of insects and creepy-crawlies."

Porcupine

Hedgehog

"Goodness! How could so many animals enjoy eating such things," exclaimed Gold.

"Oh, but that's not all: the hedgehog has been known to win fights with snakes, and it will eat the snake afterwards. Despite its small size, the hedgehog can be victorious because it is resistant to the snake's bite, although not immune to the venom. Its battle strategy is especially effective: by alternately biting with its sharp teeth, and then rolling itself into a prickly ball, it can survive until the snake is finally dead. No other mammal rolls into a defensive ball better than the hedgehog. A pair of special muscles pull the skin forward over the head, another pair pull it backwards over the animal's bottom, and then a big circular muscle operates like a drawstring of a duffel bag.

"Hedgehogs have sharp little claws, too. Even so, none of its defences stop the fox, or a human hunter. Nomads say the flesh of the hedgehog is tasty, and its skin is useful. It can be tied around the neck of a timid camel to cure it of its fears. After one month, the Bedouin claim that the camel will no longer be afraid."

"Perhaps the camel cannot imagine anything worse than having a smelly dead hedgehog right under its nose," suggested Gold.

"You may be right, Gold. The body of a hedgehog is somewhat primitive and similar to the earliest known fossil mammals. It is an animal that always adapts well to wherever it finds itself, and I don't mean around the neck of a camel. The hedgehog may be small in size, but it has a gigantic history that stretches back at least 25 million years. This insectivore survived by adapting successfully to the earth's changes. It is interesting that one of the theories on the extinction of the dinosaurs is that some primitive insectivore ate the giant's eggs. Perhaps the culprit was an early hedgehog.

"The Arabian Peninsula has shrews, and these are insectivores, too. This animal is called ZABA ABAH in Arabic. There are many different species of shrew in Arabia, and they breed rapidly. Some are endemic, or found only in the Arabian Peninsula. It is believed that the shrew's ancestors were probably the first true mammals on earth. It is Arabia's smallest mammal. The shrew is very small indeed – a slender, soft, furry, mouse-like mammal with very small ears, tiny beady eyes, and a long, finely pointed muzzle, covered with many long bristles. The ears and eyes are often partly hidden by fur. Its four legs are thin and bony, and the tail very long and thin. It has special odour glands on its flanks.

"Shrews tunnel along in leaf or ground litter, and are most active at night. It is possible to locate them by listening for their high-pitched squeaks. Although shrews are so small, they have a large reputation for being querulous. They quarrel among themselves and they can be quite vicious. And, although they are supposed to have singing contests, these events sound more like arguments to see which shrew is superior. I am told that if shrews are handled, they will bite. It

may be that their saliva has toxic properties, so it is wise to leave them alone. Apparently, they tend to lead a solitary life."

"I'm not surprised. They sound most unpleasant to me!" judged Gold.

"Shrews do appear to live up to their reputation for being cantankerous. It is amusing that women with vexatious, scolding manners, are sometimes called 'shrewish'. Personally, I think they are attractive little creatures. I hear that the shrew eats a great deal of food, and it cannot go for long without a meal. Unless it eats every third or fourth hour, it will die. Shrews apparently consume more than their own weight in food every day. The reason for this is that their bodies are so small that they can lose body heat very quickly. To keep the heat up, they must constantly eat.

"Shrews are basically insect-eaters but they will eat almost anything, even carrion; and they have been known to attack and eat snails and worms, too.

"Another Arabian insectivore is the mole, which is also a prolific breeder. It is known as HLEND in Arabic. Moles are burrowing mammals and their front legs are short and strong. The mounds of earth thrown up by its burrowing, are known as 'mole hills'. In Arabia, moles inhabit the shallow valleys, and their tell-tale 'hills' are visible in these places."

"Rabbits don't make hills! We smooth out the earth we dig and make it nice and flat. Does a mole look anything like a rabbit, Susan?"

"Not at all. The mole has a more rounded body with a fine, velvety coat that is blackish-grey, and its head joins its body with no apparent neck. And, quite unlike you, the mole has tiny, dark, darting eyes.

"One Bedouin folk tale tells how the mole helps the owl, frog, moth and swallow look for a lost camel. The Bedouin talk of the badger, too. It is known as ZARBUL in Arabic. The badger was once hunted, and tribesmen would try to trick the creature by crying out that it should run away even though they knew it was hiding in its den. Its enemies must take great care because this animal can squirt an offensive stream at them which is most discouraging. The badger is of the same family as the skunk, which has a similar ability.

"The Arabian variety of badger is a species known as ratel, or honey-badger. As its name implies, this mammal has a passion for honey, so, it is fortunate that the ratel's hide can withstand the sting of angry bees. The honey-badger is classified as a carnivore, and its normal diet consists of rats, mice, gerbils, jerboas, birds, frogs, and lizards. The Bedouin believe it to be a robber of graves, too. It can be found around the Al Hasa Oasis where there is plenty of honey and water, but it also survives in arid places."

"And what does this one look like?"

"The Arabian honey-badger is a handsome creature. A bit smaller than the average dog, it has a long body, long tail, and a dog-like head with beady eyes and human-shaped teeth. Its coarse fur coat is a creamy-grey colour on the top of the

Badger

head and back, the rest of its body being dark brown or black. Honey-badgers have powerful claws for tunnelling and digging a den. They are rarely seen because they are nocturnal creatures, and hibernate in dens throughout winter."

"The honey-badger sounds like someone to keep clear of."

"Not really. Its body does have a special odour, but the animal will not spray unless upset. If a young one is caught and tamed, it becomes a 'well-behaved', and even a playful pet.

"Other carnivores that might interest you are the mongooses."

"What's a 'mongoosus'?"

"Ah, the 'mongoose!' It's a funny name, isn't it Gold? In English, the plural of the bird: goose is 'geese', but, for the mammalian mongoose, the plural is 'mongooses'. In Arabic, it is called NIMS. It belongs to the Viverridae, or civet genus: a group of species, many of them notable for producing a strong-smelling secretion from anal scent glands, used in the manufacture of perfumes.

"There are at least two different species of mongoose living in Arabia, and they are mostly found along the eastern and western shores. The Indian grey mongoose inhabits desert and open scrubland and varies in size and appearance according to the environment. It rests at night in a burrow that it digs for itself, and hunts under cover during the day, feeding on almost anything such as rats, mice, snails, scorpions, centipedes, wasps and other pests. The young are born blind and hairless, and the mother carries them about, defending them fiercely. The white-tailed mongoose emerges late

Mongoose

afternoon and hunts alone or in pairs at night. It eats insects, frogs, reptiles, snails, crabs, fish, eggs, ground-living birds, berries and fruit."

"What does a mongoose look like?"

"It is a small to medium-sized, short-legged, furry mammal, with a body a bit longer than the average rabbit. The males are somewhat heavier than the females. It has a fairly long fluffy tail, an elongated head and a pointed face with small eyes and ears. And, their claws are partially retractable. The white-tailed mongoose is larger than the grey mongoose, with longer legs and a very bushy tail.

"The mongoose is a great hunter and a fearless fighter. This is a creature normally found in hot and humid places that produce abundant vegetation, so often full of snakes, which the mongoose feeds on extensively.

"The mongoose is an attractive little animal and it can become a friendly pet. It will serve humans by clearing the house and garden of undesirable or deadly creatures. Exciting stories have been told about the predatory expertise and skill of the mongoose. It will fight with powerful snakes that are much larger than itself. And, sometimes this small mammal has saved people when they were about to be bitten by a snake. The most famous story is 'Riki Tiki Tavi' by Rudyard Kipling. Perhaps Christopher will read it to you sometime."

"Yes, please."

"There is one fascinating small mammal in Arabia, with astonishing powers. I wonder if you will like it. It is the bat, known as WATWAAT in Arabic. Few people appreciate bats, which is a shame, because, apart from insectivores – and the peculiar Australian animals – the bat is the mammal with the oldest history. It is a flying creature that has been on earth longer than primitive humans – and it is the only creature of the order Chiroptera. I have never seen a bat, as they are nocturnal, but there are many different species found in various parts of the Arabian Peninsula.

"The bat is a small mouse-like creature with a peculiar face, and leather-like wings that spread to cover the forelegs, hindfeet and tail. Some species in Arabia have a wing span of about half a metre (20 inches). Bats group into colonies and roost by day in hollow trees, rock crevices, ruins, old buildings, and in caves mainly found in mountainous places.

"Bats have been feared because there are many horror tales made up about similar creatures. There is no such thing as a vampire for instance; although in tropical America, the small vampire bat drinks blood from living creatures, stealthily and silently attacking cattle at night. Some bats are especially dangerous because their bite spreads diseases such as rabies which can kill humans and animals. There are species of bats that do not live on blood of course. Most are content to eat insects, especially mosquitoes; and in this way, they are extremely useful. Others live totally on fruit.

"Bats are very agile and they can walk just as quickly on their thumbs as their toes, whether they are on the ground or going up the walls. As they are nocturnal, they roost all day – hanging upside down. Shortly after dark, they leave their hideaway roosts and fly noiselessly, sometimes skimming low to the ground. A bat has an extremely acute sense of hearing, and it finds its way about in the dark by a method called echo location. (You will remember from the stories about Aquatic Creatures that dolphins also use this method.) As the word implies, the animal locates things by their echo. A bat makes high-pitched sounds that cannot be heard by most other animals, and then it measures the distance between itself and an object by the sound waves that bounce back."

"That is very clever."

"I'm glad you think so, Gold. The bats deserve some appreciation. Wasn't it a long story, today? There were so many small Arabian mammals to tell you about. Well, that was good timing. Here comes Askalu with your supper.

"TAFADAL Gold," I said, as an invitation.

"SHUKRAN, Susan." he replied, thanking me with a twinkle in his blue eye and a glint in the gold one.

8
The Camel

old came 'galloping' towards me in a carefree fashion one morning, looking as perky as I had ever seen him. The cool weather had come at last, and this was always a great boost for our rabbits – and also for us.

"Hello, Susan, have you got time to tell me a story?" he asked, with a puff, as he pulled up. "Can you tell me a funny story? I feel like hearing something amusing."

"As a matter of fact, I do have time right now, Gold, but an AMUSING story . . . Well, let me see . . . I suppose you would like it to be about an animal?"

"Oh, yes please, Susan, if you can."

"Let me think. Let's sit right here on the diving board. We can catch a little of this gentle autumn sunshine while I try to think of a story that will entertain you. Are you comfy?"

Suddenly, I had an idea: "Gold, I shall tell you about the time that our friend, Charles, offered us his baby camel. Her name was JAMEELA, which is Arabic for 'beautiful'. The word appears to come from the same root as JAMAL, and that means camel. This suggests to me that Arabs find the camel beautiful. Yet, it is often described as the most inelegant of creatures. Someone once said that it was an animal designed by a committee. I'm sure you must have heard how people on a committee never seem to agree. In any case, THIS baby camel was very appealing indeed, although not attractive enough for us to accept the generous offer."

"Oh, but why, Susan?" cried Gold.

"We had our reasons, Gold. We just thanked Charles and explained that our villa was less suitable than his for keeping a camel."

"But, if the little camel was so appealing, Susan, how could YOU turn it down?"

"Well, you see: it had only been a week since we had dined with Charles and his mother. I remember because it was a truly memorable occasion. The evening began as a very formal affair and everything was beautifully done – as was Charles' way. There were other guests whom we had never met before, so the atmosphere was polite and friendly, but restrained. We sat down to an elegantly laid table, and had reached the second course when it happened."

"What happened?" asked Gold, tense with anticipation.

"A camel burst through the doorway. That's what

happened. Everybody leapt to their feet, and all feelings of propriety instantly vanished. It was actually a very small camel, but the dining room was not large and the young camel seemed enormous. It just stood there, and so did we. Charles was the first to recover his senses and he began shouting orders to the houseboy and cook. They peered over the top of the camel's rear end, framed in the doorway.

"On our side, we tried to turn it around, but all our efforts were in vain. Then, the boys came around another way, bringing bunches of green stuff into the dining room. They were going to try to coax it to turn around and go outside. Eventually, when she was ready, the camel did turn, and we guests lent a hand to push and shove. Even very young camels are heavy creatures, we discovered. In the desert, at a distance, camels seem slender and light-framed, but at this close range . . . I formed quite another opinion for always."

"So, it was Jameela, the baby camel," mused Gold. "Why did she come inside?"

"I believe, Gold, Jameela had become so fond of Charles that she just wanted to be with him. She probably missed her mother, and he had taken her place. This sort of thing is called 'imprinting' – occurring when baby animals accept another species (including humans), as a natural parent."

"Oh, what a hoot! What happened then?"

"Bit by bit, we urged Jameela forward while Charles and the boys dragged her along inch by inch. Every slap sent clouds of dust rising out of her woolly coat which sat like a saddle on her back. When Jameela reached the back hallway, she stopped and just slumped to the floor in a heap. She had made up her mind to sleep inside that night. There was nothing to do but leave her and return to the table. And, as you might have expected, the rest of the evening was relaxed and jolly."

"That was a great story, Susan. Have you got another one about a camel?"

"Yes, Gold, as a matter of fact, I have. Let me tell you about a camel that did belong to us. His name was Clyde, and he became as well-known as Jameela because of his looks."

"Wonderful!" said Gold enthusiastically, as he shuffled his front paws, sending a ripple down his furry body. When he was comfortably bunched up, I began:

"It happened just before EID AL-FITR, the Muslim celebration that comes at the end of RAMADAN (the Holy month of fasting). All of the western women, living on the Dhahran airbase, had decided to decorate the company's dining room as a surprise for the Muslim employees. They had intended using only tinsel and streamers; but then it had been agreed that any novel form of decoration would also be welcome. I was seized by one of my compulsions, which, incidentally, I cannot explain. The vision I had was of a life-sized, green, papier mâché camel called 'Clyde'.

"Within the hour, I had gathered piles of old newspapers from the neighbourhood, and I filled the double-bowled kitchen sink with boiling paste. It was best to work in the kitchen because it had a marble floor and I was sure to make a mess. Then, I set to work cutting and bending some old meshed wire, using it to make a frame for the camel's body. This part of the project left my hands sore and bleeding. As Clyde began to take the shape I had visualized for him, I felt no pain, but I did have a great feeling of elation. Creating something always gives me that feeling. Covering the wire skeleton with the gluey paper was much easier than the first stage, and it was even more rewarding. I could see that Clyde was going to be a handsome camel.

"Although RAMADAN is always the ninth month in the Islamic calendar, or HEJIRA, it occurs at a different time each year. This is because the months are shorter than the western Gregorian months, as Islamic months begin with each new moon. That year, RAMADAN fell in one of the hot months. The kitchen was the hottest room in the house and I was beginning to wilt. Clyde was doing much better. His paper was drying almost as quickly as I worked, moulding him to 'life'.

"On the second day, my camel was ready for some real character building. By far, this was the most enjoyable stage. It was great fun sculpting his face, with the mushy paper squelching under the pressure of my hands. Needless to say, by the time I had finished, no one had been able to enter the kitchen for days. The floor was caked with glue and stuck with bits of paper. Each evening when I went to bed, I had to leave my shoes behind.

"During the day, familiar faces occasionally peeped around the doorways and through the back door. The comments were good-natured and encouraging, which was nice considering that they had really come in search of refreshments and meals. Seeing my preoccupation, my family and friends were then kind enough not to ask for anything. They were even kinder, when, at intervals, they offered me hamburgers, pizzas, or fish and chips. No one commented on the state of the kitchen, and everyone said nice things about Clyde. They seemed to like him. In particular, his long feathery eye lashes caused admiration and amusement. Yes, he was going to be a success.

"My paper camel turned out to be larger than I had intended, his size not permitting much movement in the kitchen. The only negative comment about Clyde, cast through the doorway, concerned his size – and it was beginning to alarm me a bit, too. It seemed that he could never leave, making the kitchen a lost room forever; or we would have to cut him into pieces to get him out. I decided not to think about it and to face the problem when the time came. Meanwhile, I spray-painted Clyde green, choosing the same rich green colour as the Saudi Arabian flag. The final touches were the halter and saddle, made from a fake gold chain and a circular table mat which I fringed with tiny brass bells.

"When the hour came for Clyde to depart, John borrowed a truck and we managed to move him from the kitchen by taking two doors off their hinges. Amid shouts and laughter, we set off for our company's dining hall. Clyde caused a small sensation. They liked him so much that he was kept on display long after the festive dinner. After that, our telephone would ring with invitations for him to attend oil conventions, exhibitions and dinners. I am told that some Aramco oil men still talk about Clyde."

"I want to see Clyde. Where is he now?" demanded Gold.

"That's another story, Gold: it happened several years later, when we returned to live in Riyadh. I did not want to part with Clyde, but I almost had to do so because we had too many belongings. These had been loaded into a very large truck. It was already piled high with furniture, carpets and suitcases, and there was no more available space. It was clear the driver thought we were crazy for wanting to take huge fossils, heavy petrified wood and enormous geodes. And, when I insisted on taking my green paper camel, he almost cried.

"To him, 'Madame' was completely mad. Finally, he agreed to strap Clyde to the top of the load.

"We set off on the five-hour journey, in convoy with the truck, sailing along the highway with the wind whistling through Clyde's eyelashes. The driver's worst suspicions about me were confirmed at our destination when I threw my arms around my tattered Clyde.

"After all that, we could find Clyde no suitable place in our new villa. We decided to store him at the local stables. At least we could see him several times a week when Christopher took his riding lessons. And, Clyde would have his own place amongst the theatrical society's scenery and costumes. The Riyadh Amateur Theatrical Society, RATS, was producing a series of Horse Operas at the time, and I thought, too, that Clyde might eventually land a small part. But, he never did. As time passed, bit by bit, Clyde just fell to pieces."

I felt a little sad at the end of my tale, but I was cheered to see Gold laughing. When his mirth had subsided into an occasional chuckle, Gold apologized. "Sorry, Susan, I know you must have been fond of Clyde. I wish I could have seen him. Do you have a picture of a camel?"

"Yes, Gold, I do, and I suppose you would like me to tell you about the Arabian camel."

"Oh, yes please." Gold almost pleaded.

White camels are rare

A cow camel with her calf

Camels on the horizon
seem so small

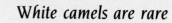

A bull camel takes a solitary walk

"Don't you think
I look smart?"

Jameela
the baby camel

"As you know, Gold, from our previous stories, a group of any kind of animal is called a genus. Well, in the genus *Camelus*, there are two kinds, known as species: the Arabian camel and the Bactrian camel. The Arabian camel is the dromedary, and it has one hump on its back. The Bactrian camel has two humps and comes from the area called Bactria in Central Asia. The dromedary is thought to have evolved from the Bactrian, so somewhere along the trail, it must have lost a hump. These animals are found in arid areas all over the Old World."

"What do you mean, 'the OLD WORLD'?"

"It is a term for Eastern Hemisphere lands, excluding the Americas, which were discovered later. (The centre of the Old World used to be called the Near East, but is now generally known as the Middle East. The United Nations, however, still refer to it as the Near East.) Arabia is near the heart of the Old World.

"The dromedary has been in Arabia since the great ice age, which ended ten thousand years ago, Gold."

I knew rabbits had no comprehension of any great number of years. Gold and I had discussed it several times. As clever as he is, large amounts of time and distance seem incomprehensible to him. I think it might not matter if I just said: "Long, long ago . . ." and "Far away . . .", but I wasn't sure.

I glanced around at my audience which had grown to about fifteen rabbits, plus Mamapuss the cat and Samantha, the dog. Gold was the only one paying close attention. The others seemed to be happy enough, just to be fanned by the breeze, as they dozed beside the pool.

I continued: "Camels belong to the Camelidae family sub-order, called Tylopoda, meaning 'pad-footed'. Whether a camel has one hump or two, it remains a quadruped, or four-footed creature with an enormous body, long slender legs, a long tapering neck, and a long thin tail with a tuft on the end. It usually weighs between 300 and 500 kilos (about 1,100 lbs) and a big bull camel can be heavier, the height can be over two metres (about 7 feet).

"The camel is an ungulate, or mammal with grinding teeth and modified limb bones with one or two toes known as hooves. The camel's are solid or cloven, meaning that each foot is split into two toes. The average camel has very broad feet with cushioned soles. Its bulging eyes are intelligent-looking and have a soft expression. The upper eyelids overlap to keep out sand and the thick eyelashes help, too. The protruding eyebrows shade the animal's eyes from the sun. Camels have small ears with hairs that protect them; while their very large slit nostrils can be shut tight against a sand storm. The prehensile upper lip is cleft in two, like a rabbit's, the top lips hanging over the lower. The jaws are very strong indeed and the formidable teeth capable of breaking a man's arm. Their true purpose is to tear branches off trees."

"What's prehensile?" asked Gold.

"Prehensile means capable of grasping. The camel's cleft upper lip assists this herbivore to gather vegetation. They are generally gentle feeders, nibbling foliage, shrubs, grass and other ground herbage.

"Camels vary in beauty as well as quality, I am told. I have heard them described as 'dignified' and sometimes as 'disdainful'. A fine riding camel must have an erect head, an arched neck, and small pointed ears that are pricked up.

"It must have long, slim legs with no thickening around the bends and joints, and the feet should be smallish. A good camel has broad ribs and chest, and the hump should be immediately above the abdomen. A healthy animal has a hump that is plump in the middle. The flank should not be hollow and the skin must be free from scurf. Most of all, the eyes should be shining and wide open; although they may be half closed or shut when the camel is chewing its cud."

"Chewing what?" asked Gold.

"It means that it ruminates, Gold; its food is stored for a time in a special first stomach, or rumen. You see, camels feed quickly, but later on, they chew it more thoroughly a second time. This is called ruminating, or 'chewing the cud'. However, camels have incisors and canine teeth in their upper jaw, which true ruminants do not.

"A camel sometimes feeds for up to eight hours and then takes further time to chew the cud. This requires that the food be regurgitated back into the mouth from the first stomach. The camel's insides are like a factory. There are two principle chambers in the stomach which process food by fermenting and breaking down tough plant fibres, allowing the camel's body to extract and digest as much goodness as possible.

"Camels can survive on very poor vegetation. Even when there is little of that, grazing herds generally (but not always) avoid eating toxic plants, however good they might look. In low rainfall areas, where there are few leaves to eat, they can make do with very coarse vegetation.

"Its long neck allows the camel to stretch up to a height of over three and a half metres (about 11 feet), to seize and tear branches off trees. Munching up twigs and prickles, and even large thorns is not a problem, because the lips and insides of the mouth are tough and spongy, with no sensitive nerve endings.

"Many desert plants wear an armour of thorns as protection against animals, a defence that works against all but the camel and goat. The thorny acacia tree which is naturally flat on top, becomes flat below, too, because camels crop as high as they can stretch. Even so, it is not destructive. When browsing, they take only a few mouthfuls from one tree or bush and then move on to the next. Even when food is plentiful, a browsing animal habitually wanders for up to 70 kilometres (44 miles) per day, eating along the way. It consumes a variety of plants including saltbush which is good for its health.

"The camel is a hardy animal, very well adapted to living in harsh desert conditions. It is a remarkable creature because it can live and work in barren places, withstanding extreme heat

and dryness. Its ability to live without food and water for long periods is ideal, making it the perfect desert mammal. Its body structure (the anatomy) and its various body systems (the physiology) are unique.

"For instance, a unique flexible body temperature, like a 'thermostat', makes it possible for a camel to conserve the water it drinks. Its breathing is slow, and it does not pant like a dog in order to lose heat, since it can allow itself to become much hotter than any other creature before the need to sweat. When the camel does become too hot, the moisture given off its body acts as an insulator on its fine layer of fur – before this liquid is ultimately lost as well, of course.

"Now, although the desert is very cold at night, the camel can use stored heat to keep itself warm. This body heat, built up in the daytime is released very, very slowly during the cool hours of darkness.

"To conserve moisture a camel sends very little liquid out of its body as waste. Its droppings are almost dry; and it has special kidneys which extract most of the important contents before excreting the highly concentrated salty waste liquid that is left. Even so, some camel urine smells sweetly of aromatic plants as a result of what has been eaten. It is said, some tribal people collect it to use as a hair rinse! And, they use camel droppings as fuel because there is so little wood available in the desert. So you see, a camel is a very useful creature for desert dwellers.

"The camel's greatest asset is its hump, useful as a pantry or larder where food is stored. The largest dromedaries can store over 150 kilos (about 450 lbs) in the hump. When the animal has eaten more than it needs, some of the food is converted into a special fat, chemically bound to water. Much of this is stored in the hump. When energy and water are needed, the body draws upon this store. In good condition, the hump is firm and upright. When the animal has been hungry for some time, or it has been ill, the hump shrinks, becomes floppy and almost disappears. That is why camels need to eat beyond their immediate requirements when food is plentiful."

"What a marvellous idea, Susan," said Gold. "But, I can't say that I would care to wait as long as a camel for a good meal."

"Going without food for a long while can make a camel unhappy, too, Gold. Even quick changes in diet can cause it to have tummy upsets. Just how well this animal copes without food and water depends on its past diet, its age, breed, habitat, climate, workload and care."

"But, Susan, why should a camel have to go without food and water?" asked Gold.

"Well, Gold, sometimes it might not rain in the desert for years, and the camel has grown used to this. Mankind has learned to take advantage of this creature's incredible physiology. For instance, its best known characteristic is an ability to live for long periods without water. It survives without drinking, better than any other domesticated animal. Even though camels can go without food and drink in hot and arid country, it does not mean they enjoy it. If long marches are to be undertaken, they should be trained to go without water beforehand. Moreover, there should be a good period of rest afterwards.

"In the past, camels have performed great feats of endurance. Some stories tell us that they have gone without drinking for two weeks. Of course, the success of such journeys has depended on the weather and the amount of the camel's exertion. When temperatures are moderate, plants contain more moisture, so a camel may go several weeks without water. With adequate pasture, it can easily do without drinking for about a week, but in summer should drink every two or three days, even though it can survive for longer.

"Rain is always welcome in the desert, and should it fall heavily at night, the Bedouin rouse their camels. They urge the herd to drink from the deep pools of water. Despite the rumours you may have heard, Gold, camels do not consciously drink for the future. Whatever they drink replaces what the body has lost. Yet, when fresh water is available, it is usual for a camel to drink a lot.

"A well-nourished beast usually drinks at the rate of 10 to 20 litres (35 pints) a minute, and it may consume 100 to 150 litres (20–30 gallons) in about 10 to 15 minutes. This creature's blood and body tissues have the ability to soak up and store large amounts of water. Camels have been known to drink brackish water, too, but they prefer it to be fresh and clean. A dehydrated camel that has not drunk water for many days can look very thin and sad. Amazingly, its usual appearance soon returns when it reaches water. Sometimes when it drinks too quickly, it may stagger about a bit."

"I'll bet it makes a sloshing noise when it walks."

"Certain Arabian breeds of camel are said to resist thirst the longest. Some breeds are reputed to be better workers in difficult terrain. Others are known for being swift. And, all camels have an uncanny sense for finding water, and sometimes have helped their masters locate a well or oasis.

"Folklore tells us of times when men have survived because of the camel's ability to store water in its stomach paunch. Far from a well, with the last of the water gone, a man tormented by thirst could kill his camel and drink from the rumen. The liquid is an unappetizing green sludge, so the man would need to be desperate."

"Even if I were desperate, I just couldn't do that," said Gold, as he sat up squarely on his bottom with his slender front paws stretched forward.

His posture reminded me of something I had read:

"Did you know, Gold, the ancestors of the camel were no larger than rabbits?"

"What a funny idea. How do you know, Susan?"

"I read it in an animal encyclopedia. It also said that the history of the camel is not completely known, but it is believed that their small forebears originated in North America. The descendants apparently made their way to Asia across ancient land bridges.

"There are primitive rock pictures of uncertain date in Arabia, that show men riding camels. Arabian dromedaries are believed to have been domesticated over four thousand years ago.

"At first humans probably captured and tamed cattle, sheep and goats for their use. It is most likely, domestication of the camel came about after some orphaned calves had been brought to live with the other tame creatures. It is known that camels carried cargoes of frankincense and myrrh from southern Arabia about three and a half thousand years ago. These valuable tree resins were to be sold in countries to the north of the Arabian Peninsula. Before this, donkeys had been used for riding and as pack animals, but camels proved to be the best means of travelling overland. Their pathways eventually became important trade routes, and all sorts of commodities went back and forth. For the first time, foreign products reached people living in remote places within Arabia. Camels also carried water to these isolated people.

"It is believed that camels were first kept for their meat and then for milk. Later, they were used for riding, carrying loads, for working in agriculture (to pull ploughs and irrigate the land) and as draught animals, giving power to simple mills, and drawing water from wells by pulling ropes.

"In the olden days, merchants travelled in large groups. This was for safety on the long journeys across barren deserts. The groups were known as caravans. There might be as many as one thousand or more camels in a caravan, and sometimes they moved forward, abreast. More often, they would travel in single file, and this became known as a 'camel train'.

"Heavily loaded beasts would move slowly towards their destination at about 90 paces a minute, averaging 4 to 5 kilometres an hour (2.5–3 mph) for 8–10 hours a day. They would be given a short rest from time to time, and could average about 30 kilometres (about 20 miles) a day for weeks on end. Usually, they worked in this manner for about eight months before the yearly rest period.

"Caravans normally confined their travelling to the early morning and evening. The camels grazed midday. Sometimes, the animals were 'night marched' to make up time, or because it was the hottest time of the year. Some caravan routes became very famous. One is known as the 'Silk Road' because it brought the treasured silk textile from China. The one from southern Arabia is called the 'Incense Route'; and the 'Pilgrimage Route' brought caravans to Makkah five times a year for over one thousand years, until early this century.

There are said to be 5,744 different names and epithets for the camel in Arabic literature. In English, it is often called the 'Ship of the Desert'. Certainly, the lurching, rolling gait of the camel often leaves passengers feeling quite 'seasick'. Now, modern aeroplanes and buses ferry the faithful followers of Islam to and from the holy places: Makkah and Madinah in western Arabia."

"I think the pilgrims must be pleased that they don't have to travel by camel any more." said Gold.

"Yes, I am sure; especially so, since many pilgrims travel vast distances. You know, Gold, thousands of years ago, carts, wagons and chariots existed in the Old World, and the Romans used these wheeled vehicles in the Middle East. Eventually, they chose to give them up in favour of the camel because it was much more suitable in the deserts. Wheels are only good when there are roads or smooth, firm terrain. But, camels were cheaper, too.

"Wood for making and repairing vehicles was expensive because suitable trees were rare. So, the camel reigned supreme for well over three thousand years. It remained popular in Arabia until this century, when the motor car was introduced. Yet, even then, camels were still the only means of transport between many towns which had no roads to connect them. Today, modern roads criss-cross Arabia, and the motorized vehicle has taken over completely from the camel as a means of transport.

"JAMAL is the everyday Arabic word for a camel. The dozens of other names that tribal people use, describe exactly which camel they are talking about. There is a name for the animal in each year of its life until it is fully grown. There are names for the various breeds, and to describe the sex; whether it is an adult or calf; if it is a cow bearing young, or a barren female. There are also names for the camel's state of health, and to describe whether it is a pack animal, a herd animal, or a riding camel. Other names distinguish the colours, qualities, defects, habits and special features.

"There are two principal races of camel in Arabia, the Najdi and the Omani, and each has several breeds known for different qualities.

"The colour of a camel was always considered important, too. In the north, the favourite colour was white, and such camels were called WADHA. To the south, a very dark brown-coloured camel, the HUMRA, was prized. Yet, the most commonly seen camel in Arabia is a sandy-beige. Many consider, in the Najd, that the finest of all were the black ones, the AL SHARUF, meaning 'the honoured ones'. They are also called SAUDA. This special breed is still treasured; yet, when it comes to woven camel-hair cloth, white is the most desired.

"Bedouin folk tales often include a white camel. It has been said that many a Bedouin girl and woman dreamt of riding in a fancy carriage on the back of a pure white camel. In the past, when a bride went to her new home in the bridegroom's village, or a faraway town, she travelled in a decorated carriage affixed to the back of a fine camel.

"Before the motor car, tribes moved from one camp site to another on camels, continually searching for pasture. Hundreds, and sometimes thousands of camels would swarm forward at a command. Many bore carriages tied to their backs above the saddle. The womenfolk would sit inside with their babies, small children and treasures, screened from the hot sun and blowing sand. The pretty curtains also gave them privacy from the gaze of others.

"Camel carriages have many names. Western people often refer to them as litters or howdahs. In Arabia, they were known by several names, according to their type. The most colourful was the MAKSAR. It had arched framework made from tamarisk wood, ornamented with colourful woven rugs, streamers and tassels. The great Rwalla tribe in the north of Arabia used the DHALLA, a spectacular carriage with great wings that stuck out each side. It was covered with gazelle skin and brightly coloured decorations. The MARKAB served as a banner in battle. It was very elaborate indeed, and decorated with the feathers of the Arabian ostrich which is now extinct in the wild.

"For centuries, rearing camels was the main source of wealth for the Bedouin. And the Arab of the desert once devoted himself to breeding them. The finest camels were considered pure-blooded and noble if the parents, or sire and dam were recognized purebreds. The tribes that bred the best were considered noble themselves. Because of the unique qualities of this animal, the illustrious tribes could live in the three great Arabian deserts, the northern Nafud, the central Dhana and the southern Rub al Khali, providing they were not too far from their wells. The Najd, in central Arabia, is an inaccessible region with an abundance of camels. They were especially valuable because these creatures were healthy and isolated from disease. The Shammar and Anaizah tribes raised the AL HURRA, which were once the most famous Najdi camels. They had a reputation for resisting thirst in tough conditions – even when working on a stony ground in the hottest months.

"In days gone by, camels were a source of strength and income. They were mobile wealth and represented power. As wealth, they were commonly offered as part of a bride's marriage dowry."

"What's dowry, Susan?" asked Gold.

"Dowry is a gift for a girl when she gets married, Gold. In Arabia, it is a tradition for the man she marries to provide money to the bride's father, which he invests for her future security. Sometimes the money was used to buy camels. Many brides preferred to have flocks of sheep and goats. As a rule, sheep and goats were bred by the less important tribes, who lived on the fringes of the sandy deserts, where water was more accessible. Their animals could not survive without drinking daily.

"In Arabia, camels were once booty in battle. When tribes raided each other, the camels that were taken, would pass back and forth between the tribes year after year. Raiding appeared to be a test of skill and bravery. Men rode camels to battle taking horses with them. Then, over short distance attacks, both camels and horses were ridden. A horseman would ride behind each camel until they were within striking distance. The final charge would be on horseback with the camel riders acting as a supporting force. On every adventure, water for the men and horses was carried in a goatskin called a JIRBA.

"The camels needed nothing to drink until the attack was over and they returned home.

"There are battle stories about the great AL SHARUF. These black camels are said to have moved forward as a wall, which no animal would break. It was as if they understood that they had to protect the men behind them.

"Not so long ago, before the rifle was invented, the Bedouin hunted on camel back, carrying long spears. High on a camel's hump, a man had tremendous advantage with spear or gun.

"It is the menfolk who traditionally tend the camels, and often a great affection grows up between the master and his special riding camel. In the days of raiding, an owner would sometimes not rest until he had discovered the whereabouts of his beast, and who had it. After a raid, it was the custom to hire a spy to locate the camel, but this man could not be from either of the tribes involved."

"How could the spy find it, Susan?" cried Gold.

"Certain Bedouin tribes had a great reputation for tracking, and they depended a great deal on camels for their success. They could tell exactly what kind of camel had passed by, where it had come from, what it had eaten, and how long ago, just from observing the camel's spoor, or tracks and droppings. When the camel was finally found, the spy sometimes paid money to get the animal back. The owner was usually quite willing to pay for the return of his camel because he loved it so much.

"I am told, a Bedouin never ill-treated his camel, and its needs came first. And, this was not just because the man's existence depended on the animal. He really cared about its welfare. Even so, when a beast was sick, it was often treated severely in the past, in the belief that the right thing was being done. One common cure was cauterization, a treatment commonly called 'firing'."

"Firing?" repeated Gold with a questioning tone.

"Cauterization or 'firing' is an ancient method of treating ailments. It means placing a red hot object on the area of pain. It hurts a lot and leaves a scar, but, strangely, it sometimes works. Perhaps by causing a new pain, or 'counter-irritation', the patient was able to forget about the original ailment.

"On a march, the Bedouin kept a close eye on the condition of their camels. This was essential because these creatures are tenacious, and keep walking even when they are not well. Any tremor in the hind legs, when the camel crouches down or rises up, can be serious. When a camel is in poor condition as a result of a hard summer, or if it is suffering from arthritis, it will have difficulty rising in the morning. A mouthful of dates is usually offered as encouragement.

"To the same end, herdsmen sometimes sing a strange-sounding song, promising beautiful grazing ahead. One traditional song asks a camel to trust him to be its guide and helper. In response, the camel allows itself to be helped up, although protesting with growls and burblings. There are a

number of useful camel songs. A herdsman has a special one to sing as he rides to pasture, encouraging the herd to follow and not stray. Another traditional song was once sung by the caravan drivers to keep the camels moving along smartly at a steady gait.

"Some people say the camel is called the 'ship of the desert', because it crosses an ocean of sand. A person who rides one for the first time is convinced that it is because of the camel's motion. Rabbits hop, cats and dogs run, snakes slither, and a camel paces – well, most of the time. They can be taught to trot. Pacing means that the right hind leg and fore foot move forward at the same time, alternating with the left hind leg and fore foot. This rock and roll motion can make a beginner 'travel sick'.

"Camels are sure-footed in gravel and sand. They do not do quite so well in rocky terrain, although they have been used successfully to take loads up steep escarpments. The broad feet are well padded with heavy leathery soles. Camels living in sandy territory have softer soles with tattered strips of loose skin. Those from the gravel plains have foot pads polished smooth. All have pads of hard skin on the elbows, knees, hocks and chest, having developed over the years where the creature's body touches the ground. These pads give protection when kneeling in hot, dry places.

"Should there be a sand storm, a camel will turn its back to the prevailing wind, fold its legs under the belly, and collapse to the ground. To keep out the whirling, stinging sand, it shuts its double row of long, thick eyelashes, and closes its nostrils flat. A rider would have halted his camel in good time to make it kneel. With the tail turned half to the wind, he can crawl under cover of its flank and draw his cloak, the ABBA, over his head. Thus, master and beast lie protected for as many hours as it takes for the storm to pass."

"The Bedouin man is very lucky to have a camel to shelter him. I've seen a bad sand storm. Flying sand hurts." confirmed Gold.

"It certainly does, Gold. The camel is unique because it has adapted so well to the desert and also helped humans to survive there. The nomad considers this animal to be God's greatest gift because it serves him better than anything else.

"No wonder the tribes took good care of their herds. In difficult times, when grazing was no longer possible, men have fed camels on the last of their dates and barley. And then they sometimes had to offer them dried fish and tree bark. Of course, fodder and grain are best if there is no natural grazing, but this was sometimes impossible.

"Tribesmen took care not to lose their camels. Well-trained beasts did not have to be tethered in any way, and they came when called. They rarely strayed too far at grazing time. But, badly-behaved camels had to be hobbled so they moved about slowly. At night, the herd was brought into a circle close to the tents and fed from the centre."

"How long does a camel live, Susan?" asked Gold.

"The average camel can live to be well over 30 years of age,

Gold. Some surpass 40 years. The cow camel can be bred from the age of two years, although they are not often mated before they are three years old, or more; and often, shepherds do not wish to mate the cows until they are six years old. A bull camel can be a father at about two years of age, but it is not normally mated until five or six years old, or more.

"Shepherds hope that the calf (which can also be called a colt) will be born in the cool weather when there is good grazing for the mother. This would ensure that the mother had plenty of milk for the baby. Unfortunately, this is not always the case because camels can breed all year round. Usually, mating occurs at rutting time, in the cool spring season between January and April – a period known as HEJ in Arabic. The female gives birth to one calf, and sometimes two, every other year. The gestation period is 410 days.

"Soon after birth, the calf's legs quickly become long and strong. At first, the baby will have a woolly coat, which is shed at the end of the first year, leaving a tuft on the top of the hump. Even the tuft falls out eventually, and adult hair begins to grow in autumn.

"Cow camels are protective and affectionate with their young and should be approached with caution if you want to touch the baby. A dead calf will upset the cow too much for her to travel. To ease her misery, should the Bedouin need to move on, the skin of the dead baby is taken along. Otherwise, she will stay behind with the body. A lost calf will not move, either, until the mother comes to fetch it.

"A calf is permitted to drink from its mother for 12 to 18 months if the Bedouin family can spare the milk, Occasionally, the suckling period is extended to 24 months. When the family needs the milk, the calf may be allowed to suckle for only a few months. Normally, calves are fed only at dawn and dusk, and often half of the milk goes to the calf and half to the Bedouin. It is interesting that cow camels usually give their milk only if the calf is present, or if she has been deceived into thinking it is there.

"To prevent a calf from drinking all day, a bag is tied over the cow's udder, or the four teats are plugged. When the calf is to be weaned, a sharp piece of wood is tied across its nostrils. This will prick the mother if the calf attempts to feed and it encourages her to reject the calf. Gradually, the young camel begins to eat tender grass and delicate leaves. By the time that it is three years old, it can eat whole dates and barley, its food sometimes mixed with milk.

"Camels have an astonishing ability to produce rich milk even when their diet is poor. And, they produce a volume well beyond the capacity of other domestic animals in the same conditions. It is therefore not surprising that herds are still kept in Arabia for their milk. In the past, it was the chief nutriment of tribes, nourishing every member of a Bedouin family. In times of drought, the nomads who lived in remote places, without wells, would have died without cow camels. In a difficult season, many tribes had to live on their 'she' camel's milk exclusively for months."

"Oh, how could they? I HATE it!" cried Gold.

"A Bedouin, in times past, could not afford to hate it, Gold. But, it would be difficult to dislike. I have tried it and found camel milk unique and quite different from cow's milk. It is more like a yoghurt drink. A nomad could help himself to a fresh and frothy drink when he was thirsty, squirting the milk into a special wooden cup. I am told, the taste varies depending on the animal's diet. It can be sharp and salty or slightly sweet tasting. It is fortunate, too, that camel milk does not sour easily. Being low in fat, it will not make butter, although, it can be boiled to a curd to make small cheeses.

"Milking the herd occurs only at dawn and dusk as a rule. With plentiful grazing, a good camel can give five or more litres of milk (7–9 pints) daily and suckle her young at the same time. It is a Bedouin belief that the cow camel will go dry if she is milked with dirty hands or into a bowl that is soiled with meat. That is why the desert folk, in the past, kept special wooden bowls for milking and drinking. Today, plastic and metal are used."

"But didn't the Bedouin ever get tired of milk, Susan?" asked Gold.

"I suppose they did sometimes, Gold. Whenever they could, the tribes would go to an oasis and refill their bags with water, rice, and grain; and, at an oasis, they could have a variety of fresh food – and dates. They would fill as many bags as possible with dates because this fruit keeps exceptionally well. Today, most Bedouin have vehicles as well as camels, so they no longer depend on the camel and its milk. However, its meat remains popular.

"In the past, the tribal people rarely ate meat, and it was a great honour if an animal was killed to feed a guest. Now and again, a male camel would be slaughtered for a very special occasion. The meat of the adult -male animal was tough, so usually only young ones under five years were eaten. Camel meat was popular in many towns, so calves were sometimes sold at birth to traders who travelled about the desert. In olden times, they gave calico in exchange for animals."

"What's calico?" asked Gold.

"Calico is a tough cloth that withstands abrasive sand, and, in the past, the Bedouin used it to make slippers and clothing.

"Many camels were sent to markets outside the Arabian Peninsula to be slaughtered for food. Tribes were able to trade their animals for most of their needs. But, since oil was discovered, Arabia's wealth has provided trucks and cars and the camel is no longer in great demand. The time has passed when the tribes could be independent because of the camel. In fact, the Bedouin have ceased to rely upon camels as a source of revenue. Yet, recently, some herds have begun to increase again.

"Long ago, when nomads enjoyed their independence, they learned to make full use of the camel, whether it was alive or dead. It was essential to do so if they wanted to roam free and survive. For instance, each year, the nomadic people of Arabia could collect camel hair. Cloth made from camel hair was treasured all over the world, often described as being softer than silk.

"In the autumn, as the weather cools, the dromedary begins to grow long hair over its hump, shoulders, head and neck. Some long hair grows on its upper forelegs and the tip of its tail, too. Each camel produces between one and two kilos (2–5 lbs) of hair each season, which begins to fall out in early summer. Whatever is left can be removed by hand. The best hair comes from young camels. The hair collected by the Bedouin, was first spun by hand and then sold, exchanged or woven into fine cloth for clothing and cloaks. Sometimes camel hair was mixed with other fibres, to be made into rugs, blankets, bags, tents and rope.

"The hide of the camel was made into shoes, sandals, belts, scabbards, pouches, bags, basins, buckets and waterbags. Camel fat was boiled down to make suet which kept for months until needed as enrichment for bread and rice. Camel bones could be made into useful items, too, such as needles and fertilizer, while the shoulder blades were once used as slates in school."

"It reminds me of the video film we saw last night, Susan: 'Wanted, Dead or Alive'." said Gold.

"In this case, Gold, it was 'Needed, Dead or Alive'. I doubt that the early Arabians could have developed the arid centre of Arabia without the camel."

"I wonder what camels think, Susan."

"It is hard to know, Gold. Camels are basically docile by nature, and they have been described as 'nonchalant' because they seem cool and indifferent to whatever is happening. They accept their role in life and have been known to endure privation and pain with seeming indifference. Overworked, camels, that have had insufficient food and water, have dropped dead while carrying heavy loads. Females can be angry sometimes, and they might growl, but mostly they appear calm. The females are especially biddable, but no one will ride a bull camel."

"Why not, Susan?" asked Gold.

"Bull camels can be very dangerous, especially during the breeding season. A rutting bull can be aggressive and unpredictable. That is why male calves are often killed or sold. Some bulls are kept for breeding, but others that are needed for work have to be castrated, or de-sexed to make them stronger and easier to handle. The average breeding herd might keep only two bulls, mating only one at one time. To keep a bull under control, and to prevent it from straying, the front legs can be tied together – or one leg can be tied with the knee bent. Bulls have been known to break these hobbles to search for a cow that is ready to mate.

"A vicious bull camel will attack other males, and humans, and its bite can be serious. With their great teeth and jaws, they can inflict appalling injuries, so really bad-tempered bulls wear a muzzle over their mouths. It is common to muzzle camels while transporting foodstuffs, because they can easily rip open the sacks.

"The bull camel is particularly difficult to handle because it might kick. Usually, camels kick to defend themselves against wolves and dogs. The hind legs can kick at great speed – as high as a man's shoulder. The forelegs can reach a man's back and hit with tremendous force.

"It is important to watch out if a camel becomes upset or excited. You will recognize an excited male at mating time, because it inflates the lining of its mouth to puff it out like a balloon. This soft palate is called the 'goola pouch'. Furthermore, if they get very excited, both male and female can forcibly project a stream of green liquid from their first stomach. It is very unpleasant if it hits you."

"Ooooo. Yucky!" said Gold. "How does anyone manage to get near a camel, Susan? How can you be sure it won't kick, bite or spit?"

"I didn't mean to frighten you, Gold. Camels, like most animals, respond to kindness, and they are excellent in the hands of a good owner. It is true that some can be difficult, or they might take fright and panic if handled by an unsympathetic person, and they also bear resentment against anyone who has been cruel. Compared to the horse, the camel does not seem very intelligent, but it is a patient animal. Handled kindly, camels can be taught what is expected."

"How?" demanded Gold.

"A young camel's training starts when it is still with its mother. Firstly, the calf must become familiar with its handler. Then, when it is two years old, it is taught control and discipline, commencing with its being lead by a head rope, or by a peg in its nose. Depending on the camel's future, it will be taught to obey commands. Some light pack work may begin at this stage.

"The riding camel (called DHALUL in Arabic) is not broken in until the third year. Both baggage and riding camels must first learn to kneel down. This is called BARRAKK in Arabic. The camel will need to learn the appropriate words for sitting upright, sinking down, and tucking its feet under the body. They are also trained to obey many other words and noises.

"A camel does not wear a conventional halter. It is controlled by a simple headstaff that is attached to a long rope. This is called RISAN in Arabic. The RISAN may have been handmade by the Bedouin men and women and it can be very pretty. A hand-wrought chain, worn over the nose, connects to a hand-woven band that passes behind the ears. This strip usually has intricate geometric patterns, and colourful tassels are sometimes attached.

"A riding animal must pay attention to the camel stick, the MISHAAB. The rider uses this long, thin, flexible stick to tap the neck and to indicate where he wants to go. To stop the animal, some riders make a clicking noise with their tongue. A riding camel is taught to kneel for her master to mount, rising only after he is firmly seated. Otherwise, he would be dislodged, because a camel first unfolds her long forelegs and then her hind legs, thrusting the rider sharply forwards and then backwards.

"The hump makes riding bareback very difficult. Most riders use a saddle, known as the SHADAD in Arabic. The SHADAD is a wooden frame that fits firmly around the hump. Sheepskins, and brightly-coloured tasselled rugs are thrown over it to make it comfortable. The rider, sitting high on the hump, either places one leg each side, or he kneels in the saddle, on top of the upturned soles of his feet. Many Bedouin prefer to kneel if they intend to gallop. Riders in southern Arabia prefer a simple straw-stuffed pillow fixed behind the hump. It is a skill that requires excellent balance.

"Bull camels are fully grown at six or seven years old, and cows reach this stage when they are seven or eight. No dromedary is really fit for heavy work until it is six, but they might begin before then with very small loads. Some experts advise that a baggage animal should carry nothing but its saddle before it is five and a half years old. To work before then could cause the camel some health problems in later life.

"A camel's prime working life is between 7 and 12 years, but pack camels continue to work until they are about 20 years old which is about half their lifespan. They are stouter and more muscular than riding camels, and they have deeper chests and heavier bones. These special beasts of burden are sometimes called 'baggagers'. They participated in caravans, and carried the tents and household possessions in the days when tribes changed their camping grounds.

"A strong baggager carried as much as 200 kilos, and sometimes much more, for 30 kilometres or more (about 450 lbs for 20 miles). The load was usually kept to about a third of the camel's weight. Females were less powerful and carried less. On a short trek, a strong camel carried up to 500 kilos (1100 lbs). Travel was often divided into two marches – morning and evening – with a period for grazing in between. Throughout the journeys, short rests were usual at regular intervals.

"A riding camel is lighter and finer than a pack animal, and the females are said to be more courageous and have greater endurance than the males. Apparently, the female will keep going until she drops from exhaustion and thirst – even though she may be displaying her misery by moaning and crying real tears.

"These fine animals are usually ridden only by one man. Unless the camel is a racer, it should be able to carry some equipment or baggage as well as its master. It can be ridden for approximately 70 kilometres (45 miles) for up to 14 days, if the country is flat, but it must be well rested afterwards before further work. This is a lot for the average camel; yet a really fit animal can do almost twice that speed, as long as it is not for more than a two-day journey – and it would require at least a week of complete rest to recover.

"The pace of the normal riding camel is a jog of 8–10 kilometres per hour (5–6 mph). At this pace, a distance of 50 kilometres (30 miles) can be maintained for days. The rider usually sings as encouragement to keep the animal going. Camels are walked at 4 kilometres per hour (about 2.5 mph).

A fast run is about 16 kilometres per hour (10 mph). This can be kept up for an hour or so.

"Camel racing is very popular still, and a good racer is very valuable, and is often pampered. In some cases, special care must be taken, particularly as the finest racers are said to have tender and sensitive feet.

"A racer, known as DHULUL, is capable of surprising speed, being particularly swift in a short race. Over a long distance on soft sand, it is claimed that a really fast camel can outrun a horse; and in short distance races they will reach 30 kph (about 20 mph).

"In the Kingdom of Saudi Arabia, the camel's speed is tested each winter in weekly races. The most exciting race occurs in the spring. It is the largest and most important of its kind in the world, and known as 'The King's Camel Race', because it is held under the patronage of the King of Saudi Arabia.

"One thousand or more camels race on the 22 kilometre (13.5 miles) circuit at Al-Janadriya, 60 kilometres (37 miles) north of Riyadh. Contestants come from afar and very young riders compete with agile men to win this prestigious afternoon race. They gather weeks before to prepare their mounts. The camels are tenderly cared for and carefully trained with special diets and exercise. It is a great honour to be the winning rider and owner – the prizes are grand and they are presented by the King himself."

It had been a particularly long story, so I was not surprised to see Gold beginning to nod off. The garden was so peaceful and the sun was gently warming. I looked around and saw all the animals stretched out enjoying the perfect weather. As I rose, my movement brought a twitch to a fur coat here and there, but they were all too drowsy to move. I did not want to disturb Gold. He was still awake, but only just. I could hear what he thought about camels tomorrow.

9
The Horse

It was a typically quiet and lazy Friday in May, with the sun shining out of a clear blue sky. John had taken Christopher horse-riding and I lay back on my garden sofa, appreciating the peaceful ambience. The weather had been fine for weeks and we could expect it to remain dry for some time to come. The average yearly rainfall (less than 13 centimetres – about 5 inches) had fallen early in April, and summer was well on the way. The heat would increase rapidly from now on, but it was a dry heat in Central Arabia. Riyadh residents do not experience the intense humidity that occurs around the coasts, making the atmosphere in the cities of Jeddah and Damaam, quite stifling and 'sticky' in high summer. Fortunately there is little concern about having fine weather for the 'weekend' – consisting of only one day for most working people. Rain and dust storms do occur, but they are rare, so, Friday, the 'day of rest', is usually pleasant.

I had just refilled the rabbit's water bowls, and Askalu had fed them. Samantha joined us to see our lagomorphs eagerly devour their mound of 'grins'. I watched her as she 'inched' forward, bit by bit, until a coarse cabbage stem was within reach. She quickly seized it and slunk away, hoping I would not notice. Mamapuss raised her head to see what Samantha had. "Foolish dog!" she seemed to say with great disdain and put her head back down to rest on her front paws.

Dogs probably don't enjoy eating raw vegetables but they do seem to like stealing food. Samantha was now holding the fat stalk between her paws. She gnawed away, as if it were a bone. Shreds and bits lay all about, so I doubted that she had swallowed much. Meanwhile, Gold who had finished eating, had begun asking me a lot of questions. I was feeling a little sleepy, and answered him automatically without paying too much attention. As I continued to watch Samantha with her 'pretend' bone, my mind had been occupied with nothing more than wondering if she had consumed any of the cabbage stalk.

After a while, I became aware that Gold was desperately trying to transfer my attention to himself, so I decided to tease him a little.

"You know, Gold, not so long ago, I might have been burned alive because of you."

"What? Why?" said Gold in alarm.

"Once upon a time, women were called witches for MUCH less than talking to a rabbit. You would have been called 'an agent of the devil', and I would have been burnt at the stake."

"But, Susan, Christopher said scientists spend a lot of time trying to communicate with animals, so it must be alright. It is alright for us to talk, isn't it, Susan?"

"Of course it is, Gold. I was just teasing you. That was long ago, and not in Arabia. Nowadays, research in the field of animal communication is acceptable and quite commonplace. I have often thought it strange, though – that humans have probably had more to do with the horse than any other animal, yet they have done very little about 'horse talk'."

"You mean horses have TALKED?" Gold almost screeched, perhaps at the thought of a rival.

"No, not exactly, Gold. But horses do communicate with each other and they do, to some extent, 'talk' to humans. Between themselves, scent is thought to be much more important than sound. The visual exchange of signals and gestures is more important still. Even an overall body posture tells something. There is, indeed, a very elaborate body language amongst horses and some statements resemble those made between humans. They don't quite raise their eyebrows as people do, but their gestures are the same sort of thing. There is the set of the mouth; lip movements; rolling of the eyes; the angle of the head; stamping of the feet; flaring of the nostrils; and swishing of the tail; but, the most important of all, is ear position.

"Horses have more subtle signals too, such as feints and challenges which confirm their 'pecking order'. You know exactly what that is because rabbits also have an order of importance; and it is reinforced by the reprimanding of inferiors, too. Amongst groups of horses, messages confirming the order of superiority are said to ripple back and forth like static on a radio. Although silent, and only the horses can 'hear' it, everybody can easily see the signs. Usually, when a horse bares its teeth, it is nothing more than playful bluffing, especially if it is accompanied by a calm eye, relaxed facial muscles, and perked ears. Even friendships may be reaffirmed by a nip. Horse friendship is mostly maintained by mutual grooming, where they nip each other very gently for several minutes.

"It is believed by some people that horses can send each other their 'news' telepathically. They say these animals send 'mental' pictures to each other, transmitted and received by the brain in a similar fashion to television. I wonder if this could be possible?"

"Most animals can do that sort of thing." said Gold a little depreciatingly.

He added thoughtfully: "Susan, I know Christopher goes horse-riding, but I don't know much about horses, really. Is there an Arabian horse?"

"But of course! Arabia has a very special horse indeed. It has been described as a 'magical' animal, and it is prized above all creatures on the Arabian Peninsula – even more than the camel."

"Surely not more than the camel?"

"Oh, no animal could take the place of the camel, Gold – at least, in the eyes of the Bedouin – but the horse has always been the most desirable animal in Arabia. To the Bedouin, it was the same as a luxury car might be to a Westerner. Even many Western horse-lovers dream of owning a pure blood Arabian horse, for it is acclaimed world-wide as one of the finest breeds. But, long before this superb creature was discovered by the outside world, it was treasured by the Arabian Peninsular people.

"Over a thousand years ago, in the seventh century, A.D., the Prophet Mohammed said: 'It flies without wings – the horse – as if the Lord had made it from the speeding winds'. The Prophet encouraged men to feed their horses well, and, it is written: 'As many grains of barley as thou givest thy horse, so many sins shall be forgiven thee.'

"So you can see how special this creature is to the Peninsular people – AND to the rest of the world. An air of mystery enchances its glamour. You see, this mammal's origins are veiled by the mists of time.

"The horse family, Equidae, includes asses and zebras – all highly adapted for fast, graceful running. In this group, the foot has evolved into a single-toed hoof of horn. In the wild, equids live in herds of up to twelve females and young, led by a dominant male. They feed mainly on grass. Their elongated skull accommodates large teeth adapted to grass-cropping and grinding. They defend themselves by kicking and biting.

"Most scientists agree that horses originated in North America and migrated to Asia where they were domesticated around 4,000 years ago. But, the history of the horse in Arabia remains incomplete, and the origin of the Arabian breed is unknown. For this reason, legend and tradition have provided most of the information about this very special animal.

"Some fanciful folk tales exist about the origin of the Arabian horse. One story tells us that Ishmael, of Biblical times, received a mare in foal as a gift from Heaven, and all horses are descended from it. Another one recounts that King Solomon's horse was drowned, and seven young horses emerged from the waves where the royal horse went down.

These are supposed to be the ancestors of the seven different strains from which the famous Arabian horse is said to have descended. One historian believes he can trace its heritage back many thousands of years, to the time of Baz, a man who is said to have tamed wild horses in Yemen (to the west in southern Arabia).

"Some nomads have claimed that horses were captured wild and tamed in Arabia at a time when the land was fertile and green. Yet, most Bedouin say that there were no horses in Arabia long ago, and they were originally acquired by raiding. After that, they say, the captives were taken to the inner desert where nomads perfected the breed.

"It is quite likely that horses first came to Arabia from Mesopotamia, the richly fertile region to the north of the Peninsula. This crescent-shaped segment of land lies between the Tigris and Euphrates River that flows into the Arabian Gulf. Water is abundant there and the vegetation is perennial. Horse breeding could have begun in any of the fertile areas on the Arabian Peninsula.

"It is probable that the Arabian breed originated about five thousand years ago either in Arabia or North Africa. However, and wherever it happened, there is no doubt that this horse is different. There are rock pictures of similar horses in Arabia, although these are said to be only about three thousand years old. To add to the mystery, an ancient Eyptian illustration exists, depicting what appears to be a perfect Arabian horse. These animals are known to have been introduced into Egypt by the Hyksos invaders from Syria about three-and-a-half thousand years ago.

"Wherever the breed originated, it is generally agreed that this fabulous horse kept its unique characteristics, because it was bred for centuries in the remote and inaccessible Najd. This is largely a desert region in the centre of Arabia, and framed by a range of high mountains on the Western side, and a desert wilderness on the other three sides. Much of the Najd is a harsh place, where in olden times, only a strong horse could survive. Yet the dry air would have helped it to develop sound lungs – and the Arabian horse is especially renowned for its soundness of wind (meaning that the animal does not get puffed out easily). There are many tales about its incredible endurance.

"It is astounding that a fine horse could be bred in the merciless desert. Horses are delicate creatures requiring the greatest care. Proper feeding is considered essential. Feeding a horse in the inner desert, long ago, often meant that a Bedouin family had to go hungry themselves. In the most difficult times, it had to be fed dates, dried locusts, and dried meat as a substitute for normal horse food. Barley was given whenever it was available. But, if grain was in short supply and vegetation poor, the horse might even be fed camel's milk. There were times when it had to go without food. Some scientists believe that, after many generations, this meagre diet resulted in a lean, small-framed horse. Despite all the setbacks, a horse of incredible beauty emerged.

Najim, an Arabian stallion

Haifa, an Arabian mare

"There is great romance surrounding this fine animal. Both ancient and modern Islamic literature describe its beauty, courage and speed. The breed is said to be a combination of grace and refinement; intelligence and friendliness; dignity and courage. The harsh and frugal lifestyle of the Bedouin helped to create a horse of exceptional character, patience, high spirits, and physique, with an aristocratic bearing. Its stamina and legs were strengthened by galloping on sand and over hard desert terrain. The leg bones are described as 'ivory hard' and the tendons are strong.

"There are many stories about the very special care that a Bedouin would bestow upon his horse. Desert people will tell you: NOTHING causes as much trouble to raise as a mare: and, it is easier to bring up five children than a single filly. Children, they say, require special care for only the first two years of their life, but the care of a mare has no end."

"But, Susan, if horses were such a nuisance, why did the Bedouin keep them?"

"The horse was valuable, Gold, because it was an investment, and it helped people to survive in the desert. This creature was prized simply because it surpassed the camel in speed and manoeuvrability. It was much easier for a warrior to repel attack on horseback than when mounted on a camel. With horsepower, enemies could be defeated and a tribe keep its honour. The horse could also be used for transport and hunting as well as in warfare. Also, when the Arabian horse became known to the outside world, a tribe could sell one abroad for a very good price.

"An Arabian steed, or horse, had to have speed, as well as intelligence. And, it had to be able to endure hunger and thirst, and not be frightened of the dark, because raiding was often carried out at night. The Bedouin prized it for its speed, strength and endurance, and not so much for its beauty. Nevertheless, a fine-looking horse was a source of pride and honour, and a beautiful animal brought pleasure to her owner."

"I suppose everyone just HAD to have one," commented Gold.

"Oh, no. That was not possible. There were never MANY horses in Arabia. And, especially, today, they are rare. A nomad rarely owns a horse, nowadays. Rarity is another reason why ownership has always been a source of immense pride; and it was the female that gave the most prestige. Long ago, when a mare foaled or gave birth and a male (known as a colt) was born, it was often sold or killed. This prevented the mother from being needlessly weakened from feeding the foal. You may be interested to know that the gestation period for a horse varies a little between breeds, but it is about 11 months.

"A foal is called a colt or filly up to 3 years of age. Their lifespan is about 25 years. The birthday of a horse is always on the 1st January, following its birth, and in the year following, it is referred to as a 'yearling'. Its age is judged by its teeth.

"If the mare gave birth to a female, or filly, there would have been great rejoicing amongst the owner's family. Kinfolk and friends would send their congratulations just as if a boy child had been born. You see, traditionally Bedouin men preferred to have sons, because they felt that boys would strengthen the family. Daughters always married and went away to be part of someone else's family. With a horse, a mare was preferred because it was considered to be more manageable, and to have greater endurance than a stallion. Furthermore, a mare could provide the Bedouin with more horses. With that hope in mind, the little filly was gently reared – and with great tenderness. She would even be given camel's milk in addition to suckling from her mother.

"Some of the largest tribes kept only one male horse, but it would be the finest stallion that they could breed or buy. Only the very best would be considered as a stud horse for breeding, expecting it to 'sire' a new generation of excellent mares. (After giving birth, the mother would be called the 'dam' of her fillies and colts, the father known as the 'sire'.)

"Traditionally, great desert tribes kept scrupulous control of breeding. They were especially careful to keep the purity of bloodlines. A pure Arabian horse is one that has no other than Arabian blood. This sometimes required a mare to be taken hundreds of miles for mating. And then, the owner would expect witnesses to be present, just to make sure the offspring's pure breeding could be confirmed.

"Yet, with the Arabian breed, it is possible to produce excellent offspring from one that is less than the finest example. It can happen because of a unique trait called prepotency. It means that even a poor Arabian, whether male or female, may pass on to its future generations the true characteristics of the ideal animal.

"All over the world, the Arab horse has been used to renew and strengthen other strains. It has a reputation for being an excellent stud horse, improving and upgrading about one hundred distinct types and breeds. 'Breed' refers to light horses and ponies with recorded histories such as thoroughbreds, hackneys and Anglo-Arabs. The term 'half-breed' refers to those with one thoroughbred parent. A 'type' refers to horses such as hunters, hacks and polo ponies – as distinct from the breeds. A pony is a small breed of horse.

The Arabic word for horse is HISĀN, KHEYL or KDIS and the plural is AHSINA or KUDS. A true Arabian horse is called FARAS, but the common word for a personal and revered horse is KEHILAN AJUZ, meaning 'purebred horse of great antiquity'. KEHILAN, is the English equivalent of 'purebred', but the Arabic word for an Arabian horse with a pedigree is ASIL (plural ASAJEL) meaning 'pure and noble lineage'. Around the world, such a horse is simply called 'The Arabian'.

"The Arabian people have many descriptions for horses. There are names for the different sizes, and for herds of horses, horses grouped for a race, a horse leaping, prancing or led. There is a name for a horse just foaled; at seven days after foaling, and when a horse is feverish from thirst or

swollen from running, and so on... There are said to be 60 different words for the paces of a horse, and there are names for each part of the animal to indicate if it is 'undamaged' or 'injured'. These words do have a counterpart in the Mongolian language but probably no other. Individual names are usually given to denote a quality. For a stallion, it might be MANSOUR, Arabic for 'victorious' or AKBAR, meaning 'great'. Mares might be called JOHARA meaning 'jewel' or RAJUAH, for 'hope'.

"The official colours of the Arabian horse are Chestnut, Grey, Brown and Bay. Chestnut is a ginger or reddish colour with similar mane or tail. Those that have both black and white hairs throughout the coat, or tufts of dark hair, (known as 'flea-bitten') are officially called 'Grey'. A horse is never correctly described as 'white'. It is interesting that they only become white or lighter with age. The traditional colour of the Arabian is Bay, which can be varying shades of brown with black points. Some can be very light in colour, and quite yellowish.

"The Bay is said to be the fleetest, and the Bedouin believe it has the most endurance. Yet, many nomads say light-yellowish-coloured mares are the fastest over a short distance. They are known as SAFRA. The Najdi Bay, claimed to be the purest, has a dark-blue tinge that shimmers through the coat (which is also known as a pelt). Black horses are uncommon and they have a reputation for being the most spirited, but many Bedouin do not like them – unless they have some white on the feet or forehead. A horse of any colour with a white forehead mark is believed to be blessed. There are less brown ones than the other colours. The brown must be dark with brown points. If there is doubt about classifying the colour, it is taken from the 'points': the tips of the ears, mane and tail, the fine hair on the muzzle, and the extremities of the forelegs. White is not considered a colour but a lack of it.

"The desert folk once believed in the wisdom of their horse. If a Bedouin woman was having difficulty bearing her child, a mare would be encouraged to eat barley from her lap. If the animal whinnied and ate the barley, all was considered to be well. After the baby's birth, if the mother seemed too weak to speak, the mare was sent for again and would be given more barley.

"It is likely, when the Islamic religion went out to the world from the Arabian Peninsula in the seventh century, it carried with it exciting news about the Arabian horse. Although there are great gaps in its history, there are some clues. For example, records show that by the thirteenth and fourteenth centuries, an Egyptian Sultan had acquired three thousand Arab horses.

"Long ago, horses were considered booty, leading them to become weapons of influence. The more horses a tribe had, the more it was feared by its neighbours, and the greater, therefore, was its power. At the beginning of the nineteenth century, their worth led them to feature in the history of Saudi Arabia. It had become known that the Najd, or Central Arabia, had some magnificent horses, and that the Saud ruling family housed an excellent collection of them in their stables. Thereafter, on two occasions in that century, Egyptian armies raided the Najd and took horses. The first time, they ran off with two hundred, and the second time, they seized all that were in the Saud stables. The horses were taken to Egypt, and kept by the Viceroy, Abbas Pasha, who loved them. Then, to add to his stock of Arabians, Abbas Pasha arranged the escape of an imprisoned member of the Saud family, in exchange for some very special examples of the breed.

"Abbas Pasha began to keep records for each animal until, eventually, it became the first complete documentation of the Arabian horse. Such a record is called a 'pedigree'. Previously, records had been committed to memory. The Bedouin kept no written details – it was only written down if a horse was sold to a dealer.

"Nevertheless, the immediate history of each horse was known by heart. Many Bedouin could remember the names of each ancestor of his horse for many generations back, and recite them in the correct line down to its own dam and sire. Yet, the details were considered accurate, despite being handed down by word of mouth from father to son. Only in 1946, were written records officially substituted for Bedouin memories.

"Each line of descent is called the 'genealogy'. In the Western world, the genealogy of a horse is traced through the stallion. But, traditionally, Arabs traced horse-breeding lines through the mare, because they valued the female more highly."

"What happened to the horses that Abbas Pasha pinched, Susan? Are they still in Egypt?" enquired Gold.

"Abbas Pasha was assassinated, Gold, and all the horses were sold. Most of them were taken to Syria to be kept by the Governor, Ali Pasha Sherif. The records were maintained until the time that his stables became run down. Fortunately, two wealthy English travellers, Lady Anne Blunt and her husband, Wilfred Scawen Blunt, remembered the stables in their prosperous days. They had a deep love and knowledge of horses. In the late 19th century, after purchasing some of the best stock, they took it to Egypt, intending to breed the horses there. But, Egypt was not ideal for horses so they were eventually taken to England. It was then that British society's great interest in the Arabian began.

"Horses, and the people who are interested in them, are a special part of society known as the 'Horse World', or the 'Equine World'; and, within this sphere, there is a world of horse-racing. Three Arabian horses in particular, that were imported into England in the 17th and 18th centuries, made their mark on the racing world. They are generally called Arabians although some experts say their blood is mixed, they were the DARLEY ARABIAN, the GODOLPHIN BARB, and the BYERLEY TURK. They were bred to English horses and became the founding fathers of the English thoroughbred, the breed that produced some of the world's fastest mounts. Later, the

Arabian was cross-bred with the thoroughbred, and their progeny (the colts and fillies) were officially named 'Anglo-Arabians'.

"At the end of the 19th century, the intrepid Blunts returned to the Middle East and ventured into the Najd in search of fine horses. Few foreigners made such a difficult journey at that time. They brought out of Arabia the best pure horse stock available, and these were used to improve the Arabian breed in England. The first major stud farm for Arabians outside the Middle East was then established by the Blunts in England. The breeding of Arabians spread from there to France, Germany, Poland and Russia – and then westward to the Americas.

"Some of the finest Arabian stock in Britain today, results from horses that have been imported from the Middle East quite recently. In the 1930's, three Arab stallions (bred in the Najd) left Arabia and sired some fabulous race horses. Another stallion, called MANAK, was given as a gift in 1937, to King George the Sixth, from Prince Saud. He was the son of King Abdul Aziz Ibn Saud, who founded the Kingdom of Saudi Arabia, and destined to become King himself.

"The descendants of MANAK became famous racehorses. There have been famous names, too, from the Najd. One of them was called DAFINA, and she was the foundation mare of a fine stud farm, and the progenitor, or forebear of a long line of distinguished horses.

"The definition of the Arabian took precise form in 1918, when the Arab Horse Society in England was founded. Its first English stud book began the following year. Modern breeders, world-wide, have usually concentrated on the physical development of the Arabian, keeping it along the same lines as those valued by the Bedouin. Lady Wentworth, the daughter of Lady Anne Blunt, wrote a book called: 'The Authentic Arabian Horse' and a pamphlet entitled: 'The Arabian Type and Standard', which clearly set out what is required in the perfect Arabian. As the most important breeder of this horse in modern times, her definition is upheld as the most correct. By using her work, it is fairly easy to recognize an Arabian horse."

"Could I tell if a horse was an Arabian, Susan?"

"I believe you could, Gold. If you know exactly what to look for, you can recognize it at a glance. In fact, it has been said of this unforgettable animal: 'unless the characteristics strike the eye at first glance, it is certain that it is not of the highest class'."

"Imagine that! I hope you're going to tell me how. You will, won't you, Susan?" Gold was wondrously excited, shuffling his paws beneath him, while the glint in his gold eye and the flash in his blue eye, begged me to tell him quickly.

"The Arabian is a small saddle horse ranging from 14 to 15½ 'hands' at the withers or lower neck, which is 142–157 centimetres (56–62 inches). You see, a horse measurement is called a 'hand', which equals almost 10 centimetres (4 inches), but, that won't help YOU, Gold. It seldom weighs more than 453 kilos (1,000 lbs). That won't help you either. First, you must look at the head. The Arabian has a small head, and it must be very short in comparison with other horses; and nothing is more essential on the head than the JIBBAH. That's an Arabic word for the scooped hollow at the top third of the horse's nose – just below the eyes. In English, this concave shape of the horse's head is often called the 'dished' profile. It sets the appearance of the Arabian apart from all other breeds.

"The JIBBAH is made more obvious by the broad and bulging forehead, and the large, wide-spaced eyes which are prominent and set low in the head. The eyes are not slanting as in other breeds. The Arabian's eyes are shaped like the human eye – and set at the same angle." I used my hands to show Gold the rounded forehead, bulging eyes, and the scooped-out nose, tapering down to a pointed muzzle.

"A lot has been written about the eyes of the Arabian horse. They are dark in colour and deep-looking; and said to have the sparkle of a diamond; also, they are alert, expressive and intelligent-looking, without ever appearing wild. The head tapers to a small and soft muzzle; yet, the rounded jaw must be very deep and wide. The slim and delicately-flared nostrils are extremely flexible, extending to become an oblong shape when the horse is excited. The ears are beautifully curved and pointed, and they nearly touch each other at the tips. Oh, and the mare's ears are longer than those of a stallion.

"The next most important feature to look for, is a gracefully-arched neck. It is a long neck, but not at all out of proportion to the body. MITBAH is the Arabic word for the unique angle at which the neck joins the head. It matches the angle of the windpipe in the Arabian's large throat; and it is this which gives the head its renowned flexibility. (The well-developed windpipe accounts for the horse's legendary good 'wind'.) The Arabian is quite remarkable for its ability to endure prolonged and extreme exertion without distress.

"The tail is another unique characteristic of the Arabian. The root of this long-haired tail, known as the dock, is set very high on the end of its short back. The tail itself, curves beautifully upwards to match the arch of the neck, and gives the appearance of an unfurled flag when the horse is galloping. In olden times, the arch of the tail would prop out a rider's long cloak. The short back of the Arabian is said to be responsible for a graceful movement. The hind-quarters, or croup, are long, wide and flat. At the other end of the horse, the chest is wide but not too broad.

"The forelegs should be slim and short compared to most breeds. And, it is particularly important that this horse has straight hocks. (The hock is the hindleg joint between the true knee and fetlock. The fetlock is the place above the horse's hoof, where a tuft of hair grows.) The hair of the Arabian is very fine, particularly in the mare, and the mane and tail of a well-kept animal have the appearance of spun silk."

"It sounds very pretty, Susan," said Gold with a twinkle and a glint in his odd-coloured eyes.

"The Arabian is also a gentle horse, Gold, and intelligent, with a desire to obey. These are qualities which make it easy to teach – if it is handled correctly. Arabian horses have been used for any and every purpose for which the light horse is known – even as circus performers; but their speciality is endurance. They are not as fast in a short run as some other breeds, but they are fleet and tough, and renowned for carrying heavy loads at faster speeds for longer distances than other breeds. Consequently, Arabians are regular performers in endurance competitions, where the horses run long distances over long periods of time. And, Anglo-Arabs have been specially trained for dressage competitions, where horses execute certain movements with extreme precision and smoothness.

"Although not many ordinary people own horses in Arabia any more, there is still the opportunity for everybody to ride. Races continue to be a traditional entertainment throughout the land. Although such events are organized by the settled folk, it is not at all unusual to find that the best riders are nomads or semi-nomads. A highlight of the year is the annual King's Cup Race, organized by the Riyadh Equestrian Club. Many sons of tribal men ride Arabian horses in the Royal Guard, the Saudi Guard, and for the Public Security of Saudi Arabia. Arabian desert horses are also the mount of various police forces in other countries on the Peninsula."

I paused to watch Gold, who was deep in thought. "Gold, it is almost time for me to put on the kettle for tea. So, unless you have any special questions about the horse, I shall finish today with a little story about Christopher and HIS horse." His ears perked up at the offer.

"Oh, please, Susan. So, Christopher had a horse?"

"No, he has never had his own horse, but, before he went away to school, he rode three times a week in Riyadh. As you know, Christopher loves all animals very much, but, when he was quite young, he was especially fascinated by horses. He asked questions about them all the time, and wanted to learn to ride. He was so keen, that we arranged for him to have lessons.

"Neither John nor I had ever had enough courage, or any inclination to pursue this sport – and we were apprehensive when Christopher began to ride. He was a fearless child and we thought that he might not be careful enough around such big, strong animals. As it turned out, the greatest danger for him was learning on horses that were not suitable for beginners. Nevertheless, we kept up the lessons – and the warnings – until the time spent at the stables became the highlights of Christopher's week. He joined the Pony Club's Riyadh Branch, and we were pleased to see him so keen to learn to ride well, and to care for a horse.

"We are convinced that his confidence, and divine protection, saw him safely through those years. Sometimes, much-needed help came from an earthly direction. On one such occasion, his horse took fright and ran off with him. A stallion had startled his mount. Until quite recently, Arabs did not geld their stallions. Gelded, or castrated male horses are generally considered safer to ride, although not all 'entire' males rear up or bite and behave dangerously. But, stallions were kept amongst the other horses, and one of these had been responsible for the disturbance.

"Christopher had been riding in the large ring that day and, fortunately, the openings to the desert were shut off. The horse gathered speed with every length it galloped, and if the gates had been open, it may have raced off into the desert. We were amazed to see that our son kept his seat and rode it out beautifully. He did not seem to be upset, but fear gripped us and everyone watching. As the horse flew past for the second time, it looked as though it wanted to jump the rails. If that happened on the far side, Christopher would either fall at the brick wall, or later on the rocky desert ground beyond.

"We were terrified. The horse did not jump, and it was coming around for the third time with a mad look in its eyes. We could only be grateful that Christopher had seen so many 'Westerns' on television. It used to amuse us to see him mimic a 'cowboy on horseback', waving at us, holding the reins with one hand. Perhaps his 'make-believe' played a large part in keeping him seated on this occasion.

"On the third time around, Christopher was still seated. Hopefully, the wild ride would not last much longer. We could only watch and await the inevitable fall amongst those flying hooves. This must surely be the outcome. Then, as the horse straightened up for the gallop past us once more, a small slim stable boy slipped into the ring and glided towards the oncoming horse. The startled horse slowed sufficiently for him to lunge and grab the reins, dragging it to a halt. Christopher was instantly dislodged, and slid gently down the flank of the great horse. In one movement, the stable boy used his free hand to reach under the agitated animal, and drag our child free. We were overwhelmed by the stable boy's courage, and babbled our gratitude. The hero modestly shrugged off our praise and thanks, and melted into the crowd that gathered about us. We were unable to find him later."

"Oh, Susan, you were scaring me to death. Haven't you got one little light-hearted story to finish off?" pleaded Gold.

"Well, yes, Gold. As a matter of fact, I do, and it is another one about Christopher and a horse.

"On this occasion, I was at the stables, waiting with a group of mothers and governesses, and trying to catch a glimpse of Christopher taking his lesson. Suddenly I saw him mounted and gathering speed as he headed towards a jump. I leapt to my feet and shouted to the instructor: 'Stop Christopher! He has never jumped before.' By the time I had finished speaking, the horse and boy had successfully completed the jump, and the reply came: 'It's alright, Mrs. Blake, neither has the horse.'"

As Gold burst out laughing, startled eyes turned upon us where we sat on the terrace, surrounded by a dog, cat, eighteen rabbits – and an almost tangible image of the Arabian horse.

10
The Donkey

usan, why did John say Mr Brown was a 'donkey'? A donkey is not a kind of human, is it?" Gold was apparently very curious, because he had hopped up two flights of stairs to ask me this question. It obviously resulted from eavesdropping – a habit he had begun, partly because no-one realized that the little rabbit underfoot could understand everything that was said.

"Gold, it isn't very nice to listen to a private conversation and then tell someone about it. I'm sure John was joking; although, it is true, Mr Brown does seem quite dull at times. Of course, it was wrong in the first place, for John to suggest that a donkey is stupid. People have a habit of calling anyone a 'donkey' if they don't seem to be very bright. It is insulting to the animal as well as the person. You know that some people say 'silly as a rabbit' – it's the same thing."

"Are donkeys like rabbits then?" asked Gold, looking even more perplexed.

"Oh no, Gold, not at all, but the intelligence of the donkey is generally thought of as low, and its behaviour has led people to believe it is a stupid and stubborn animal. Donkeys work for man as horses do, but they think differently to similar animals doing similar work. If this creature refuses to do something, humans have to find a way for it to perform with which it agrees, or nothing gets done. Giving it rewards will assist training, but too many treats spoil the animal, and then it may nip if it doesn't get anything."

"That's naughty!" judged Gold.

"Perhaps, but donkeys are special. And, they really do enjoy human companionship. They are very patient with children, according to an English expert, Elizabeth Svendsen. She has been honoured by Queen Elizabeth II of England because of her kind and clever work. Mrs Svendsen began 'The Slade Centre', where disabled children are taught to ride.

"She has saved many unwanted donkeys and the Centre gives them something to do that they like. Apparently, these creatures are gentler than ponies. And it is easier for the child to obtain the correct riding position on a donkey's back because it is narrower than that of the pony. Furthermore, a donkey is cuddly, and more attractive to youngsters. Once disabled children are accustomed to them, many can go on to riding ponies."

"What is a donkey like, Susan? It must be like a horse if you can ride it. Are there any in Arabia?"

"Oh, YES, Gold. It is almost certain that the donkey originated in North America, or perhaps North Africa, but no one is sure how this mammal spread throughout the world. It is considered native to Southern Asia and North Africa, but as it became part of traditional Arabian life in olden times, it can be thought of as a local animal.

"'Donkey' is the common name for the Ass. In Arabic, it is called HIMĀR. Although not indigenous, or belonging naturally to the Arabian heartland, the Syrian Wild Ass and Asiatic Wild Ass once ranged widely in the far north of the peninsula. Numbers declined because of human settlement on its range, and grazing by domestic stock, as well as hunting. Grasses and fresh water are critical to its survival.

"The Ass is a quadruped, belonging to the same family as the horse and zebra. They are ungulates; an order of mammals that have grinding teeth, and hooves with one or two toes on each hoof. The ass, horse and zebra have only one toe on their hooves and it is made of horn, similar to the nails on human fingers and toes.

"In captivity, there is insufficient rough ground to wear the donkey's hooves down, so they must be trimmed regularly to prevent them from growing too long and making the animal lame. The horn on a donkey's hoof is more elastic and less brittle than on the horse; so, in dry climates, the feet harden naturally, and rarely need metal shoes.

"The Middle East is a most suitable habitat for the ass, because it is an animal that can survive well in a harsh environment, being content with fairly poor vegetation, and requiring less water than the horse. They have been known to go for long periods without drinking, although the happiest ones are those with a constant supply of fresh water. Ideally, they must not have too much protein. A rich diet can result in stomach cramps, leading to serious illness. Rough grass and thistles are best. When even this bare diet is not available, groups of females with their young, led by a dominant male, will gather together with others to migrate.

"Do you know Gold, donkeys have helped humans since the earliest times and they are still working in many parts of Arabia. It has been a most useful animal.

"Apart from being ridden, it can carry heavy loads through rough, trackless country, and up steep and narrow mountain paths where vehicles cannot go. Donkeys have helped in agriculture, too, carrying loads out of fields. They replace machinery, and they are sometimes harnessed to water wheels and corn grinders. In Arabia, donkeys were used for hire, and to carry small tanks of water and fuel.

"It is an animal of various colours, but many of them are white. The coats of the white ones used for hire in Saudi Arabia, were traditionally stained with patterns of orange henna. And, very often, the donkeys and their little carts were strung with brass bells and colourful trappings. To me, donkeys always look sad, so these decorations help to make them appear a little brighter.

"In remote places, desert people still depend a great deal upon the donkey, just as they did centuries ago. Folklore suggests that, in the earliest times, the ass retreated to the foothills where food was scarce, allowing the horse to remain in the lush plains. And, because donkeys tended to scatter themselves about, they developed a loud bray and big ears in order to keep in touch with each other."

"Is THAT how you tell a horse from a donkey, Susan?"

"The large ears are one way, Gold, but the tail of the donkey is quite different from that of the horse. A donkey's tail is long, and there is a little tuft at the end. This is useful for swatting flies and insects. Many donkeys grow a long shaggy coat in winter to keep warm, but it is not waterproof. The healthy ones shed their long hair in summer and become smooth-coated like the horse.

"The donkey is much smaller than a horse – approximately 10 hands high. There are 10 cms (4 inches) to the hand so that makes a donkey just over one metre tall (40 inches). Like the horse, the eyes are on the side of the head, so it does not see well to the front. It is important to remember that a donkey must be approached from the side. Although it is not as nervous as the horse, it will kick out as protection when frightened.

"The female donkey is called a 'mare' or 'jenny', and the male is known as a 'stallion' or 'jack'. A female foal is a 'filly', the male a 'colt'. Donkeys interbreed with horses sometimes, and then the foal is known as a 'mule', providing the father is a donkey and the mother is a horse. If the father is a horse and the mother is a donkey, then the foal is called a 'jennet' or 'hinny'. Mules and hinnies are much stronger than the donkey, but they are also much more stubborn – more difficult to handle, and cannot produce offspring."

"But how can you tell if it is a mule or a hinny, if you don't know its parents?" queried Gold.

"It is difficult to be absolutely certain, Gold. However, a true mule tends to be rather standard and of uniform conformation – usually standing 13–14 hands high; and almost always bay in colour with virtually no white markings. A hinny tends to exhibit nearly as much diversity as the parent pony stock, being thin or fine boned, large or small, white or skewbald (odd-coloured) and so on. A good guess would be that it is a hinny if it is not bay-coloured.

"Donkey stallions are much noisier and usually difficult to handle; and, they can be quite bad-tempered. They are known as 'entire'. Some have been so dangerous and destructive that they have had to be gelded, or neutered, to become tame and biddable.

"Although a donkey does not have to be broken in for work as horses do, it must have some simple training. Its back is not strong enough for work or being ridden until it is about three years old. Before that age, the bones are not properly formed and can be distorted. The age can be told by the six front teeth which become more slanted and shorter with age.

"The legs are very strong, allowing donkeys to undertake much longer journeys than horses; but, they are slower, and average only about two-and-a-half kilometers per hour (1.5 miles) or 15 kilometers in a day (9.5 miles). A donkey should not carry more than 50 kilos (110 pounds) and the load must be properly packed and evenly distributed. Adequate rest is important for a working animal and food and water should be given every six hours. They can live for 40 or 50 years, but many only reach 20 years because they have been overworked."

"How many do they have in a litter, Susan?"

"Female donkeys are mature at one year, and give birth to only one foal after a gestation period of between eleven and twelve months. The foals remain delicate in health for about one year and, in some parts of the world, their main danger is wet and cold. Although the Middle Eastern climate suits them very well, it's still only the strong that survive because a baby donkey is supposed to be more delicate than the young of similar animals.

"This creature has a very interesting character. One day, everyone may agree that it is intelligent. Elizabeth Svendsen believes that donkeys are VERY intelligent. She has seen evidence of their conveying messages between themselves, and has known them to seek help for each other. For example, one donkey gave warning in the night when another was in trouble. It was one of her special pets. He would not stop braying until the lights came on in the house and help was on the way. Braying is a donkey's usual way of getting attention. On another occasion, Mrs Svendsen discovered that her pet raised the alarm because a little one was very sick.

"Apparently, it is better to keep two, because a single animal can become very lonely. A new female once woke Mrs Svendsen in the early hours of the morning with a mournful 'hee-haw', and it was found pacing restlessly around and around the paddock, braying incessantly for no apparent reason. After a companion was provided, it was much less noisy. Some lonely ones repeatedly bite their way out of their pen to make a noisy call upon their owners. They can be playful and mischievous, too, enjoying to tear things to pieces with their teeth. Just for fun, they might drag each other around and around by the collar or halter until it is shedded."

"What a mischief!" said Gold in wonderment.

"Yes, and domesticated donkeys can become fussy eaters, I have heard. You know, Gold, some appear to inspect their food immediately it is brought, and corner and challenge the stablehand if it is not good enough. One such donkey trotted quickly to the gate to reach it first. Then, he turned around to give the person a kick, apparently conveying that the offering was considered second-rate.

"Another of Mrs Svendsen's donkeys was greedy for attention as well as food. The more he got, the more he wanted; and, he showed contempt for other animals. He even took to chasing cats and dogs. After a while, he began nipping his owners who had been very kind to him. Then, he kept the neighbours awake with his braying. Eventually, to keep him occupied, he was given his own television set. It pacified him for a while, and he would stand for hours with his eyes glued to the screen. But, soon he became bored with it, and he had to be gelded to quieten him down."

"Animals aren't often stupid Susan. They're just different to humans, that's all. And, they are very different to each other mostly, but I'm not at all sure about donkeys. Frankly, I think THAT donkey was VERY spoiled. Imagine, his OWN television. Good grief! What next?"

"Perhaps it really was going a bit far, Gold. People have had a good working relationship with these creatures for thousands of years, so they know them well. It appears the donkey can be very determined indeed. Perhaps its temperament is dull in comparison with a horse. But, after all, it IS a completely different species, so it should not be compared just because of the similar shape. People who have compared it to the horse, quite naturally find the donkey 'obstinate' and 'uncooperative'.

"A donkey is especially hard to manage if it has not been properly handled in early life. A well-trained animal becomes good and faithful. It is a very sociable creature, and enjoys living in a family group. Human companionship can also be very important. But, if it is to work with people, careful training must begin from when it is only a few days old. The so-called stubbornness which many display, and for which they are renowned, is a result of poor training or the complete lack of it, I am told. It is interesting to see, in their own family groups, donkeys have rules which seem harsh for the smaller ones: for instance, at feeding time, the oldest or strongest will see to it that they have their fill first. This often leaves the youngsters with very little to eat.

"There is no doubt that the donkey has often been misunderstood. It is usually patient and quite humble. Its dull role as a 'beast of burden' has not helped its image either. Working animals are sometimes scorned as inferior in the manner of master and slaves in olden times.

"Mountainous climbs are natural for donkeys. They are valued especially because they can negotiate steep and rocky terrain where camels and horses cannot go. It is so sad though, to hear when they have been abused and overworked under such trying conditions. SPANA, the Society for the Protection of Animals in North Africa, is a charity formed in Great Britain in 1923. It was begun by Mrs Kate Hosali and her daughter Nina, who witnessed appalling cases of neglect and ignorance towards donkeys in North Africa. SPANA became a most effective organization with many animal welfare centres, where domestic and pack animals still receive rest, refuge and treatment today.

"It is a paradox that some people who work alongside donkeys and apparently like them, nevertheless, sometimes treat them cruelly. In one country I visited, many happy donkeys work in the fields by day and return home in the evenings, carrying the farmer and hay. Yet, other masters there, expect their donkeys to make repeated trips in intense heat, carrying tourists up a mountain. The poor creatures must climb a narrow and incredibly steep, cobbled path to the town at the top. The drivers beat the donkeys to make them go faster, so they can transport the maximum number of passengers per day. For many tourists, it is a fifteen-minute ordeal. Their experience cannot compare favourably with the scenic journey in the barely-advertised cable car, which is usually almost empty."

"How did man first get the donkey to work for him, Susan?"

"No one really knows, Gold. It is believed that the Egyptians domesticated the ass some time between five and six thousand years ago, and written records show that it was highly-prized in ancient times.

"In more recent times in Arabia, it has been practical and hardworking; yet, donkey and master often shared a great friendship.

"In the Arabian desert, you might see donkeys wandering or clustering together, apart from humans. It is amusing to watch them sometimes. They go for leisurely walks in single file, one following the other in order of superiority, probably. Perhaps they go in search of water. People often wonder what this animal is thinking about because it gives the impression of brooding over something."

"Perhaps they are wishing just to be someone's pet, without having to work anymore."

"Well, Gold, I'm not so sure. Mrs Svendsen found that what appeared to be her happiest donkeys were the ones with something to do. You know, years ago, we had a pet donkey. Although we gave him good food, and were prepared to love him just as we loved all of our other animals, we failed to make him happy. I think he was bored. He quickly became 'mean', and within one week, we learned to fear him. He seemed to mistake our kindness for weakness, but we can never be sure."

"Tell me all about it. Then I'll tell you what I think – from an animal's point of view," said Gold importantly as he shuffled his paws, sank down upon them, and flattened his ears.

"Yes, Gold, perhaps YOU may be able to figure it out;

otherwise, it will remain a mystery, most likely. It all began one December morning, here in Riyadh. The Western community was small then, and it was possible to get to know almost everyone. On special days, it was the custom to gather friends together for a breakfast, luncheon or dinner, because many were sad to be so far away from their families.

"On this day, John and I planned to entertain in the evening. We had invited only a few lonely businessmen whose wives were not living in Saudi Arabia. But, shortly after breakfast, we were surprised when the gate bell began to ring – and it rang again and again, until our villa was filled with friends. Apparently, quite by coincidence, various groups had said: 'Let's go and see the Blake's.' They guessed that we would remain at home because Christopher was still very young.

"In no time at all, every corner of the villa was taken up by this spontaneous party. We had two enormous dogs then, elegant Borzois, called Ivan and Anastasia – and we had Mamapuss who was still a kitten. The animals were weaving in and out amongst our guests, and being thoroughly spoiled with caresses and titbits.

"Ivan and Anastasia were amongst the most handsome of couples in the room, and Mamapuss looked very pretty, too. She never did enjoy being picked up, but she always loved a party; perhaps because her feline curiosity could have 'full rein'. She has been known to exhaust herself by staying up too late at evening gatherings – remaining until the last person has left. On this occasion, she padded the perimeter of the room, using the backs of chairs and the sofa, and she peered into every dish, cup and ashtray.

"At the height of the frivolity, there was a cry: 'Quickly, John and Susan, go to the gate! Go and see what Omar has brought you!' Everyone, including the dogs pressed forward to the porch and balcony while John and I descended to greet Omar. He led in the tiniest and prettiest grey donkey I had ever seen, bedecked with glittering tinsel and a Swiss cow bell around the neck – and there was a red Egyptian fez on its head.

"We were thrilled with our gift. Omar had been very kind to us ever since our arrival in Arabia – always thinking of ways to help and please us. He knew that we loved animals, and had been with us several times when I had stopped to pat donkeys. Alas, in the days that followed, we had plenty of reason to doubt our good fortune.

"Our baby donkey circled the villa, all through the night, noisily trotting at a steady pace on the concrete path rather than on the grass. The echoing 'clop, clop', that rang in our ears, never seemed to stop. And, this noise was interspersed with his bray which came all too regularly. Each time, we imagined that he was waiting for us to drop off to sleep. He began with a kind of loud wheezing sound, building up to a noise similar to that which humans make before sneezing; 'Aaa ha, aaa ha', and it finished off with the loudest 'hee-haw'."

I was a bit put out by the memory but Gold was rocking with laughter. I chose to ignore his reaction and continued:

"Christopher was never a problem in the night and slept through it all. We could not. Hollow-eyed, after several nights of broken sleep, we tried to think of a way to cope with our donkey's nocturnal wandering. We tied him up, but he objected to that. We had already made him a nice shelter on the shady side of the villa, but he preferred our front porch, at the top of the fifteen slippery marble steps. I think he may have been happy if we had given him a place in our bed."

Gold suddenly stopped laughing and looked thoughtful.

"Then our baby donkey began to attack us, and we were soon cast into a state of seige. Fortunately, there were no pet rabbits to get kicked to death, and Mamapuss was nimble enough to leap to safety. Our fleet Borzois were wise and kept well out of his path. They were as quick as lightning and skipped out of the way whenever he headed in their direction.

"Seeking us, for whatever was on his mind, our little grey beauty would clatter up the steep steps to the porch. Once there, he would reverse to assault the iron panels at the bottom of the large glass entrance doors. The battering echoed like thunder inside the house. The little grey donkey would kick again and again, rattling the doors until our heads ached, and we thought that the glass must surely shatter."

Gold was now frowning and I wondered what he was thinking. I continued:

"We discovered that if we attempted to go out into the garden, our tormentor would rush towards us. Turning spritely, he would kick out with his rear hooves. This worried us considerably because Christopher was not yet two years old, and he could have been killed by one blow. To leave the villa, we had to escape by a side door, making a dash for the side gate. We had to move quickly. Those pretty grey ears pricked up at the slightest sound, and our little donkey would speed to attack. In terror, we would either dash back into the house or quickly pull the outside gate shut behind us – depending on how far we had gone down the path before he spotted us. If we had not been so frightened, it would have been amusing.

"Our decision to admit failure and part with our gift, came after the visit of Rowena, a neighbour's governess who brought her little charge, Heather. On this occasion, the donkey seemed to come from nowhere. He dashed towards them, reversing quickly in preparation for 'the kill'. Being a dedicated protector, Rowena enveloped Heather in her arms, and dived into the hedge. We heard the commotion, and saw it all from the balcony above. We began to laugh despite the danger – and the obvious discomfort of the victims who had fallen out of the hedge on the other side. After all, they were safe for the moment. In the chaos that followed, we lured the little terror away and came to the rescue of our guests.

"John finally paid to have our donkey removed and housed until a new owner could be found. It was an expensive lesson about ill-considered pets. You see, admiring an animal is an

"Let's go
for a walk"

Can you find the donkey?

"A working life is not so bad"

108

Mother goat cleaning up
the new baby

A sheep takes
a sneaky nap

insufficient reason to adopt it as a pet. The decision to have one, must take into account the size and nature of the animal, and the place where it can be kept. We did not know a thing about the care and training of a donkey, so our grey baby's behaviour had come as a complete surprise. Choosing a pet is a serious commitment that should be undertaken for the lifespan of the animal."

Gold had been listening intently, and now sat straight up, as did his ears. "Well, I have an opinion alright: there are nice people and there are awful people – and there are all kinds in between. It is the same with animals. I know you don't like to hurt them, Susan, but I think he was perfectly rotten to you, and you should have given him a good clout."

Perhaps Gold was right. But, really, I believe this donkey missed its companions, and we were too inexperienced to train it and solve the problem.

Our story over, our minds turned to mealtime.

"Well, Gold, it looks as though there will be no 'grins' for you today. Hussein could not find any lettuce or carrot tops in the SOUQ, so I shall cut up some apples for you. Askalu gave you the last of the carrots yesterday, but she is bringing some sunflower seeds when she returns tonight. For now, I'll tear off a few sunflower branches and nice young leafy eucalyptus twigs."

The rabbits loved these as a treat, especially the huge flowers. They would eat the petals eagerly, and then devour the leaves. Finally, even the thickest and toughest stalk would disappear. Gold hopped along beside me towards the garden in eager anticipation. Nigel was sitting on the diving board as usual, and the other rabbits were scattered about resting – until they saw where we were going.

Suddenly, we were surrounded by them. I began dropping leaves and twigs at my feet, Gold almost hidden from view as the rabbits jostled for position and craned towards the newest pieces. You would think that they had never been fed before, I mused. It was obvious that Gold's interest in stories had vanished for now, so I stepped out of the turbulent sea of fur and walked quietly away, with Samantha plodding along behind me. No doubt, Mamapuss would be waiting for us in the kitchen, as it was her mealtime, too.

II
The Baboon

One troubled morning, when Gold and Ginger had ceased squabbling at last, I went out to the terrace to speak to Gold. It looked as though Ginger was still the 'Chief Buck' because he was moving confidently among the rabbits. Poor Gold meanwhile, had retreated to a far corner, and just sat there brooding. I went over and tried to cheer him up.

"Hello, there, Gold. You may not be the Chief Buck, but you are a very special rabbit, you know. I must say, it is a privilege to know you."

"Oh, Susan, you are just trying to cheer me up. Ginger thinks I'm jealous of him, and I'm not. I was just enjoying a game with the youngsters and the does. I know Ginger is the strongest – and the most handsome. He has nothing to fear from me. It's so unjust."

"Believe me, Gold, you are very VERY special, and you are attractive too – and, furthermore, one day, it will be your turn to be the Chief. I believe Ginger is just jealous of your popularity; and, I agree with you, there are better things to do than quarrel. I'm glad you are popular in the warren – and I am more than delighted that I can have a conversation with you. That makes you very special indeed. We love you very much, Gold, and you have become even more precious to us, since we have been able to share your thoughts. They show us that you are very interesting and kind."

Perhaps I had gone too far. I seemed to be embarassing Gold – although he was clearly pleased. He puffed out, shuffled his paws and huffed a bit. As he shyly lowered his odd-coloured eyes and looked away, the light shone through the little hole in his right ear. It was time to change the subject.

"I heard that Christopher read you Jungle Book again, Gold. I know you like hearing about jungle creatures, so I thought, perhaps, you might like to hear about one of Arabia's wilder animals."

"Really, Susan? You mean there are bears and tigers in Arabia?"

"Well, no, Gold. There are no elephants either, but there is a baboon, and that is a medium-sized monkey. It is called baboon in Arabic, too. They are often found in deserts and savannas, or wide, treeless plains. 'Monkey' is the popular word often used for the lower primates such as baboons, marmosets, lemurs, treeshrews, bush babies and monkeys.

"Primates are mammals with a comparatively large and well-developed brain, so they are intelligent. They are also very vocal and have grasping hands with nails instead of claws. Their eyesight and sense of smell are well-developed too. All monkeys and the upper primates, such as gibbons, chimpanzees, orang-utans, gorillas, apes and humans are similar.

"The Arabian baboon, named *Papio hamadryas*, can be recognized by its dog-like snout, prominent cheeks and sloping back. The brows overhang to shade small, closely set eyes. It is a hairy creature with a bare face – and the adults have colourful bare patches on their buttocks. Males are nearly twice the size of females, and have a heavy mane of long hair around the neck – and their facial skin is a blend of light grey and pink. The coat is grey, while the bare skin on the buttocks can be a brilliant red to deep pink. The facial skin of the female is darker than that of the male, the female's buttocks less brightly-coloured except when she is in her breeding season. Then the colour maybe even brighter than the males. The long, straight tails, with a tuft on the end are held up high when walking or running. The hair of an adult baboon is a greyish brown with light overtones, but an infant has black hair until it is about six months old.

"Baboons are the creatures that seem to have the most fun in Arabia; when they are not resting, they are marching, running, tumbling, jumping, leaping, climbing and swinging."

"Climbing trees?" enquired Gold.

"No, Gold, unlike many other monkeys, Arabian baboons are seldom seen climbing trees. This seems to be a result of there being few suitable trees. You know, it is strange: although they have a good time, they never appear to be happy. In fact, the male seems grumpy most of the time, sometimes roaring or barking. Of course, the males – and especially the 'alpha' or lead males, are constantly pre-occupied with protecting their rank and females. Baboons have long sharp teeth, so humans must be very careful if they are close by. Fortunately, this creature is wary of man and cleverly avoids contact if possible.

"Baboons are omnivorous creatures which means they eat

both meat and vegetable material. The Arabian hamadryas has to be nomadic because of its constant search for food and water. When leaves, blossoms, fruit, grass and herbs are absent, nourishment often comes in the form of dung beetle larvae that live in cattle droppings. Baboons also eat butterflies, beetles and lizards. Abandoned Bedouin camp sites are one place to forage for the remains of human food, so they move from one site to another. They also like to congregate around city dumps where there is a wide variety to be found; and they visit water holes. At feeding time, the adult males dominate the best patches.

"Many that have access to town garbage, become fat and overfed as a result. The females gather what they can. Juveniles eat whatever is available on the edge of the feeding group, and usually content themselves with a more natural diet of greenery."

"Did you ever see a baboon, Susan?"

"I certainly did, Gold, and it was a memorable event at the brink of a mountain cliff in the south-west of Saudi Arabia. I was astonished to find myself quite close to a group of baboons who were eating from a large metal rubbish container. I managed to take only one photograph before retreating to safety. You see, baboons have been known to attack if they are surprised or irritated. Fortunately, this lot soon ran off in the opposite direction. They disappeared into the woods, their pink bottoms bouncing and their long tails flying, as they leapt and scampered over boulders and across the carpet of spring greenery. The band were swallowed up by the swirling mist which threaded through the beautiful landscape, rich with herbs, shrubs, and bushes set amongst tamarisk, juniper and acacia trees. I soon learnt that they had not scampered away because of me, for another troop of baboons bounded up the rocky cliff-face, swinging themselves over the iron guard-railing to get to the rubbish bin. They had come up from the depths of the mysterious wild gorge far below, from where a mighty wind heaved up spray that showered me every now and again. I felt like an intruder in this untamed Arabian 'Eden'.

"In such wild places, baboons find water in the deep gorges. They have been known to dig in dry wadis for water, too – and for roots."

"That woodland sounds marvellous, Susan. I had no idea that Arabia had such a place. Wouldn't you think the baboon would put on a 'smile face', just because he can live there?"

"The baboons don't live there, Gold. They just visit the area to scavenge. Usually baboons live in bleak places which are inaccessible to humans, such as rugged mountainsides that are sometimes vertical. They find suitable and safe lairs there. Baboons inhabit the mountainous regions of the west and south-west. Only now and again have they been sighted in open rocky country further inland or on the Red Sea coastal plain.

"It is interesting that the Arabian baboon is the same species as the Ethiopian one in North Africa. The origin of these hamadryas baboons is obscure, and how they became distributed is uncertain. They appear to have been separated at some time, not too long ago. As they do not exist in the other mountain ranges of Arabia, it is unlikely that these creatures are Arabian in origin. And, their behaviour is so very similar to that of the Ethiopian species, it is probable they came from Africa on trading ships in olden times – perhaps brought across the Red Sea by the Ancient Egyptians. That would be time enough, it is thought, for their behaviour patterns to change somewhat. It is a fascinating clue, that the hamadryas baboon was sacred in Ancient Egypt, and mummified upon its death. It is also known that the Egyptians imported these animals from the land of Punt. The mystery remains unsolved because it is not known for certain if Punt was on the southern Red Sea coast of Africa or Arabia.

"The Arabian populations of hamadryas baboons appear to have more female members than in Ethiopia. And, the Arabian males have been found to be more tolerant amongst themselves. There is also a tendency for the females not to antagonize each other so much as those in Ethiopia. This suggests that there is less competition between females when it comes time to mate and form family units. In Ethiopia, with fewer females, the males must compete for them."

"Do they have families like humans or like rabbits?"

"Baboons have complicated social ways, Gold, but their system is somewhat similar to that of rabbits: Their smallest units are families, usually consisting of only one adult male, and several adult females. However, the hamadryas females usually remain faithful to the male, mainly because he punishes them if they go astray. A few families like this usually join together to form a clan. When several clans group together, they become a band of about 40 to 100 baboons. Quite often, several bands will tolerate each other sufficiently to pass a night on the same cliff face. Such a gathering is called a troop."

"How long do they live?" queried Gold.

"The average lifespan of the hamadryas is forty years, Gold. The females give birth to a single baby and sometimes two at anytime during the year, after a gestation period of about six months. A baby clings to the hair of its mother's chest soon after birth, allowing her to travel with her family when it is time to move. The young baboon is referred to as a 'juvenile' until it is four to five years old. Juvenile and young adult females often move about freely between families and eligible young males, until they are about three years old.

"When the time comes for a young male to form his own family unit, he shows an interest in a juvenile female. Gradually, he lures her out of her mother's unit, and they begin to build up a relationship. Firstly, he must teach her to follow him, and sometimes he might bite her to help the lesson along. One young male was seen to use 'cave-man' tactics, and hold his chosen female by the tail for hours, sometimes pulling her along. The initial step towards a full

Baboon

family has been taken when the female has begun to groom the male and to follow him willingly.

"According to scientific studies, it seems that Arabian baboons are less fussy than their Ethiopian counterparts when selecting safe sleeping places. This is believed to be because there are fewer predators in Arabia. Occasionally, the baboons have been sighted roosting in easily accesible hill slopes, indicating that they have no great fear of being attacked. The troops vary in number each night, but the small family units and clans remain the same. They need have little fear of their natural predators: the wolf, the leopard and the striped hyena, because these animals are not plentiful in Arabia today. Disease is the other constant enemy of the baboon, although the Arabian ones do appear to be in fairly good condition."

"It must be nice for the families to keep together, especially for the youngsters, Susan."

"Yes, Gold, the juveniles appear to enjoy life, despite a fairly strict code of behaviour. Observation has shown that although a clan might move from place to place together, they usually keep a certain distance between each family – and the male often takes especial care to stay between his family and humans.

"In cold weather, baboons cuddle up and move very little; and, in bad weather, they come out only to eat. At night,

families shelter together from the cold wind, mostly hiding in shallow rock caves and in hollows between and under boulders. Normally, early in the morning, they abandon their sleeping caves and ledges to go foraging in various directions. They depart in almost military order, forming a dense column which eventually divides.

"Clans frequently split up into very small foraging parties, and a single male unit may go off by itself. They might even divide at the sleeping lair, or shortly after leaving it. When males disagree about the direction taken, they usually just part company; but, sometimes, a leader looks back at the departing group, and turns to follow them, apparently seeing some wisdom in the choice. Generally, a large male brings up the rear as protection. A common travelling column consists of about fifteen baboons, sometimes covering several kilometres to find food, taking their rest when the leader decides. At night, the parties assemble again at the sleeping cliffs."

"I wonder if baboons communicate with each other like other animals," said Gold thoughtfully.

"Quite a bit of research has been done on primate communication, Gold. People who have spent a lot of time watching them, have come to recognize their moods and a kind of language. A raised brow and a jumping lunge is a way of threatening, while lip-smacking is a friendly gesture. They sniff each other's mouths, too. Perhaps this is a cautious way

of finding out the other's intentions. A gentle tap or a prod is known to be an invitation to groom. Grooming is a social activity, and appears to be a way of expressing feelings for each other. It is practical, too, helping to rid their coats of ticks and fleas."

"It would be fun to watch them," said Gold, as he wiggled with enjoyment and settled down again.

"All monkeys are interesting, and often they are entertaining to watch, and none are more so than the Arabian baboon. Unfortunately, it is difficult to do. They are hard to discover because their size and colour merge perfectly with the greyish, boulder-strewn terrain. And, of course, it is dangerous to get too close. Nevertheless, people have managed to listen to their noise-making which is called 'vocalizing'. The bark is a warning, and possibly a good method of communication between separated parties. Baboons also cackle and squeal in different ways for different purposes. Then, there are several well-known facial expressions which communicate intention. For example, it is aggressive to pump up the cheeks or gape with bared teeth. In preparation for a fight, they may fence with the jaws before grabbing and biting. Such an argument can develop into a full teeth-to-teeth battle, which females have been known to interrupt by grooming their mate. This gives her an opportunity to plead with him and discourage further fighting."

"I'd say she would be taking a chance of getting bashed herself," Gold announced, somewhat indignantly. "Women ought to keep out of such things," he added, with prejudice. It seemed a buck rabbit had strong views about such matters.

"You may be right, Gold, but sometimes the females fight: when Arabian baboons move about in an almost military order, it is amusing to see female after female in single file, obediently following a male. You will see the male looking back every now and again to check on his family. He may have to stop his females squabbling sometimes, although he will often allow them to have a good fight before intervening. Sometimes a male chases off one female to break up a fight. Both females might then come to groom him as a sort of apology. Mostly, however, females are tolerant and friendly, and they will even groom one another and fondle each other's infants. Just sometimes, squabbles arise over food or males.

"It seems that the females mostly follow the male by choice. But, just occasionally, a female does stray. Her mate might bite the back of her neck as punishment, making her scream. This rarely happens though, and usually, slapping the ground threateningly or raising eyebrows at her will be sufficient.

"Juveniles and young adults often have slow and gentle playfights. When angry adult males compete over a female, one might simply chase off his adversary. But, sometimes, serious contact fighting develops into a full and fearful fight where the combatants leave each other with dreadful gashes that disable them permanently. Baboons can be fierce.

"Baboons can be peaceful, too. They take long rest periods, dozing, scratching and grooming. The mothers take very good care of their babies, and the clans watch out for both the mothers and their children.

"Babies are popular, so it is not unusual for adult baboons (other than the parents) to give them a hug. Although the young ones quarrel sometimes, they play often. The juveniles can be amusing when they play together, exuberantly leaping and tumbling. The adult males occasionally become short-tempered with their antics, if they come too close, and they might reprimand them gruffly."

"They sound very much like rabbits, don't they, Susan?"

"They may behave in a similar way, Gold, but baboons are not as cuddly as rabbits!" I said as I scooped up his wriggling body to give him a thorough cuddle."

12
Ruminants

Spring had arrived, and it was once again the mating season for our rabbits. Now that their neutral winter season was over, we could expect fewer calm periods between their activities. We had grown accustomed to seeing cozy knots of lazing lagomorphs. Now, instead, there were pairs, groups, or a single rabbit at each of the far corners of the garden. And, there was a lot of frenzied squabbling and pairing off.

Soon, Ginger, the 'Chief Buck', would have to re-establish his quiet, well-ordered society. He would sort out his subjects in order of importance. They needed to be shown the limits of their power and individual territory. In this way, serious fighting might be eliminated, and aggressive displays less frequent. Except in the case of humans, nature has provided animals with a wide variety of ruses, strategies and inter-actions as ways to resolve conflicts. This reduces bloodshed. Bad injuries are kept to a minimum, and thus animals have a system with a total, or near absence of loss of life.

As a senior citizen and privileged buck, Gold had been chasing Rupert to 'put him in his place'. Rupert was one of the younger rabbits, and Gold had already chased him around the swimming pool several times this morning. Obviously, the youngster had been paying too much attention to Harvette. Our precious Gold had made his point-of-view quite clear, by delivering a good nip to Rupert's bottom. I had just watched him chase Rupert again, almost twice around the pool. He broke away now to finish by flopping down next to me on the terrace.

"Goodness, Gold, you can run fast – and you took those corners rather well. Though, on the second circuit, I felt sure you would either crash into the wall or fall in the water."

"Whew! I know what you mean, Susan. I'm not as young as I used to be. But, I can still show THAT young whippersnapper I'm not too old to teach him a lesson he'll remember."

"They do say rabbits are very fast over a short distance. But, to escape a fast predator in the wild, I've heard, they must resort to a zig-zagged path. I bet, if you ran in a straight line as fast as you did just then – and if you were the size of an antelope – you could run as fast as it does. I am most impressed with your speed, Gold."

"Thank you," Gold said, looking quite pleased with my praise. And, taking advantage of the situation, he asked: "Can you tell me a story, Susan – while I catch my breath? Perhaps you could tell me about those 'anty' things."

"Antelopes. Why not? Are you quite comfortable now, Gold? Good.

"Antelopes are most interesting animals. They are ruminants which I talked about in our camel story. For a time, they can store food in a special first stomach, or rumen. This allows them to feed quickly, and later on – by regurgitating it back into the mouth – they can chew it more thoroughly a second time. This is called ruminating or 'chewing the cud'.

"All cattle are ruminants, and so are sheep and goats. They belong to the family Bovidae. Perhaps I shall tell you about the ibex and tahr, too. All of these animals are quadrupeds, or four-footed animals, and their four legs have divided hooves known as 'cloven' feet, so they are ungulates, too.

"But let's begin with gazelles, a small to medium-sized antelope. The common name for a gazelle, in Arabic, is GHAZALA, or ZBI. It is one of Arabia's larger herbivorous mammals. It is one of several 'look-alike', swift, long-legged, horned animals that live in Arabia. And all have been threatened with extinction. Sadly, the gazelle has almost become extinct in the wild. It is a slender creature that is mentioned frequently in Arabic poetry, sometimes used as a symbol for women; perhaps because the running motion of the gazelle is so graceful. Maybe it is because the gazelle has large, exquisitely expressive eyes that are quite bewitching. Its beautiful, serene face does suggest a gentle and feminine nature; but it must be kept in mind that the gazelle's exquisite looks can be deceiving. The horns are sharp, and it knows how to use them – so, BEWARE!

"There are several species of gazelle, and at least three kinds inhabit Arabia. One is the Arabian or mountain gazelle (called IDMI in Arabic). It has almost straight, ringed horns which slope backwards. It is also recognizable by distinct facial markings and a flank stripe. Otherwise, it is a dark reddish-brown. The IDMI is mostly seen in the west and south-west, sharing its habitat with another gazelle, known as AFRI in Arabic. It is the rarest, having long straight horns but larger

ears than the IDMI – despite having a smaller body and shorter legs.

"The third, the RHEEM, has horns shaped like the musical instrument, the lyre. They are wide apart at the base near the head, with the tips hooked forward and slightly inward. Most female ungulates have shorter horns than the males, and this is so with the gazelle – in fact, they are finer, and sometimes absent. The calves are born without horns, but they grow quickly within the first year. The hooves of these creatures are pointed and the short tail is tufted. Rheem are the most abundant species, and their habitat was central and northern Arabia. They do not leap and bound as other gazelles do, but run very fast indeed.The females usually give birth to twin kids while the other two species generally have only one.

"The colour of gazelles varies, but mostly, they are a golden brown or greyish-beige with white markings, which blends well with the terrain. Many people keep them as decorative pets in their private gardens, but their true habitats are mountains and foothills and sometimes the plains and dunes, where they gather together naturally. Once upon a time, many gazelles grazed on the open plains of northern Arabia. They also followed the green valleys in the south-west, as well as wandering in arid parts of the central region.

"Gazelles were hunted for food and sport, so their numbers are now greatly reduced. The skin is fine, and it was once made into garments and covers for camel carriages.

"In bygone days, gazelle hunting was an annual ritual, requiring strength, courage and endurance.

"The nomads prepared for the hunt well in advance through the changing seasons. In spring, when the weather was cool, tribal women had a chance to sew gazelle skin and textiles. They had the time, too, to take walks and enjoy the desert, while the menfolk tended their camels and horses and practised riding skills. After summer, tribesmen revitalized themselves on fresh homemade milk products and dates, preparing for the strenuous activity of hunting the gazelle. They would often hunt on horseback to tire their swift prey. A rider sometimes carried his saluki hunting dog, and released it to catch the gazelle when it was tired.

"When wheeled vehicles and modern weapons were introduced, life was much easier, but sadly this brought some Arabian animals to near extinction. So it was with the gazelle, until they became protected. Today, these beautiful creatures are breeding successfully on an open range, sponsored by the Saudi royal family, and in Saudi Arabian zoos.

Arabian Gazelle

"In olden times, tribes had different ways of hunting gazelle. Some had no horses or even a saluki. One such tribe (who were well-known as clever gazelle hunters) worked in pairs. One man wrapped skins around his knees and elbows, and crawled along on his stomach in the direction of the herd. He drove them towards the other man, who was hidden. With this method, it was possible to kill up to twenty gazelle in one day. Other tribes used the SALUKI. The dog would panic the gazelle into jumping a low wall, to fall into a pit that had been dug on the other side. Sometimes gazelle were driven through narrow passes and killed.

"There is a Bedouin tale about the gazelle having dreams of running to its death through narrow openings. And, if a tribesman wished to stop a gazelle in flight, he had only to shout: 'A narrow opening is in front of thee, O gazelle!' AZ-ZEJŽ JÂ RAZÂL! and the gazelle would stop at once and look around.

"It is also written, that if a Bedouin saw a gazelle when he was undertaking an important task, he had only to shout: 'Gazelle, gazelle, let the misfortune vanish as well!' RAZÂL, RAZÂL W-SARREN ZÂL! and afterwards he would become successful.

"The Bedouin are particularly fond of animal stories, just as you are. Here is one simple tale about the gazelle and hare which goes like this: A grazing gazelle happened to startle a sleeping hare. As a result, the gazelle took fright. But, when he came to his senses, he was annoyed. So he shouted after the hare, that it had little value other than to please children. He added that certainly there was not enough meat on his bones to satisfy anyone. The hare – not to be outdone – shouted back: 'Gazelle, you lose your mind whenever you see pasture.'"

Gold's eyes twinkled at these bandied insults.

"The gazelle belongs to the same family as the Arabian oryx, Gold, a traditional trophy of the Arab hunters, the oryx has probably been hunted to extinction in the wild. The flesh was said to be very tasty, with the ability to prevent and cure some illnesses and even render the Bedouin bullet proof. Its

Arabian Oryx

Ivan and Anastasia

Samantha makes
herself comfortable

Camera shy

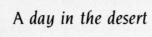
A day in the desert

"At least it is cool"

"I wish it were over"

blood was supposed to be an antidote for snakebite. The hide was once made into water bags and other useful items. The thickish skin at the back of the neck was especially prized and made into gauntlets, worn to protect the hands against sabre wounds in olden times. I am told this patch of skin was like the beast's armour, because that is where a predator took hold.

"The habitat of the oryx was once widespread. In the early part of this century, the few survivors retreated to the inaccessible sands of the vast southern desert.

"Now this creature is protected. But, it remains one of the rarest antelopes. When its timely conservation began, the oryx was initially bred in captivity. By nature, it is said to be unapproachable and wild – and especially dangerous when wounded. In the wild, its only enemy was mankind, as it was well able to defend itself, even against larger animals. Remarkably, it is easily tamed and becomes docile in captivity.

"Conservationists eventually decided to re-establish it in fenced open areas in Saudi Arabia, where it is beginning to multiply successfully. Soon it will be released. Many of these beautiful creatures now live peaceably in the Omani deserts of Southern Arabia, cropping the sparse, straw-like grasses and shrubs that grow there. It has very few animal predators in this tranquil place. Today, the tribesmen (whose people once hunted oryx) stand guard to protect them"

I saw Gold almost bursting to ask me something. "I know what you are going to ask."

He giggled and nodded in answer.

"The Arabian oryx is a middle-sized antelope about the size of a small donkey. It stands a metre (39 inches) high at the shoulders, where there is a slight hump. The backward-sloping spiral-shaped horns are long, fine, sharp and almost straight. They measure about half a metre (20 inches) long." I used my hands to demonstrate. "Like the gazelle, it is graceful and elegant, with beautiful eyes. Its coat is mostly a shining, silvery-white, while black patches decorate the head, nose, neck and under the eyes and chin. The legs are brown. The white tail has a brown wispy end.

"This spectacular colouring serves as an excellent camouflage against pale-coloured sand and the dark shadows cast by outcrops of rock.

"The mythical unicorn of legend is believed to have originated with the oryx, because its pair of horns appear as one when seen in profile. According to mythology, the one-horned unicorn once triumphed over the lion – 'the mightiest of animals'. Today, it is said that the oryx is truly a 'unicorn' because it has overcome the threat of extinction.

"It is said that a huntsman wearing white can get very close, especially if he advances against the wind, behind a white horse or camel.

"The Bedouin call the oryx, BAKAR AL-MAHA or BAKAR AL WAHAS or AL-WADAHI. They say it will not stop running for a whole day if it is badly frightened – perhaps because this

creature has poor eyesight. Yet the oryx will stand and fight with its horns if neccessary.

"Old reports show that this creature grazed openly during the day; but it sometimes pastured only at night, perhaps to avoid the heat, and because desert plants contain more moisture at night. It is supposed to be fond of sheltering in the deep tunnel-shaped natural pits, found in the sandy deserts, or on the shady side of dunes.

"Oryx herds are nomadic and once wandered the sandy regions of the Arabian Peninsula, roaming the northern Nafud, the central Dahna and the southern Rub al Khali deserts. Dunes are its natural habitat, its feet large and specially adapted for walking on sand. The oryx uses the front feet to scrape a cool spot to lie down, and to dig for edible roots. It will also eat grass, trees, shrubs and desert gourds, licking the morning dew off leaves. It can exist without water if there is sufficient plant life to provide moisture. Yet, the oryx apparently has a remarkable ability to find water, and it has been known to travel hundreds of miles just to reach it. It is quite astonishing that any animal survives in a land that is largely arid, considering the basic needs of shelter from heat and cold, and adequate regular food and water.

"Belying its shy, and perhaps sensitive appearance, the oryx is said to be one of the toughest species on earth with the ability to survive in extreme temperatures in forbidding terrain."

"There was once another beautiful Arabian antelope, known as the Lesser Kudu. In Arabic, it was called WAOUL. It was not so lucky as the oryx, and would seem to have been extinct for about 20 years. All that appears to be left are its thick, wide-spiralling horns that have been kept as hunter's trophies. Of course, it is just possible that the Lesser Kudu still exists in remote western mountains, far from civilization. It was always a rare animal and very timid. Proof exists that it once shared terrain with the moutain gazelle. Its natural habitat was the mountainous areas of the Arabian Peninsula, but to some extent this antelope also roamed desert dunes, wadis and plains, moving in small, widely-scattered groups."

"That is all very worrying, Susan. I hope they will be saved from extinction. It is good that no one will hurt them any more because they are protected."

"It is now possible to save them, Gold. Would you like to hear about some other Arabian ruminants? One is a mystery animal!"

"Yes, please, Susan, if you have time."

"We have just enough time before tea, to tell you about several ruminants that are each very special in their way.

"Let's begin with the mystery animal. I believe, Gold, that it may be a wild goat. The Bedouin describe it as being about the size of a young lamb, with the top of the head resembling that of a human. It was reported to be a herbivorous creature that they once hunted, called SEJD AT-TAS'A. Its habitat was the western border of the northern desert, where lava flows cooled millions of years ago, and became blackish rock, gravel and

Tahr

Ibex

sand. This small mystery mammal is said to have been grey or brownish-grey in colour, so as to be well-camouflaged. Because it was sighted at the edges of the desert, it is likely that it needed regular water. Western people have also spoken of its existence, and the description given of all sightings indicate that it was probably a goat. It had a beard, giving it an 'old man' look, which was perhaps why the Bedouins say the face appeared 'human'.

"The ibex is another wild goat. It is said that the ibex was the symbol of a moon god on the Arabian Peninsula in pre-Islamic times.

"The name of the ibex in Arabic is BEDEN or WA'AL. There is evidence that a similar goat existed on the Arabian Peninsula a very long time ago. Ancient pictographs, or rock pictures show that it lived alongside other creatures that are now extinct, such as the wild ox and ostrich.

"The ibex has rather large pointed ears, and the male has a black beard. The coat is coarse, and light-brown in colour on the back, and even lighter underneath. The large and powerful scimitar-like horns can be dangerous. A scimitar is a broad, curved dagger, and the ibex can use its horns just like this weapon (which is correctly wielded in an upsweeping motion). The female protects her young with them.

"Not so very long ago, the habitat of the ibex was widespread. But now, this creature appears to have retreated into the volcanic rocky recesses and mountains of western Arabia. It is especially scarce because it too, was hunted. Pictographs show that men hunted these goats with bows and arrows, spears and daggers.

"The ibex seldom descends from its secret mountain places to the plains. It knows that wild dogs can overtake and attack it on level ground. Perhaps it remains aloof because it has weak eyesight like the oryx. It must rely upon keen hearing and a good sense of smell to avoid predators.

"In the last century, some Arabian hunters tracked the fresh spoor that the ibex left as it went to pasture at night. A group of between five and ten men would then follow the animal into the mountains. They would crouch in a rocky hideaway and wait for it to pass – one man taking up a position on the ridge of the mountain, the rest stopping at fixed intervals down the slope. During the day, they would search likely places where the goat might rest, not giving up until it was found and killed."

"I suppose they would eat the ibex."

"Yes, Gold. They needed the food so their families could survive. That's not the same as hunting for sport and killing more animals than is necessary.

"In the south there is another species of wild goat called the Arabian tahr, and it is almost extinct. The timid tahr is rarely seen, but it is known to inhabit the inaccessible steep and rocky heights and gullies of the mountains in Northern Oman. In this habitat, the goats survive very well on a rich variety of plant life and fruit. They require water daily, and drink from mountain streams. The tahr possibly owes its survival to an ability to go where humans cannot follow. Its chief enemy was the leopard, but this is another creature that is rare in Arabia today.

"The tahr is known to have originated in the Oriental lands east of the Arabian Peninsula. It came to Arabia many thousands of years ago, from southern Persia (now Iran) across a land bridge that once existed between these two countries.

"It is a smallish-sized goat with horns and ears that are similar to the ibex. But, unlike the ibex, its coat is shaggy, and lightish-brown to pale beige, with blackish-brown markings and tail.

"Goats are attractive creatures and they can make nice pets, providing they are fenced off. Most ruminants will destroy a garden, and goats eat almost everything.

"Herds and flocks of domesticated ruminants are known as livestock. In the past, many such animals had to make do with poor vegetation for most of the year. Yet, the females retained the incredible ability to produce rich milk. I have often thought it marvellous that however parched the desert becomes, the animals mostly avoid eating the poisonous plants."

"Perhaps those plants don't taste nice, Susan."

"I'm sure they do not taste as nice as lettuce, Gold, but hungry desert animals do eat some bitter-tasting plants. Sometimes they make mistakes. I recall a tragedy in our household when an animal ate poisonous leaves from our garden."

"Ooo! What happened, Susan?"

"It all began because we could not resist buying a baby goat in the SOUQ. The young of a goat is called a 'kid'. We suddenly decided to have the little kid for our garden, especially as Christopher was small. They could play together, we thought.

"It seemed a delightful idea. We used Christopher's discarded baby bottles to feed the little goat at first, because it had been taken from its mother too soon, and was not weaned, or accustomed to food other than its mother's milk. It drank hungrily for two days, and was very lively, but then it collapsed. I felt awful, and imagined I had been responsible in some way. Kids were normally sold in the SOUQ, as meat for the dinner table, and perhaps I should not have interfered. Maybe, the milk we gave it had not been rich enough.

"The only thing I could think to do was to search for the little Bedouin girl who drove her flocks of sheep and goats past our villa twice a day. So, John and I drove around the streets searching for her.

"At least, she would have a goat in milk, and surely she could save our kid. But, we could not find her. In desperation, we drove to her tent which appeared to be deserted. Nevertheless, I carried my little goat into the encampment, hoping to find someone there. Inside, in the silence of the big, dimly-lit tent, I saw no one. Then, in the far recesses something moved. It turned out to be an old Bedouin woman who had been resting beneath her covers.

"I pleaded for her to look at my kid. She said, with finality, MOAT! which means 'dead'. But, I would not give up. MISH MOAT! I argued. All I need is goat's milk. Where is the girl? Where is the flock? Please help me." The old lady waved her arm in one direction, but assured me my little goat was quite dead, and I could throw it away. We thanked her and dashed off in the direction she had indicated.

"We finally found the young shepherdess and she agreed to help. Grabbing a female goat by a hind leg, she dragged it into the shade. Then she squirted some milk down the kid's throat but it could not swallow. It was too late and the poor little thing died in my arms. We were very sad. The Bedouin girl did not seem at all disturbed. She told me to throw the body away. It was useless. Although her family raised sheep and goats for milk and meat, an animal must be slaughtered according to Islamic tradition, if it is for the table. No animal that dies in any other way can be eaten, which of course is very wise. We would not have eaten our pet, in any case. We gave our pretty little kid a nice resting place in the sandy soil nearby.

"Later, a zoologist visited our garden, and explained that the kid had probably eaten oleander leaves which are poisonous. We had many of these leafy green shrubs which bloom with spectacular pink flowers. Apparently, our kid had been too young to know that it meant death to eat them. Animals have many natural instincts, but much of what they know is learnt in their early days at their mother's side.

"The zoologist laughed to hear that we had thought Carnation milk might not be good enough. Teasing us, he said: a goat's digestive system is most efficient indeed, and a female goat can convert a cardboard carton into rich milk. I know you hate milk, Gold, but this nutritious beverage has been as good as treasure for the human race. Flocks and herds have been kept for thousands of years for their milk and it was just as important as meat.

"Sheep are believed to have been the first domesticated ruminants. Humans kept sheep about twelve thousand years ago, before they kept goats, and long before they had cattle. Once, wild oxen roamed Arabia, but they are now extinct. Perhaps oxen were herded, but they would have been more difficult to bring under control. There are said to be wild sheep still roaming parts of the Arabian Peninsula, and many have remarkable horns that curve into a circle. But, maybe they are feral sheep, having returned to the wild.

"And, now, Gold, it is time for tea. Oh, and it looks as though it is time for Samantha to be fed. Did you notice how she just got up and ran inside, and, there goes Mamapuss. They know it is teatime, I believe they may hear when Askalu clinks their food bowls. It will be your turn next. She will soon be here with your tray. But let me give you fresh water."

"Thank you, Susan, and thank you for the story. What animals will you tell me about next?"

"Perhaps you would like to hear about some smaller creatures. I don't mind. You may choose, my precious Gold."

13 Dogs

"Oh, do look at Samantha, Gold. Isn't she marvellous when she looks like that? Samantha is never more charming than when she puts on that shy and coquettish look. She always does it after her bath – when John is flattering her."

"It's because she feels so good, Susan. Bathing makes her cool and comfortable."

"I know, Gold, but Samantha also likes to be pampered and flattered.

"She behaves that way, too, after a 'hurt', when we are consoling her, or when we are apologizing for taking her photograph. She is very self-conscious, and especially 'camera shy'."

"I think she is a bit soppy. But, I know nothing about dogs, Susan – only Samantha," said Gold thoughtfully. "What is a dog exactly? Where do they come from?"

"Dogs! They are of the animal family Canidae, often referred to as 'canines'. They are mostly long-legged good runners, with large ears, a long muzzle and a bushy tail. But, there are many kinds. No one can agree on the exact ancestry of the domestic dog, although it is usually said to be descended from the wolf. You will remember, Gold, I told you about the wolf and fox – relatives of the domestic dog. It is believed that the canine family descended from a carnivore which evolved at the same time as the cat and bear. These early creatures developed separated toes in an Age that commenced about 40 million years ago, lasting 15 million years.

"Some researchers believe that the dog was the first carnivorous mammal to be fully domesticated, when early humans hunted and gathered food. At that time, dogs would have been camp followers, providing the service of 'cleaners' by scavenging around camp sites. Once tamed, they became sentinels, guarding and protecting. It is likely that the first ones were caught as puppies, and quickly and easily tamed. Humans would have encouraged this animal because it could be of great service, with its superior speed and acute senses of hearing and scenting. For instance, they could assist in hunting, and as a guard – possibly the canine's earliest duty was to act as a watchdog.

"For at least ten thousand years since then, this animal has been mankind's constant companion. And their various uses or functions have led people to breed them to perform better. To be truly domesticated, breeding must be controlled. Thus, humans have been responsible for the many types of dog which vary greatly in appearance, size and temperament. Of course, this can only occur over a long period of time."

"Has the dog always been the favourite of humans?" Gold sounded a tiny bit jealous.

"No. History once gave the dog a BAD image. You see, in the Old World, and especially in the Middle and Near East, many dogs carried the dreaded disease, hydrophobia, commonly called rabies; and the fear of catching this fatal sickness, made people reject canines for thousands of years. It was a paradox. The dog was despised and hounded at the same time that it had a reputation for being faithful, obedient, a loyal friend, a good companion, and a protector.

"Many different races discovered that it could be a good hunter. Ancient Egyptian vases are engraved and painted with the greyhound and dachshund types. Both were valued servants in this way. Today, the dog is said to be the leader of the pet world, and carries the title of 'Man's Best Friend'.

"Many domesticated dogs, returned to the wild, (and known as 'feral'), will hunt in packs, while others are solitary hunters. Scent and speed are important to them when tracking. Some have been known to sustain high speeds for considerable distances, and long pursuits are often an important part of their technique. Alone or in a pack, feral dogs habitually pursue their prey steadily and relentlessly, until the victim is exhausted. Hunting in a pack enables them to bring down animals much larger than themselves.

"There are feral canines roaming the deserts of Arabia. Such a dog is called KALB in Arabic, but British residents usually refer to them as 'pye' dogs. This is an abbreviation for 'pariah', the name given to lowly dogs in India when the British ruled there. In Arabia, the desert dog mostly keeps to its own pack, but sometimes it has interbred with Arabia's fine hunting dog, the saluki, and various domesticated dog breeds. Mostly, these have arrived in recent years. Certain tribal people believe feral dogs have bred with wolves and jackals.

"The desert dogs CAN be lured from the wild and tamed sometimes. The males often have a fierce, shaggy appearance,

and they can be powerfully built with broad heads, similar to the bull terrier. The females are more lightly built. These dogs have been enticed into gardens by people providing food. Some remain and tame well. Others run off to rejoin a pack, which might contain several families and number up to thirty dogs. Such packs once roamed the inner Arabian cities at night, howling and barking as they searched for food and water. A pet desert dog usually answers their call and will run to meet them if it is not shut in. Many never return."

"Is the desert dog like Samantha, Susan?"

"No, Gold. Samantha is a pure bred 'golden' cocker spaniel – a domesticated hunting dog. The common colour of a Central Arabian desert dog is a light beige, generally matching the terrain. Around Taif, where the rocks are grey, it is difficult to spot the feral dogs because they are usually shades of grey and black. In the Empty Quarter, the dogs' colours blend with the red sands. Occasionally, the female (correctly referred to as a bitch) will produce about eight multi-coloured puppies. I saw such a litter that was born in a city rubbish dump. The puppies were perfectly camouflaged, and it was difficult to find them, unless they moved. Once the pups were weaned, this family continued to live there. For weeks, they fed on the carcass of a camel that had been dumped after being accidentally killed by a car.

"If a feral dog is not kept and fed, it leads a difficult life, surviving only by hunting and scavenging. Even if kept by the Bedouin, it is not fed very well, to encourage it to find its own food. Yet, the nomads do pamper the Saluki. Desert dogs often have to be content with scraps. Sometimes there is left-over bread or rice, and occasionally, a kind master might give his dog some dates. None of this is ideal nourishment for a carnivorous animal, of course.

"Once upon a time, the Bedouin kept feral dogs in their camps to serve as watchdogs. It was believed that they would become fierce fighters if the tops of their ears were cut off when young. The ears were cooked and given to the dog to eat. This custom was said to make them bark at night when necessary. I cannot imagine how this would work except to make the animal resentful and aggressive. Then, there is an old Arab proverb: 'Beat the dog and the lion will behave itself.' It could mean that a well-disciplined watchdog will protect its master from wild animals. There were once lions roaming Arabia, you know.

"Desert dogs were trained to prowl around the tents throughout the night, and ward off wolves and unwanted visitors. Guests, who were strangers, had to keep these dogs at bay by a continual motion of a stick. In camp, the dogs usually slept outside the women's apartments. They were never allowed to enter any tent because they were considered 'unclean'. The Saluki on the other hand, was regarded as a 'clean' dog, and was permitted to enter tents and sometimes to sleep there.

"Naturally, a Bedouin did not want a desert dog to breed with his Saluki. To prevent this, when the Saluki bitch was ready to breed, a leather thong would be tied from her collar to her hind legs, thus forcing her to remain seated until the breeding time was over."

"Sounds uncomfortable to me; yet, it might be a good rest if everyone brought her good things to eat." Gold looked at me enquiringly.

"I am sure a kind master would see that his Saluki was comfortable, well-fed and provided with a bowl of water. In a nomadic society, the dog is the sole property of its owner, whereas in a settled community, dogs belong to the village, and everyone makes some effort to provide for them.

"In the wild, the female desert dogs are often the chief sentinels, and they are very clever. When anyone approaches the lair, the mother will leave her young well-hidden, trotting off swiftly, hoping to draw the intruder away. However, the puppies are innocent, and therefore unafraid and friendly. They quickly forget what their mother has told them about staying hidden. So if you want to see them, the trick is to remember where the mother was first sighted. The den is sure to be close to that place.

"Remembering that a desert dog's colour blends with the countryside, spotting one can be very difficult. A thorough search will usually reveal the den. If you are quiet, after a short while, the puppies will come tumbling out to play. Puppies enjoy being petted and they can quickly become tame, giving up their freedom in exchange for loving care and regular food. However, it is not wise to become too fond of them. Time and again, we have seen the call of a roving pack lure an affectionate pet out of the most comfortable home, never to be seen again."

"What ungrateful things," rebuked Gold.

"It is a normal instinct: 'the call of the wild'. You cannot blame them. Even if the pet remains, it will most likely bark a lot. At night it might howl endlessly, if it knows a pack is about and it cannot get out. A feral dog never really belongs to you. Such animals are known to become snappish and irritable with age, too. It is because the re-domestication process takes a very long time, perhaps requiring many generations.

"In the desert, John, Christopher and I once saw the savage side to feral dogs at close range. It is rather frightening. At first, this aggressive kind of behaviour is only a warning, and usually given if the dog is a member of a pack. Alone, these animals can seem well-mannered, and even friendly. The single dog may even wag its tail. In my eagerness to take photographs on this occasion, I remained too close and too long to an exposed litter of puppies. The mother returned and climbed a small hill close by. She set up an incessant snarling and barking that brought responses from her pack. One by one, they mounted small neighbouring hills to bark at me. Bit by bit they moved closer, still barking. Finally, I had to retreat backwards, quickly yet cautiously, to the waiting car where John had the engine running. I have no doubt that the pack would have attacked me if I had remained."

Mother spies an intruder

"Come, follow me!"

A desert dog's nest

The mother calls for the pack

The pack gathers

A young dog's curiosity

The puppies emerge from hiding

"Oh, Susan, wasn't that foolish. I don't think you should have anything to do with this kind of dog."

"But, Gold, I wanted to take photographs. I shall show them to you. Do you know, our first dog in Saudi Arabia was a desert puppy. We called him Mark. Our friend Charles brought the fluffy little fellow the morning of Christopher's first birthday. He placed it in the cot just as our son was waking. Christopher loved Mark instantly, and they shared many happy hours together.

"Charles said the puppy's mother was a creamy-coloured feral dog, and he suspected that the father was a pet German shepherd that lived close by. The puppies had been born about eight weeks earlier, in a small dirt cave, hollowed out by the bitch. She had apparently come to the edge of the city in search of water at the onset of summer. She had stayed on to have her puppies because kind people had put food and water out for her. Thousands of thin and thirsty desert dogs come into the towns and cities each year when summer's cruel heat advances. Yet, even if a bitch is not fortunate enough to get good food and plenty of water, her puppies are always beautiful, plump and fluffy. Unborn pups take their nutrition from the mother, who generally has many litters. This is why the females are usually left thin and old before their time.

"Mark had been the prettiest of his litter, inheriting his father's handsome mane of long hair. He grew large and very strong, and became rough in play. He also tended toward over-excitement. Little Christopher was often injured."

"I don't like these dogs at all!" frowned Gold.

"Mixed breeding can produce a genetically stronger dog, Gold. Although, it did not do so in Mark's case. Within a year he suddenly became very quick-tempered, and he began to snarl at those who had been very kind to him. He started to bark and howl much more. Our houseboy, Abdullah, who had the greatest patience with him, was the first to be cornered and threatened. On this occasion Mark seemed ferocious and crazed. His 'savage' moods became more frequent and they were quite unpredictable. We began to fear Mark, yet we still cared for him.

"Eventually, we gave him to a caring American Colonel who did not have young children."

"There you are, Susan! I knew it was not wise to keep these dogs. Good riddance, I say!" Gold said with finality.

"On another occasion, a man gave us a different kind of dog, and this time, it was a real 'pussycat'."

"Whatever do you mean, Susan?"

"I mean, it was docile and friendly, Gold. It came unexpectedly one very, very hot summer afternoon when we were resting. We were awakened by someone ringing the bell at our front gate. It rang at least twenty times before anyone could answer it. Whoever was out there must have been most anxious to call at this unusual hour, when people were napping after lunch. Irritated, John arose from his favourite couch and padded sleepily to the gate to see who it was.

"Standing in the slender shade of the great decorative archway, he found a plump young Saudi gentleman holding a rope. There appeared to be a very small sheep attached to it, its matted hair hanging to the ground.

"It was almost impossible to tell one end of the animal from the other, except that the rope was attached close to where the tip of a panting pink tongue could be glimpsed. The young man wanted to know if we would like to have his pet dog. He was clearly upset at having to part with it. He explained that he had to depart shortly to study overseas, and his family could not keep his dog. John was confused about what to do. And, he had never seen such a breed of dog before.

"I called from the house to ask if something was the matter. I was curious, but, without shoes, it would have been too hot to walk across the brickwork to see for myself. John called back to say that we were being offered a dog. I peered around the door in an effort to see it. It was uncomfortable standing between the cool air-conditioning and the furnace-like blast of heat from outside. Irritably, I replied that we had a dog already, we did not want another and it would be best to send the young man away. This seemed to take a very long time for John to translate.

"Enough time passed for me to reflect. My next message to John, was that he should take the dog – and invite the young man to return in a week's time to see if we had found someone to adopt his pet. I could not bear the thought of the master and his dog going from door to door in the heat.

"John led the panting creature indoors. Instead of returning to our naps, I stood in the bath, ankle deep in suds while John stood by with shampoo and towels. Our new dog turned out to be a bright black and white Llasa Apso. I took some scissors and hacked away at the hair until its body took shape. He was beautiful, and in excellent condition. And, he was very grateful. I doubt he had ever been so cool. By way of saying 'thank you', the dog would not let me out of his sight and trotted along wherever I went. This gave us a problem, because he was a male and Samantha was a female. We knew that we should keep them apart for a while unless we were watching. They might either fight or mate.

"Difficulties arose immediately. Samantha was used to coming into the house, but the Llasa Apso would not go outside. He would not tolerate being separated from humans, even for five minutes. We tried to leave him in our bathroom one night, and he scratched the door badly. Thereafter, he slept in our bedroom while Samantha remained outside. She looked hurt and confused. It could not go on. The young man did not return, so we began to look about very seriously for a new home."

"What a brat," judged Gold.

"The Llasa Apso remained perfectly behaved, Gold, as long as we were in sight; and every one of our pets accepted him, although they remained somewhat aloof, as if they knew he would not stay for long. We soon became used to his ways, and were a little sad when he departed to live with a wealthy family in Beirut, Lebanon. He settled there into a life of rare

luxury, visiting poodle parlours, and eating expensive fresh meat. I wonder how he is faring now in poor Lebanon's troubled times."

"I'd say he was a very lucky dog to get such a chance," Gold sounded a bit grudging. "Have you known any other dogs, Susan?"

"Yes, Gold, long before we had Samantha, we were practically given a PAIR of wonderful dogs. We intended to buy the two, but ultimately, we could only pay for one, so that meant we received the other one for nothing. The owner would not accept money for the second one because of the unusual circumstances."

"Oh, Susan, it sounds just like a riddle," squeaked Gold, excitedly, sensing a tale. He shuffled into his comfy egg-shape and looked at me expectantly.

"You see, John has always loved fine pure-bred dogs, and one day he had a chance of a lifetime. When this opportunity came by, we had been living in Saudi Arabia for almost three years, and Christopher was just three years old.

"He had not had a dog since we parted with Mark, the 'pye' dog.

"That morning, John saw our friend, Sally, returning from horse-riding. Riyadh was a small city then, with a few major roads linking the various special places, such as the University, the Engineering College, the Racetrack, and the City Centre. Looking out from our villa, and far away across the desert, we could see the horse stables – although they were a good walk away. Sally mentioned that she had just glimpsed two fine dogs at the stables. They looked like the fabulous hunting breed, the Borzoi, yet they were penned up in a dark stall, looking thoroughly miserable.

"John went immediately to the stables to investigate. There, in a dimly lit stall, he found two sad dogs, one male and one female borzoi. A groom told John that the dogs had a fine history. They had hunted under royal patronage in exotic places such as Addis Ababa in Ethiopia, and Tehran in Iran. They had belonged to an Arabian Prince. According to the groom, the dogs were past their prime, and they had been given to a servant who left them at the stables.

"John offered to buy the dogs, but the groom wanted to speak with his friend before agreeing. He would have to come back the next day. John was very excited and full of hope when he set out across the desert the following day. Convinced that he would be able to pay and collect the pair of borzois, John was terribly upset to find that he could only have one. The other had escaped in the night. It was the bitch. She could perhaps survive by hunting, but as a domesticated canine, she would more likely remain close to humans and be killed in the city traffic. It seemed too unfortunate to be true. The pair had been within hours of rescue. Their condition was so poor, that time could not be lost if they were to survive. The men at the stables had not given the dogs more than bread and rice. They had lived on this for weeks. It seemed a cruel trick for fate to play.

"The next afternoon, John was at work. I intended to take a rest after seeing Christopher off to a children's party, in the care of our maid. Abdullah was to drive the car. I stood at the great iron gates to wave them 'goodbye'. Then, something happened that seemed like a small miracle. I saw a borzoi loping lithely across the desert. I cried out in disbelief. I glanced quickly to check that the male borzoi was still resting in our garden. Yes, he was there, and, yes, the dog in the desert was a borzoi. It must be the missing female.

"I closed the gate quickly, and ran after her as fast as I could. Half-an-hour later, hot and exhausted, disappointed and disconsolate, I returned to the villa. I had lost sight of her. I wondered how I could tell John that I had seen the female and lost her. Sadly, I began to close the gate.

"I stopped when I saw Abdullah driving fast across the desert towards me. He arrived smiling broadly. I waited, impatient and despondent as he wound down the window. 'Look, look, Madame! Look – here in the car!' He pointed to the front seat. What did he mean? There was no one there. Christopher was with Mary in the back seat. I peered in to where he pointed. There, on the floor, with her long legs folded up, was a very miserable borzoi.

"'How marvellous! How wonderful! How did you do it Abdullah?' I cried.

"Abdullah was very kind to animals but he had no special feeling for pets. His beaming face told me that he had done this for us. He knew that we would be pleased. Abdullah was always thoughtful and generous. On behalf of the rescued dog, and John, I gave him my grateful thanks. All tiredness forgotten, we opened the gates wide, while carefully watching the other dog, in case it got up and tried to escape. We need not have worried. It had no intention of rising because it badly needed to rest.

"We took no chances, and made sure the gates were secure before encouraging the female to get out of the car. She would not move, or could not. What were we to do? We could see that one front knee had been skinned to the bone, and there seemed no way to lift such a big dog out without hurting her. And the poor thing seemed too tired to move. What terrors had she been through last night and today – dodging traffic, and possibly stones thrown by naughty boys?

"Then we had an idea. We would show her Ivan. Already we had named the pair Ivan and Anastasia. Gently, we led Ivan around to be in full view of his soulful Anastasia. Have you ever seen a dog 'smile', Gold? Anastasia's face lit up in the most beautiful 'smile' when she saw Ivan. There was no mistaking this look of happiness – and relief. She slowly and painfully unwound herself, and stepped out sedately to stand beside her best friend."

"That's a beautiful story, Susan. Did they live 'happily ever after'?"

"The rest of their life was not quite that simple, Gold. Anastasia's knee eventually mended, but she was totally deaf, and had a severe case of canker in both ears. We hoped that

her hearing would come back after she was cured of this infestation of minute creatures. It did improve but only slightly.

"Gradually we brought Ivan and Anastasia back to health and beauty. They were probably too slow for hunting now, but with a proper diet and care, they would be good pets – and they might breed. Christopher loved them, and he was not a bit frightened, even though they were much bigger than he was. They were very gentle with him, and he could reach up to hug Anastasia easily because she was smaller than Ivan. He would try to climb on to Ivan's back, but slipped off the silky coat.

"Anastasia's front legs were slightly bowed, which indicated that she had probably lacked proper nutrition at an early age. She could never have been as fast as Ivan. Yet, she was very pretty and refined-looking. He was regal and strong. Anastasia had a coyly feminine way of looking at us through long eyelashes. We loved these gentle dogs and they returned our affection. We were proud of them, too, dreaming of the fine puppies they might have. But breeding proved to be difficult because they remained more like best friends than a mated pair. This is usually the case, if a pair of dogs remain together all the time.

"After several happy months passed, spring was in the air again. The sky was the clearest and most beautiful blue. And life was wonderful, until disaster struck. Prior to this, the dog days were perfect for Ivan and Anastasia, and it was easy to believe that their trials were at an end. Then suddenly, late one evening, we heard the terrible sound a hound makes when in pain. Fearing something dreadful, we all ran outside to find poor Anastasia with a broken front leg. Poor, sweet thing. Perhaps she had fallen down the steep and shiny marble steps. Ivan moaned with compassion, offering Anastasia sympathetic licks and nudges. It was moving to see how upset he was.

"Eventually, the vet came. He was a horse specialist, and did not care for dogs – especially those with such big jaws. I did my best to reassure him that Ivan and Anastasia would not bite, but in vain. He was clearly terrified. He directed me to hold Anastasia's bound-up muzzle while he set the leg. We shut Ivan out during this operation. But he did not leave the other side of the door, moaning and wailing pitifully each time Anastasia made whimpering sounds.

"Next day, when our household was tranquil again, and we were beginning to relax, Anastasia began to moan once more. Her leg had begun to swell badly because the plaster was too tight. The terrified vet returned, and we spent a ghastly hour carving away the plaster from her leg. The vet sweated, Anastasia moaned, Ivan wailed, Christopher whimpered, and I wept. Whenever the vet became impatient, he accidentally hurt the dog. Eventually, her leg was successfully reset and, in time, it healed."

"And THEN, Susan, did they live happily ever after?"

"I'm not sure, Gold. It was far from the end of their story.

Our company moved us to live on the east coast of Saudi Arabia, to the Dhahran airport. We took Ivan and Anastasia with us, but the gates to the fence around our house were not very secure, and within the first few weeks, our dogs escaped twice. The first time, Ivan and Anastasia were very excited, and took a mad romp around the entire airport camp. They ran about so fast, that we kept hearing about them: 'Over here!' 'Over there!' 'Here they are!' 'Have you seen them?' Screams told us that people were terrified to see such large dogs. Eventually, when our energetic pair slowed down, we were able to catch them. On the second occasion, Ivan and Anastasia stopped to sniff something at the open gate to the airstrip. We were lucky to catch them that time. If they had run on to the tarmac, we might have been responsible for a serious accident. We were told that we could keep our dogs no longer.

"Searching Arabia for a suitable home, we eventually found animal-loving people with a large garden in Jeddah. It was a sad parting, but we were pleased that Ivan and Anastasia got a third chance at life. Yes, we believe that they eventually lived happily ever after."

"Oh, I am so pleased, Susan. I think they deserved happiness after all that." Gold looked very pleased.

"And who gave you Samantha, Susan?"

"We bought Samantha from some Italian people in Riyadh. They bred 'golden' cocker spaniels. She was supposed to be the runt of her litter; that is the puppy that has received the least nutrition from its mother during gestation, (the length of time between conception and when the puppy is born). The dog's gestation period is about 63 days and the female may have several litters a year, with as many as six to ten puppies. The lifespan may be between 13 and 17 years, providing the dog lives a good life.

"It did not matter to us that Samantha was not the best example of her breed. We did not intend to put her in dog shows to win prizes. She was a fine-looking puppy. But, perhaps she had a neater muzzle than the usual loose-skinned, larger ones seen on the finest of her breed. A defect in her personality could be that she is very sensitive. She does not trust everyone. However, we were pleased to have Samantha remain a reliable guard dog, and it was often interesting to see just who appealed to her. Many people visited us, and Samantha would make up her mind to bark at some, hide from others, and 'smile' at the rest. We always caution visitors to ignore her totally, to give her time to relax, investigate and comment.

"When Samantha 'smiles', she makes people laugh because she does so with all of her body. I had never before seen any dog 'wag' like her. It goes all the way from the back of her neck to the tip of her feathered tail. Meanwhile, her face displays eagerness and joy. This is her most usual 'face' shown to almost everyone, especially new rabbits. Haven't you noticed, Gold, how very tolerant she is of rabbits? She sometimes approaches new ones by advancing on her elbows,

with her bottom in the air, wiggling all the way. It is very amusing. At first, some have shown caution but none have shown fear. Whatever 'waves' or signals Samantha sends to the rabbits, none can be aggressive. Have you noticed that she is respectful of Mamapuss, too, but will rarely tolerate any other cat. Any feral cats that come over the fence had better watch out. Samantha may be a domesticated dog but her breed are hunters and this instinct remains. She has proved herself to be very fast, and quite savage, when strays have dropped into the garden.

"Some people have remarked that it is a pity that 'poor' Samantha does not go for walks like dogs do in some countries. Perhaps this is so, but maybe, some of those dogs do not have such a good time as Samantha. She loves to visit the desert on Fridays when we have a picnic. And, she is rarely put on a leash as they are. Samantha can run free about our big garden, and in our large house. I think she is very well-adjusted. She is more exuberant than most dogs, but does not get over-excited or bark too much.

"Samantha is very alert and never bored. There is nothing lethargic about her unless it is mid-summer or nap time. When there are no birds or stray cats to scuttle, she pretends there are, and her fantasies seem to mean a lot to her. You must have seen her play this game time and again – dashing back and forth and up and down, barking at phantoms.

"At least once a day, she will plead with one of us to go into the garden to watch this performance. Beginning by running back and forth from the door to whoever is her chosen audience, she will then sit, quivering with excitement, until quite sure the person will step out on to the terrace for a good view. She then lures her audience out bit by bit, until convinced they will remain for the exhibition. Otherwise it is cancelled."

"Yes, I've seen her. I think she is barmy sometimes."

"It is just her way of having fun. We know Samantha very well. Once we were convinced that she was innocent of a ghastly crime that had taken place right by her kennel. I must admit, though, things looked very bad for her. And knowing everyone has foibles and idiosyncrasies, it was just possible that the victim had been 'done in' by Samantha. On top of that, I have learned to be prepared for almost anything to happen in our villa."

"What happened? You are keeping me in suspense," pleaded Gold.

"Before I tell you what happened, Gold, I should explain what led up to the drama. You see, months before, John had burst into the kitchen and asked me to follow him quickly. He looked as though something rather special had happened, so I put down my recipe book, and followed him obediently into the garden.

"Our maid, Mary, was in the habit of surprising us, so when John led me to the back of the house, I began to wonder what she had done this time. Her quarters were in the rear garden near Samantha's kennel. This part was fenced off from the front garden to prevent our dog from startling visitors. Although it was Samantha's and Mary's domain, the dividing fences and gates allowed rabbits to hop back and forth. They could be seen grazing there, especially in the morning.

"On this occasion, the maid had bought herself a red chicken with beautiful curved and colourful tail feathers. No doubt, she intended to fatten it for some future meal. So, now there was a red chicken, exactly the same colour as our young 'golden' cocker spaniel. We decided, then and there, to call it 'Golden Cockerel'. It was fascinating to watch them. The bird did not show the slightest fear of Samantha, who seemed very pleased with Golden Cockerel. Mostly, she sat by observing enquiringly, occasionally getting up to give a sniff of curiosity, following up with her famous wiggle. 'Yes, I approve,' she seemed to say: AHLAN WASAHLAN! (Arabic for: 'You are welcome to my home'.)

"I refused to allow myself to develop any deep affection for Golden Cockerel, as I had done some years previously, when another maid had brought home a chicken. I recall that, one day, we had been horrified to hear screeching followed by a dreadful silence. We discovered then, that the maid had slaughtered the chicken we had grown to love. Our pathway was running with its blood and its gorgeous feathers were strewn everywhere. This time, I would be content to see Samantha pass her days happily with her chicken. I should remain aloof.

"Samantha's only negative foible with her feathered friend was that she could not tolerate it entering her kennel. She was happy to see it strutting around or sitting on the kennel roof, but she would not permit it to go inside. Occasionally, she would return and find it had taken the liberty of resting within. For this act of gross impertinence, Samantha would deliver sharp nips at the chicken's rear end, and send it squawking.

She would then plump down in her house with a positive air, as if to say: "It is not as though I haven't told you time and time again. Not in HERE!" At first, the household was thrown into panic every time Golden Cockerel began to screech, especially if Samantha barked. We would dash to the window to see if our dog had been driven too far and savaged the chicken. But, we were soon accustomed to the game.

"It was not Golden Cockerel's fate to end up in a cooking pot, or be killed by Samantha. In total silence, he just fell over dead. The maid came rushing in with the dreadful news. Samantha MUST have killed it, she said.

"Mary was not a bit upset about Golden Cockerel's death – she just wanted the price of a new chicken. We investigated but found no marks on the bird – although it was frightfully thin. After some questions, we discovered that he had never been fed, with the exception of a few crumbs that I occasionally threw him from the window. We were horrified, of course, but the maid's explanation seemed reasonable. In Somalia, no one fed chickens. They survived by pecking food

that they found on the ground. She did not realize that our garden was no substitute for an active village where chickens found sufficient food on the ground to survive."

"It was good of Samantha to be so kind to the chicken, Susan. She must have missed Golden Cockerel when he died."

"Samantha was young and very playful then, Gold; and she was not ALWAYS good. She was especially slow to mature in some ways and we often despaired of ever being able to leave shoes unguarded; and, it was not only shoes that met with a 'chewy' end. Nothing was safe from her when she was young. She is less mischievous now, yet she has retained many endearing puppy traits. Thankfully, though, our possessions are safe in our absence.

"We had not bought Samantha with any clear intention of breeding her, but, after a time, we thought her energies might be best directed towards motherhood. We considered keeping one of her puppies. It could be a companion for her.

"Just look at her, Gold. She is ten years old and she still has enough energy in this weather for a water fight." Samantha was jumping in and out of her large water basin, and beating up the water with her front paws. It was flying all over the place. Soon, there would be little left but the usual layer of sand in the bottom.

"To mate Samantha correctly, we had to find the same breed of dog, but it had to be a male that was not closely related to her. Finding another pure-bred 'golden' cocker spaniel in Riyadh would be difficult.

We had not bothered to get Samantha's pedigree papers, so we knew she would not suit owners who required a recorded bitch for their fine dogs. Finally, we found a suitable male, and all arrangements were made and a date set. But, no one came. We contacted mutual friends, only to find the dog and her owners had left Arabia suddenly – and for good. Samantha had been 'jilted', or left by her fiance on the eve of her marriage. It was most upsetting.

"In time, we received our second chance. His name was Cadeau. He was a paler colour than Samantha, and extremely handsome. Samantha and Cadeau were the same age and both families were equally delighted with the alliance. We eagerly looked forward to georgeous puppies.

"Samantha and Cadeau were pleased to meet each other, and amused everyone with their playful antics. They were very active, even at night, and we could hear them jumping about long after we had gone to bed. However, we discovered that mating was far from their doggy minds. Cadeau did show a little interest every now and again, but Samantha would just sit down and observe him with a perplexed expression. He would then become bored and lay down to rest. Samantha would continue to look at him, until not bearing to be ignored any longer, she would go up and pat him with her paw. (She still does this to us when she wants attention.) Then, their routine would be re-enacted. But, they never did mate and Samantha has never had puppies. I think it is wise to seek advice from a specialist when breeding dogs. I have been told

since, that the female should be transported to the domain of the male rather than the other way round.

"Samantha enjoys the company of another dog whenever the opportunity presents itself, but, this does not occur often. We rarely invite a dog to visit, because of you lagomorphs. It may be natural for dogs to chase rabbits and hares, but we do not want any in our warren to have a bad experience. You would lose confidence in us. Strangely, one of our favourite visitors was an Arabian hunting dog, a saluki bitch called Charlie."

"Did she chase the rabbits, Susan?"

"No, Gold. She was very obedient. Charlie was the prettiest saluki I had ever seen. She was shy, sensitive, gentle, but she could be playful, too. Her owner told us about her speed and agility. It could easily be imagined, as these capabilities were expressed in every alert line of her lithe body."

"So, Arabia has two kinds of dog: the desert dog and the saluki, Susan?"

"Yes, Gold. The saluki is an ancient breed of dog with a history in the Middle East that can be traced back five thousand years. Its likeness appeared in ancient Egyptian paintings around three thousand B.C. There are three possibilities for how it got its name: it may have been named after the Arabian town, Saluk, noted for its production of armour and fine dogs; or Seleubia in the Greek Empire; or Sleugh in Syria. In any case, the saluki is a pure-bred hunting dog – its breeding mainly in the hands of Arab sheikhs who esteem it highly.

"It is a dignified, graceful and faithful hound dog, and one of the oldest branches of the greyhound family. (The greyhound is the fastest racing dog in the world.) In modern times, hounds have been trained to hunt animals for sport. In hunting, there is the scent hound and the sight hound. Scent hounds hunt in packs. A sight hound, such as the saluki, has long legs and hunts independently, relying on speed as well as sight.

"The Bedouin traditionally hunted with the saluki in the sport of falconry. Salukis were also used for hunting gazelle. Although the bird usually located the gazelle and attacked it in accordance with its training, the saluki would bring it down by the legs or neck.

"The population of pure blood, experienced salukis, is said to be declining in Arabia, as a result of the settlement of tribes and modern lifestyles. In days gone by, when tribes were truly nomadic, hunting occurred whenever the need arose. The saluki regularly trotted along in the shadow of the dromedary or mare. Sometimes a rider carried the dog for a time. Today, many city-dwelling huntsmen visit the desert briefly in cars and hunt with their falcons. They do not own a saluki".

"What does it look like, Susan?"

"It is a pity Charlie has gone to live in the United States of America, because you could have seen for yourself. Our rabbits were always safe in her company. She would never

harm an animal unless she received a command from her master to do so. Even then – if she were bidden to catch something – she would bring the creature back in her teeth to her master, quite unscathed.

"The saluki looks like a greyhound, but it is more attractive to my mind. There are several types and they can be different colours, such as white, cream, golden, red-fawn, black and tan, and grizzle, or tri-colour. They are elegant, tallish, lean dogs with fine bones. The head tapers to a sharp muzzle. Most varieties of saluki have smooth, soft, silky coats; and some have long hair called 'feathers', growing in fringes on the bottom edge of the long curling tail, on the edge of the ears, and along the backs of the legs. The males grow to a height of between 58–71 centimetres (23–28 inches) and the females to a height of between 51–64 centimetres (20–25 inches).

"I will show you a picture of Charlie; but, now you must hop off and join the other rabbits. Askalu has a marvellous tray of 'grins' for you today. Fortunately for you, it is an Arabian greengrocer's daily custom to cut the tops off carrots and the outer leaves off lettuces and cabbages. Hussein has found a new supplier who is happy to give us his discarded apples and carrots, too. He has brought us a a fine assortment. Off you go! Here comes Askalu now."

"Thank you, Susan. Come on Samantha. Join us for a bite," said Gold as he dashed away. Obviously, he had a new attitude towards his doggy sister.

14
Cats

The climate of Arabia is so dependable that people talk less about the weather than they do in most parts of the world. But, this is not to say that the seasons are taken for granted. The Bedouin, especially, appreciate the changes. Autumn, in particular, is favoured because it follows the harshness and hardship of summer. John and I prefer springtime in Arabia.

"On this occasion, I was taking advantage of a typical spring day and sitting in the gentle sunshine. It was idyllic weather and to be savoured because soon, the searing heat of summer would be with us once again. Today, there was not even a breeze to blow up dust and toss the odd bits of rabbit fur into the pool.

Samantha sauntered by, paused and decided to flop down at my feet. Nearby, our adopted pigeon Wuzzo, pecked at invisible things on the ground. Gold was resting close to me, and the other rabbits were in all sorts of positions, dotted here and there, either singly or in groups about the garden. Mamapuss limped slowly by, ignoring Anthony, Silver, and Modesty Blaise as she passed them, heading towards the shade of the date palm. Once there, she settled her slender body down, bringing her head to rest on one front paw. She looked back at us sleepily.

After a little while, Samantha got up and plodded towards the main entrance to the warren. She was going to peer down the holes once again. She loved to do that whenever there were rabbit kittens. It gave them such a start when they popped out. Samantha was always greatly amused by their reactions, and pranced about, coming to rest now and again on her elbows with her bottom in the air. She would never hurt them. As soon as they realized this, it was time for us to laugh at her crest-fallen look. Her respect for grown rabbits borders on cowardice, and even quite a small rabbit can make Samantha hang her head and slink away – merely by standing its ground when she sidles up to them.

"Just look at Samantha, Gold. Samantha, come here!"

Almost before I finished speaking, Samantha saw a bird and ran after it. In her mad dash, she upset a bunch of rabbits as well as Mamapuss. Mamapuss rose quickly and drew herself up haughtily on straight, stiffened legs. She slowly arched her back, seeming to look with disdain at Samantha.

Gold chuckled. "Mamapuss is so snooty," he said, and settled down to watch her thoughtfully. "Susan, is Mamapuss truly Arabian?"

"I believe that her ancestors were from the Middle East, Gold. Her shape is typical of most Arabian 'street' cats, or domestic ones that have returned to a wild state and become feral. Many domestic and feral cats in Arabia have similar head and body structure to the aristocratic Siamese, Burmese and Abyssinian purebred cats. They have the characteristic long limbs, with the back legs longer than the front ones – and the wedge-shaped head.

"In the ancient world, in countries that surround Arabia, cats were once revered. Illustrations from these old cultures show cats very similar to Mamapuss.

"Cats belong to the animal family Felidae, often called 'felines'. I was fascinated to discover that the forebears of certain modern cat breeds were used as Buddhist temple guards. Japan also kept cats to protect their temples. Ancient records from great civilizations – such as Egypt and China – frequently refer to revered cats. In China, it is said, certain people can still tell the time of day by examining the eyes of cats. And, I read that the common western tabby got its name from Attabiah (a section of old Baghdad in modern Iraq) where black and white 'watered' silk was made. It has a stripey look resembling the fur coat of the tabby. Furthermore, the Scandinavian Goddess, Freya, is depicted in a chariot drawn by two cats.

"When we first came to Arabia, the street cats were more interesting than they are today, Gold. We saw wonderful felines that looked just like purebred Abyssinians, and others with most unusul colouring. I am sure these common cats were descended from their illustrious neighbours. It seemed so unjust that they had to roam about starving and homeless.

"In most areas of the cities, the shape and colours of these feral cats have changed. Perhaps because they have interbred with domestic pets brought in from abroad. Occasionally, still, a 'replica' of the prized Abyssinian breed can be seen skulking furtively along a narrow side street, trying to keep hidden from danger, as it moves between garbage containers.

"When we first got Mamapuss, the street cats in Riyadh were very colourful indeed. Nowhere else had I seen such

beauty. The pale pinky-beige shade of Mamapuss is rarely seen anymore. Another 'style' was white with grey and orange patches, and a tail of pure gun-metal grey. All of the alleycats were gorgeous; although, sometimes, they did not seem to be so at first glance."

"Whatever do you mean, Susan? Were they gorgeous or not?"

"Well, Gold, if a cat does not have enough to drink, it becomes dehydrated, and it will lack saliva. Such a thirsty cat is unable to wash itself by licking; and, consequently, its natural beauty will be hidden under a dirty and unkempt appearance. You must have seen these poor, homeless creatures drinking from our swimming pool – their bottoms high in the air as they balance themselves to reach the water. When it is very hot, they become quite desperate, and enter our garden – even though there is a dog present. In an Arabian summer, the life of a stray cat becomes a constant search for water.

"Poor nutrition takes its toll on a cat's appearance, too. The female, who is known as a 'queen', lacks vitality because she is wearied by having too many kittens. The male, known as a 'tom', becomes ugly with battle scars from fighting over territory and females.

"It is natural for tomcats to challenge each other for females, and old toms often fight over territories. When there are lots of toms about, it is difficult to keep a pet female at home at breeding time. As a consequence, even Mamapuss had too many kittens. Her first litter was born before she was fully grown, and her body was not properly developed. That is possibly the reason why she has remained small and slender. As a general rule, it is wise to have the toms castrated and the queens spayed. Spaying is an operation which prevents conception. This can be done between the ages of 3–5 months."

"How did Mamapuss come to live with you?"

"John found her on the street when she was a very tiny kitten, under-nourished and dirty. Her skin was visible through thin fur, and she was starving and wild. Perhaps her mother was dead, or she may have been abandoned. In desperate conditions, when a queen gives birth to yet one more litter, the starving mother (who has insufficient milk to feed her young) might run off and leave the kittens. Mamapuss was much too young to be alone, and she might not have survived had John not rescued her."

"How did he rescue Mamapuss?"

"'With great difficulty' would be John's answer, I am sure, Gold. We had recently moved into our first real home in Saudi Arabia, and John was learning to find his way around Riyadh. He had just driven up to his destination one day, when he saw a little boy throwing stones at a scrawny kitten. The child ran off so John went after the kitten and caught it. It was Mamapuss, but then, we named her SEDEEKI, meaning 'friend' in Arabic. She was most unfriendly at first and behaved like a miniature tiger in the most ungrateful fashion. With needle-sharp weapons, she clawed and bit John throughout her capture and during the journey home. For her ingratitude, John threatened to change her name to BISSA, which is the common word in Arabic for cat.

"Our new cat had tremendous courage despite her tiny size, and a great will to survive, quickly learning to eat and drink. Had she been younger, we would have needed to feed her every two hours, day and night. After a while, her true beauty began to develop. Slender-boned, and beautiful, Sedeeki grew into the most elegant cat, and visitors found it difficult to believe her humble beginnings.

"Soon, Sedeeki and Christopher (who was then about eight months old) became inseparable companions. Christopher could already walk, run and climb. He had developed all three skills at the same time, bypassing crawling as a totally unnecessary phase.

"The cat rarely left Christopher's side during his rambles about the villa and garden. Our little boy could totter off at a surprising speed, with his arms outstretched sideways to give him balance. It was an amusing sight to see his kitten following. Her skinny tail would be sticking straight up when she was walking, and it would hang straight down when she sat on the balcony ledge by his side. This seemed to be their favourite place. Christopher and Sedeeki would remain there for 'ages', motionless, looking at the world outside our villa walls. At that time, Riyadh was small, and we could see a lot of desert between the villas.

"Once a day, a dainty little shepherdess in a brightly-coloured dress would pass by. She directed her sheep and goats with a stick and a call. There was very little for the animals to eat, but her flock would find sufficient food if they walked for a day in a wide circle, scavenging as they went. Sedeeki's all-knowing gaze seemed to tell Christopher that this was how it had been for thousands of years.

"A serene atmosphere pervaded the scene as a rule. Sometimes a jangling donkey cart would pass, and the cat and boy would become instantly alert. Its bell excited them greatly. Sometimes the donkey was walking, other times trotting, and occasionally it galloped as the master whacked it to make haste. The cart might hold a container of water or fuel, and at other times, the delivery made, the only burden would be the donkey's master.

"Sedeeki sometimes walked the perimeter of the high wall around our villa, and dropped down to the dusty road outside. Christopher was both fascinated and frustrated by the desert. He did not understand why he could not roam freely outside the walls. He always tried the gate latch to see if someone had accidentally left it open. Whenever possible, he quickly made off in a straight line across the desert, kicking up puffs of the dry powdered earth and small bleached stones. He would scream loudly in protest when brought back. Sedeeki, on the other hand, would return satisfied, looking smugly secretive as cats often do. She always returned when she wanted something to eat, or Christopher's company.

"One day, in her first year, a large and extremely ugly cat came to court Sedeeki. We called him Tom Jones. Almost before we realized that they had mated, Sedeeki gave birth to four babies. Perhaps because she was so young and not sufficiently mature, only two of her kittens survived. They were a male and a female. Eventually, the female vanished, and we were left with a handsome ginger and white kitten that we named Thomas.

"Although the gestation period for cats is about 63–65 days, seemingly no time at all had passed before Sedeeki and Tom Jones surprised us again. On this occasion, she chose an empty cupboard in which to give birth to her kittens. She could drop into it from the open slot above where a drawer was missing. We always thought Tom was totally undesirable, but tolerated him because he was her constant admirer and the father of her kittens. He was quite disgusting to look at – so horribly scarred and tough-looking; yet, we had to admire his tenacity for life. A lesser 'tom' would have been killed by now. He had survived to a mature age because he was so big, strong and capable; and Sedeeki seemed to adore him, so who were we to judge.

"Sedeeki was always an excellent mother. She took great care of her kittens, and they were so beautiful that we never had trouble finding them homes. One was named Chilli, and she went to Oman with her new owner who had taken a position as tutor to the ruler's son. Chilli eventually had a kitten called Hugh, who was said to have populated the palace with his offspring. These are the only illustrious descendants of our Sedeeki (whom we now call Mamapuss) – at least, as far as we know."

"No wonder Mamapuss is so proud and haughty." I saw Gold look at her with what might have been admiration.

"Another of her kittens left us to live a 'right royal' life indeed. Let me tell you about that one, Gold. The litter it came from, included five kittens, all different colours and two were long-haired. The strangest was a tri-coloured male, apparently a rare animal. When a tri-coloured male does occur, it is almost certainly sterile, I am told. This kitten was handicapped at birth. The vet said he was the runt of the litter; however, he would improve if we gave him vitamins. Poor little thing! At first he could barely stand, and he constantly shook his head. We called him Charlie Brown. It was unthinkable to end his life, and Mamapuss adored him.

"She did more for him than she did for any of her other babies. This was surprising, because cats normally abandon a weakling. Mamapuss was completely devoted to her handicapped offspring, carrying Charlie Brown around – even after he had grown far too large for that sort of thing. She jumped from high places with him in her mouth, and we grew pale when he was whacked against hard stone floors as she landed. Still, Charlie Brown began to improve, and he looked quite nice when his fur thickened. We easily found homes for his brothers and sisters, but we did not consider separating Mamapuss from her 'favourite'.

"One day, when Charlie Brown was a little older and more capable, two zoologists from the Riyadh University came to visit. They admired our animals, and confided that they liked cats best. They could not keep one, they said, because they lived in an apartment with only a small balcony and no garden. Then, they met our Charlie who would find it difficult to brave the terrors of a garden. They begged us to let him go to live with them. Charlie left that day with the zoologists who acted as though we had given them diamonds rather than a disabled cat. When we visited them some weeks later, little Charlie was eating his supper. On this occasion the men had prepared him scrambled eggs. They had also provided him with every comfort including a small swinging door cut through to their balcony for his convenience."

"What a lucky puss, Susan. Mamapuss must have been pleased for him."

"I am sure she was, and surprisingly she accepted his absence – perhaps because she was pregnant once again."

"Mamapuss does act a bit too uppity, sometimes, Susan. She seems to be just too perfect."

"Just like anyone else, Gold, Mamapuss has faults. Let me tell you a story about one of her imperfections. Perhaps you have heard that felines are notorious for being sure-footed. And they all seem to be so, except for Mamapuss. When she was much younger and more active, she continually knocked things over. Usually, it was her tail that was responsible. She would leap from shelf to shelf, weaving in and out of ornaments, causing thing to move and sometimes wobble until they fell to the floor.

"On other occasions, she might survey the room from some high vantage spot, and lash her tail. It would usually hook something and send it flying. Most nights, after we had shut the door leading to the sleeping quarters, we would hear a loud crashing sound. We were inclined to believe that she resented being shut out of the bedrooms. She was also mischievous when young, and teased Thomas unmercifully. He was the most placid of cats, even to the point of allowing new kittens to scramble and tumble over him, clawing and biting, to grip with their needle-sharp teeth and claws. Nothing seemed to shake his tolerant nature, except Mamapuss.

"She had so many kittens that, by then, she was always called Mamapuss. And we had begun to call Thomas 'Oedipuss', referring to the psychoanalyst's term used to describe a juvenile's fixation for its mother. The two played together a great deal and often shared a basket. They went to sleep coiled up tightly together, even though they had a basket each. We placed these on top of the warm, vibrating refrigerator, where they had chosen to sleep. I do believe they thought the machine was purring.

"Each day, when Oedipuss was resting on the sofa, Mamapuss would appear for her daily teasing game. She would approach Oedipuss quietly and begin to caress him about the face and neck with licks. When Mamapuss had

finally lulled him into a state of total relaxation, she would sink sharp teeth into his neck. Oedipuss would raise himself up instantly, and deliver a powerful blow with his closed paw, sending the slight form of Mamapuss reeling. Then a wild chase round and round the rooms would follow. Suddenly, their crazy flight would cease, and they would flop down to rest, completely ignoring each other as if nothing had happened. We came to expect this pantomime to be repeated about the same time every day."

"Doesn't sound very bright to me! What did he look like, Susan? You said Oedipuss was handsome."

"Oedipuss was a very large cat, Gold, and he was equal parts ginger and white. The ginger was more of a bright, rich orange, and he wore this colour like a hooded cloak over the top of his head and back. All of his underparts were the brightest pure white. His coat was thick and glossy, and he had a nice broad face with beautiful widely-spaced green eyes. His only flaw was a small nick out of one ear, where he had been bitten by an aggressive tomcat. To save him from a life of fighting, we had Oedipuss castrated by our vet. Castrated males usually stay at home, but it did not stop Oedipuss from having adventures. Would you like to hear about one, Gold?"

"What a question, Susan, you know I can't resist a story."

"His most famous escapade came about because Oedipuss was in the habit of paying calls at the houses and gardens of our neighbours. I heard that one lady tried to move him off with a straw broom, but gave up when Oedipuss just rested heavily against it. He was a confident, friendly and accomplished cat. He would knock on doors to have them opened for him, or open them himself by jumping up and pulling the handle down. His speciality was opening wire doors by hooking in his claws and pulling; and, he opened sliding wire windows the same way. Oedipuss never closed anything, so he would give himself away.

"On this occasion, he entered through the neighbour's kitchen window, and ate most of an expensive filet of beef that had been put out to defrost. He left the badly mauled remains in the hall. Then, he went upstairs and slept in the master bedroom."

"Just like Goldilocks, Susan." Gold's little body shook with merriment. "Oh, how marvellous!"

"It wasn't very funny at the time, Gold. Our neighbours were annoyed. You know, most cats like to sleep in a bed but next to someone because they like human company, and it is warm. Oedipuss had another adventure because of this trait. We were about to go on our annual holidays at the time and had made arrangements for a Saudi Arabian lady to look after our two cats. Her husband was away on business, so we thought they would be good company for her.

"Oedipuss did his job as companion extremely well. Each night, she would be surprised to find that she was gradually being shoved out of bed. It was Oedipuss. He had the habit of leaning heavily against a sleeper until eventually, he would take up most of the bed. She would get up and go around to the other side of the bed, but then, Oedipuss would start shoving in the opposite direction. The following night, she shut him out, but he appeared in her bed again. Night after night, our friend put him out, and closed yet one more door between them. But, Oedipuss was persistent and opened them all. In exasperation, she began locking him in the kitchen with Mamapuss who slept through it all. His hostess eventually won because he could not pick locks."

"Where is Oedipuss now, Susan?"

"I wish I knew. He disappeared one night when he was five years old. It was his habit to snooze for most of the day and go out in the cool of the evening. The domestic cat was originally nocturnal, or active only at night. Many house cats have adapted their lifestyles to that of their human companions, and become mostly diurnal, or active by day. Yet, some remain quite busy at night, especially when it is hot during the day, as it is in Saudi Arabia; and, their eyes can still show the adaptations that enhance night vision. Cats are said to be able to see in the dark, but this is not true; although they can see fairly well in poor light. Their eyes (which have a vertical pupil) can open very wide, allowing more light to enter. And there is a covering at the back of the eyes, acting as a mirror to reflect light within the eye for a second passage (and a chance to be collected via the optical nerve). You may recall seeing cat's eyes reflecting at night.

"As Oedipuss grew older, he stayed out later, spending hours skittering across the rooftops with other cats. I came to expect him to knock on our balcony window about two o'clock every morning. Although this habit annoyed me, I would get up and let him in, muttering a threat about leaving him out there one of these nights. Then, one night, he did not knock and we never saw him again. I deeply regretted my threats, and we missed him terribly. Oedipuss was so beautiful and friendly, we like to believe that someone fell in love with him. If they thought he was lost, they may have taken him to live far away. He was the sort of cat who might settle down to a cosy life and never attempt to return home, if it were far enough away."

"How sad! I am so sorry, Susan; but, you still have Mamapuss."

"Yes, Mamapuss is totally different. I believe she would walk miles through hostile country to get back to us. Cats have been known to do this. On one occasion, Mamapuss almost did. She had been missing for one whole day and a night, and we were very worried. I walked and walked, calling and searching. On the following day, full of sad thoughts, I was working in the kitchen, when the wire door mysteriously opened and twanged shut. I turned, to see Mamapuss, limping and bleeding, dash through the kitchen and followed her down the hall and into the bedroom. I found her lying on my bed exhausted. She was in a mess and appeared to be too badly injured for me to move her. John was in Oman, and I could not reach a vet, so I made her comfortable and placed food and water within reach.

A stray tom cat poses

Stray kittens face
a hard life

Arabian street cats can be beautiful colours

139

"She yawned continously and accepted a little water but she did not eat for several days. Cats are supposed to have nine lives, and this was clearly the end of her first.

"Eventually, Mamapuss began to get well. The swelling on her face went down and her wounds healed. Throughout her illness, she looked at me with a trusting gaze. And, she began to purr. Mamapuss could not, or would not purr before that time. Oedipuss used to purr in what we called 'three gears: low purr, second purr and top purr'. We could hear 'top purr' from across the room. When Mamapuss was well again, she ceased to purr, but she began to do so again after Oedipuss disappeared. It is said that a cat will purr when happy and lash the tail when angry. I now believe that cats purr to display ALL sorts of emotions. We have observed Mamapuss lashing her tail for various reasons, too, and especially when she looks as though she might have an excess of nervous energy or when she is feeling mischievous. It seems to me, it is a way to get rid of excess emotional energy.

"I am sure that love as well as instinct drew Mamapuss home to us. We had always cared for her lovingly and shared many experiences which surely bound her close to us.

"During the long journey by road to and from the Eastern Province (where we lived for three years) our cats travelled with us, roaming free in the car. On the first trip, we had put both cats in cages, thinking this would be best. They hated it and howled until we let them out. Cats love to investigate. They were much happier after being freed and having sniffed everything in the car. Afterwards, they settled down to sleep for most of the trip. Of course, there was pandemonium at the service stations where we pulled in.

"The cats were curious. They peered out of the windows at the attendants who were excited and amused to see cats travelling in a car.

"Although Mamapuss returned to good health and beauty, one of her front paws began to give her trouble now and again. It curled up more and more, until the fur wore thin where it touched the ground. She rarely puts that paw down nowadays. The vet said Mamapuss was not in pain and considered her too old to be put through the ordeal of surgery. So, Mamapuss limps sometimes but copes well. She can open the paw, and it is good enough to swat with, whenever she feels that a reprimand is necessary. Even when she bites you, Gold, you must admit it is gentle. That can be a cat's way of being playful. She probably misses her fights with Oedipuss.

"Mamapuss loves Christopher and all babies, but she is wary of boisterous children. You see, cats are sensitive and they do not appreciate rough handling. She will hide when noisy children visit us; yet, she will give up her nap to come and have her tail and whiskers pulled by a baby. I think she misses Christopher as a tot.

"Cats are complicated creatures. Did you know, Gold, they have teeth and a tongue that are especially designed for catching, holding, killing, tearing, slicing, cutting and scraping raw flesh, gristle and bone."

"Ugh!" Gold shuddered. He was horrified but fascinated, I could see. He looked up at me expectantly, waiting for me to continue.

"Cats keep their claws sharp at all times because they have work to do. The claws are extendable, and after sharpening on a tree or the living room chairs, they remain sheathed within the paw until the cat has to climb; to display dominance to other cats; or to use them as weapons."

"You are making cats sound like terrible, wild things."

"The domestic cat is very similar to the large wild cats: the lion, tiger, and leopard. All felines are remarkably supple and agile creatures, but despite their formidable assets, a cat's great speed is only good for short distances.

"The domestic cat has a mysterious origin, Gold, although fossils have told us some things.

"Dr Dennis Turner, a scientist and noted feline specialist, writes that it is fairly certain that the house cat was originally domesticated by the ancient Egyptians from the African Wild Cat. From Egypt it spread east over Asia Minor, and India to the Far East, as well as north to Europe.

"Perhaps one day a cat will talk, but it is not likely that it will ever tell us of its origins, even if it were preserved in folklore. You see, the cat is by nature the most secret and solitary creature in the world. It is neither completely tame nor savage. It is said to be the most independent, detached, and self-reliant of all domesticated animals. Adjectives such as 'enigmatic' (puzzling) and 'inscrutable' (mysterious) have been used to describe the mask-like face of the cat. Yet, I have never found Mamapuss to be puzzling OR completely mysterious. Some cats do seem to mask their feelings behind a 'straight face', but that is only when the cat is not a close friend. It is usually quite easy to know what is on your own cat's mind."

"Minced beef is what is on her mind," said Gold, tossing his head accusingly towards Mamapuss.

"Quite so – most of the time. Mamapuss does love her fresh minced beef, Gold, just as you love your 'grins'. Despite all the criticism, you will find most people see cats as miniature tigers, and they admire them. Some people may not like them as pets in the house, but they notice their grace and beauty. Mostly you will find that cats are kept as companions because they are an undemanding presence in the house."

"Surely not, Susan. Mamapuss UNDEMANDING? She acts as though she is the HEAD of this family, and she is CONSTANTLY demanding 'mince' – and, she ALWAYS leaves some. She DEMANDS notice, and sits ALL over the family and on the BEST chairs." Gold was obviously getting the lot off his chest.

"Now, now, Gold, you must remember, Mamapuss is getting old now. At twelve years of age, she is the equivalent of a human of over eighty years. She has earned our attention. To take a pet into the home is a great commitment. The master or mistress is responsible for the animal's welfare, from the moment it joins the family, and for the rest of its

life. The animal must be respected as an individual. And, a great deal of care must be taken when it grows old. We know that YOU like stories, Gold, but Mamapuss likes to have regular servings of mince. This probably reassures her that she is cared for. Cats are accused of being indifferent, but they are not. They have many emotions, although they do not usually display them because they are dignified and have enormous self-control. We are used to Mamapuss and recognize certain emotions. For instance, she is obviously dismayed when we pack our cases to go on vacation.

"The cat is supposed to be the only domesticated animal that has not sold its body and soul to mankind. It is quite 'self-contained', and appears to thrive in human society without the slightest desire for the approval of anyone. The cat knows what it wants – and how to get it. Cats are persistent and will not be put off lightly. They are sensible and courageous. It is a creature that will take care of itself, and in normal circumstances, it is the model of hygiene, keeping clean and in top shape.

"A feline companion will mind its own business, but it will sense your need for sympathy and give it generously. If you respect it as an equal, Gold, you will find a friend. A deserted cat is brave, and it is said to revert to a wild state quicker than any other domesticated animal. Occasionally, one is kept by the semi-nomadic and settled desert people of Arabia. Such felines help the household by keeping snakes and scorpions away. They enjoy catching lizards, too, and eat them, if the reptile does not escape minus its tail.

"Nothing is known for certain about the domestic cat prior to the time of the Egyptian Pharoahs, in the second millennium BC, which is about three to four thousand years ago. In Ancient Egypt, cats were held in great esteem, and worshipped in temples. The 'tom' cat was likened to the sun, and the 'queen' represented the moon. They were loved, honoured, perfumed and given sumptuous sleeping places, with seats of honour at festivals in return for their good service. Their job was to protect the granaries from rats and mice and kill the vermin which invaded Egypt after the rising of the Nile. Figures of cats have been found, made of bronze, copper, faience, gold and precious wood, which was scarce and valuable. Cat motifs also appear on Ancient Egyptian jewellery and in sculpture and drawings.

"In death, Egyptian cats were mourned by the entire family. Both rich and poor would have their pets embalmed and placed in mummy cases. Some were sent to Bubastes, to be buried near the temple of Pasht, the Egyptian Goddess with a cat's head.

"I am sure you will be amazed to hear, that an ancient Egyptian cemetery once contained three thousand embalmed and mummified cats. They looked very much like today's Abyssinian breed. Strangely, cats are rare in Egypt today. They were so revered in ancient times that killing one was sometimes punishable by death.

"Prior to their domestication, it is believed that cats lived in a wild state in Africa. Africans today, rarely keep cats as pets but they do appreciate them. It is said that they will go hungry rather than eat one. In ancient history, the cat's popularity went from one extreme to the other. They were first cherished by several races and creeds, and their images were worn as good luck charms. In Saxony in England, Henry the Fowler imposed a fine of 60 bushels of corn for the wilful murder of an adult mouser.

"Good Hindus in India, were supposed to shelter at least one feline under each roof. Also, there were cat 'cults', or systems of religious worship. Thousands of years ago, these groups worshipped the cat as one of their gods.

"In the 5th century, at the beginning of the Middle Ages, or the Dark Ages, the cat was no longer held sacred. For the next few hundred years, it was condemned, and nothing good was said about it. Cats were accused of being 'agents of the devil', and therefore 'unclean'. People were sometimes put to death for even feeding one; and, the poor animals were killed in the cruellest ways. Old superstitions remain today, and some people still feel it is bad luck to see a black cat cross the street from left to right."

"It is a wonder they don't bear a grudge against humans, Susan."

"Yes, Gold, especially so, when you consider how much the cat has helped us. In olden times, when it was employed to destroy serpents and rats, the ancient Greeks stole Egyptian cats to save their crops from mice. Cats were also taken to Persia, in the fifth century, to do similar work. They began mousing in China about three thousand years ago; and, it was cats that saved Japan's silk industry from mice. The Japanese were so grateful at the time, they cherished this feline.

"In Europe, the people imported Egyptian cats to rid them of rats which brought the black plague and death. Then, they were exported to the New World, to save crops, killing field-mice, black rats, grey rats, squirrels and rabbits."

"Surely not rabbits, Susan. The cat is beginning to sound like 'the enemy' again."

"The domestic cat is just a small furry, carnivorous quadruped, Gold; but, the dividing line between this charming animal and its wild counterpart is not at all clear. The domesticated feline is of the same family as the tiger, lion, puma, leopard, ocelot, lynx and the wild cat.

"The Bedouin claim that the desert wildcat has bred with their domestic cats. Arabia's wildcat is an extremely shy animal that prowls at night, hunting small mammals. Its habitat is the rocky steppe regions, or treeless plains, remote wadis, and the mountains. This feline is larger and stronger than the domestic cat, with similar colours and markings to the tabby. The broad triangular ears are black tipped, its tail bushy and black-ringed.

"Arabia has a few superb cat species. The Arabian sand cat is somewhat smaller than the domestic feline, and looks just like a beautiful fluffy pussycat – provided it does not snarl. It is a rare animal, found in the arid central and eastern parts of

Caracal Cat

Arabia, where it can survive on very little water. Both shy and nocturnal, the sand cat shelters during the heat of the day in short burrows that it scoops out of the sand. It is difficult to spot as its thick coat matches its environment. Furry mats under the paws help grip the shifting sands, and insulate the pads from the burning terrain – should it venture forth in daytime. I have held a baby sand cat in the Riyadh zoo – one of the few bred in captivity. Its broad bewhiskered face was set with appealing, wide-spaced eyes. After its initial fear, when it spat and lashed out at me, it seemed to enjoy being cuddled.

"The Arabian caracal cat is a species of lynx and is about three times larger than an ordinary cat. Caracal cats are extremely handsome, and can be recognized by the long, straight tufts of hair sticking up on the points of the ears. The curve of these large tufted ears, give the appearance of horns. The name 'caracal' comes from a Turkish word that means 'black ear' – no doubt because both the ears and tail are tipped with black. The rest of the coat is a red-beige colour. The pelt is also known as a 'caracal'.

"The Bedouin call this animal KURTA, and in Arabic, it is known as ANAQ AL ARDH, meaning 'earth lynx' because it lives in the ground. Long ago, the caracal cat could be found in many parts of Arabia, but it is rare today. It is most secretive, and those still in existence, usually keep to the remotest valleys of the western mountain range, living in rocky haunts such a crevices, chasms and caves.

"A caracal cat has powerful hind-quarters which propel it high and far, enabling it to catch a bird in flight if it is not too high. This proud creature used sometimes to feast on gazelles, when they were plentiful. It would lie in wait among desert shrubs. When a breeze moved the plants, it wafted the caracal's ear tufts at the same time. Misled, the gazelle would approach. When it was close enough, the cat would leap onto the gazelle's back, thrusting its claws deep into the throat in an effort to kill it."

"Sound fierce, Susan. I don't think I would like to go into the desert as you do on Fridays."

"You would be very lucky to see any of these beautiful, big cats, Gold. There were once many cheetahs and leopards in Arabia – and lions. Now there is little doubt that the Arabian lion is extinct, because it has not been seen for a very long time. The lion was a large beige-coloured member of the cat family, and the male was best known for its tufted tail and mane around the neck.

"The cheetah is now extinct in Arabia and the leopard almost so. Sometimes guns were responsible for their deaths. Either the cats were shot, or many of the animals upon which the cats used to feed, were killed. No one knows how and when the Asiatic cheetah came to Arabia, but it was a very long time ago. Their habitats became widespread. Hopefully, some have survived in remote places. The cheetah was a hunting leopard, and desert tribesmen tamed it to help them catch antelopes. In the wild, this cat hunted gazelle on the desert steppes. Although it is the world's fastest mammal, it had little chance if shot at.

"The graceful and agile long-tailed Arabian leopard has a gorgeous pelt (or skin), so it was hunted. The pelt is almost white with dark brown and black rosette-shaped spots – much lighter in colour than those of the Asian and African leopards. The Arabian species is somewhat smaller than a lion or tiger. Leopards once prowled the wadis of the north-eastern uplands and the mountain ranges. The Bedouin call it FAHAD, and dislike it because it sometimes preys on domestic animals. This creature was hunted until it wisely retreated to inaccessible places. Just occasionally, one is sighted in areas other than its habitats – the remote regions of the west and south-west.

"The leopard becomes chiefly nocturnal if threatened, being the most wary and cunning of creatures. It is a solitary hunter, and notorious for being fierce and brave, attacking animals much larger than itself, such as baboons and antelopes. This beautiful creature cleverly stores unfinished food out of the reach of other animals. Perhaps its superior intelligence and cunning will give the Arabian leopard a greater chance of survival."

"I do hope the leopard survives, Susan, but I don't want to meet one. From now on, I promise to be satisfied with Mamapuss. No wonder she is so uppity. Who would have imagined her to have such history and connections."

"Not all domesticated cats behave as Mamapuss does, Gold. I wish you could see my friend Ruth's cats. They resemble the wild ones in many ways. There is Calico Moma, Darth Vader, Child Bride and Patch Eye; and, my friend Geraldine also has some cats in her garden that are untamed, but they are unnamed. However, she leaves food and water for these poor homeless things. The grass is very long in her garden, and the cats can be seen there stalking real and imaginary prey. To watch them is a bit like going on safari in Africa. They move with the same stealth and wariness as the big cats. Cats have evolved as instinctive hunters. This is why a well-fed pet may catch and kill a mouse, but leave it uneaten.

"When someone new is visiting Geraldine's garden, the cats are especially shy and wary; slinking off in a wide circle, without taking their eyes off the visitor. To get a better look at a human intruder, some leap lithely onto a high wall and peer down – the body taut, ready to spring away to safety if necessary. They don't leave completely, because they are constantly hungry, remaining hopeful that there might be something more to eat. Probably, these poor creatures have internal parasites, so they don't get full value from their food.

"Your 'grins' will soon be here, Gold, so let me tell you quickly about our 'cabbits'. You know that occasionally a placid 'street' cat pays us a visit and stays a while without bothering the rabbits. Well, on one occasion before you were born, a scrawny female took up residence in a part of our rabbit warren. At that time, Samantha had her garden on the opposite side of the house, and, fortunately, knew nothing

about this cat. We all laughed about the new resident and made a joke that it may have fallen in love with our big buck rabbit, the handsome and irresistible Bugs. Then, one day, the cat emerged with five dear little kittens. And, they had remarkably large ears, so it seemed natural for us to call them 'cabbits'."

Gold looked at me in disbelief. "Oh, surely not, Susan. Is it possible? Rabbits don't even have much to say to cats. They have nothing in common."

"No, Gold, it is not possible, but the kittens did have rather rabbity ears. We eventually found them good homes, and sent the mother to live a long way away because she became a rabbit killer. It was a sad surprise, when one day, she pounced on a baby rabbit and sank her teeth into its neck. Afterwards, we found four other little bodies piled up in the shed. We did not know if she was using this store as a pantry for future food, or if she was just jealous of the baby rabbits. Of course, hunting small creatures is natural, so ever since, we have not trusted the wildness that exists in feral cats."

"How dreadful! Quite right!" Gold nodded his approval vigorously. Without another word, he hopped over to Mamapuss and took a long, hard look. Then he sped off towards the other rabbits and the tray of fresh food, that had just arrived with Askalu. I wondered if Gold's thoughts about cats would last longer than it took for him to devour his first carrot.

15
Birds

old was resting on the terrace beside me, surrounded by a peaceful ring of rabbits. Mamapuss and Samantha were there, too. Their noisy swim finished, John and Christopher had just left to go horse-riding. We, who stayed behind, must have looked the perfect picture of contentment, dozing in the autumn warmth, listening to the occasional noises.

"Isn't it wonderful to hear the birds chattering?" I asked of no one in particular. I could see that Mamapuss and Samantha had heard them, too, and I knew they would spring to life in a second if any birds came into view. Gold, of course, was the only one who could answer me.

"I saw a beautiful bird this morning," he said dreamily. "I've never seen one quite like it before." Gold was clearly impressed, and the dreamy look remained in his eyes. I imagined he was painting a picture of it in his mind.

"Yes, Gold, the exotic birds have arrived. Many have flown here from far away, and some are quite extraordinary. I wonder what your bird could have been. Arabia provides food and shelter for a great variety at this time of year. There are some that are indigenous, and belong to Arabia, and others that are found in neighbouring countries, as well as on the Arabian Peninsula.

"And, Arabia is unique because it lies on two great migratory routes. One comes from western Europe, sweeping south over the Mediterranean Sea and along the Red Sea coast to East Africa. The other – from eastern Europe – passes over the Tigris and Euphrates valley to the head of the Arabian Gulf. Then, it swings through the centre of Arabia, and onward to Ethiopia and the rest of Africa."

I sketched a quick map of Arabia and used some coloured pencils to show Gold these two routes.

"Some birds end their migration in Arabia. Those that remain for varying lengths of time, enjoy the oases, waterholes, lakes, streams and sewerage ponds. And, since the discovery of oil, a great deal of money has been spent on agriculture and gardens, so the birds have even more reason to spend a vacation in Arabia. Some stay for only a few days while certain species are here for weeks.

"I wonder what your bird could have been. Perhaps it was the Little Green Bee-eater. It is one of Arabia's prettiest and most colourful birds – found almost everywhere. Maybe it was the European Bee-eater – or, the Abyssinian Roller, passing by. There are a number of very pretty birds seen in Arabia – their colours are bright greens, blues, purples, yellows and cinnamon – while some are a smart black and white. There is an eagle with a red beak and talons, a reddish back, white breast – and a purplish-black head and wings. The wings are black and white underneath; but, I doubt that your bird could have been an eagle – not in Riyadh. Eagles prefer open country or wooded mountains.

"If your bird had a long, pointed beak, and if it were a reddish-beige colour, like cinnamon – with black and white striped wings, tail and head feathers – then it was a hoopoe. The hoopoe is found almost everywhere in the cooler months. It has an extraordinary crest of feathers on its head that fold down to a point at the back. The hoopoe can fan out this crest right across the top of its head, looking as if it is wearing one of those modern hairstyles that stick straight up. The hoopoe is mentioned in the Holy Koran; and in Biblical times, is said to have been King Solomon's messenger."

"No, Susan, the bird I saw did not have funny feathers on its head – but it was very pretty."

"The pretty birds seen in Arabia are bee-eaters, hoopoes, hornbills, kingfishers, orioles, parakeets, and rollers. I must find some pictures for you to look at. There are more than 500 bird species seen in Arabia. 200 come between August and October. The return journeys happen between February and April.

"The lark is the most common Arabian bird and its various species are found in all sorts of places. The Hoopoe Lark is often seen in the most arid, waterless places. It is not related to the hoopoe, but it has similar wing markings, which are visible while in flight. There are other birds that fly far away from water, too. The Sandgrouse is one, and it must return long distances each day to drink. And, the Cream-coloured Courser travels from one place to another in a permanent search for food and water – just as the nomadic Bedouin people do.

"Arabian birds include woodpeckers, swifts, swallows, martins, game birds, cuckoos, bulbuls and babblers, but I'm sure your bird was not one of those because they have brown,

black and grey feathers. Some do have a patch of bright colour, but hardly enough to be described as 'pretty'.

"Then, there are the ravens, but they are mostly black. Arabian farmers consider these birds to be pests and shoot at them. The Brown-necked Raven is particularly partial to dates. Arabia also has pigeons, and even magpies, but it would not have been one of those ordinary-looking 'chaps'. In any case, the magpie is usually found only in southwestern Arabia – far away from here.

"The Arabian Golden Sparrow is a pretty buttercup yellow – not at all drab-coloured as sparrows usually are, but I don't think it could have been a sparrow either. This golden bird is mostly seen in the southwest, where there is forest land and wooded countryside. In these places you also find serins, sunbirds, weavers and White-eyes. They are attractive birds. Bee-eaters, bulbuls, doves and shrikes are found in the north and east, as well as here in the Central Province, but I don't think it could have been any one of these.

"Arabia's coasts and offshore islands are the habitat of the water birds. There are bitterns, cormorants, egrets, flamingoes, gulls, herons, ibis, kingfishers, plovers, shrikes, spoonbills, stilts, storks and lots more. In addition, there are geese, pelicans and swans. They favour the calm atmosphere of the Red Sea in particular, and congregate there in exceptional numbers. Impressive flocks of pink flamingoes have been described as colouring the horizon like a coral reef, risen from the sea. They pluck their food from the sea, shallows, marsh grass and shore-line habitats. But, it is not likely that your bird was one of these."

"What funny names birds have," said Gold with a giggle.

"They do. Some seen in Arabia have stranger names. What about Tristram's Grackle? And, Hammerkop; Abdim's Stork; the Arabian Tufted Guinea Fowl; the African Silverbill; the Amethyst Starling; the Shining Sunbird; the Arabian Accentor; the Rufous Bush Chat; the Lappet-faced Vulture; the Great Reed Warbler; the Arabian See-See Partridge; the Pin-tailed Sandgrouse; and the Demoiselle Crane?"

I paused and smiled at Gold, who was shaking with laughter. It encouraged me to continue: "Also, there are the Yellow Wagtail; the Little Grey Hornbill; the White-browed Coucal; the Red-eyed Dove; the White-eyed Gull; the Yellow-rumped Serin; the Golden-winged Grosbeak; the Black-capped Bulbul; the Harlequin Quail; the Grey Hypocolius: and Wryneck!" I took a long breath. Gold now laughed so hard the other rabbits were roused, and hopped away. I went on to add some birds that I had just remembered: "And we must not forget the blackstarts; bluethroats; buntings; bushrobins; dikkops; finches; linnets; nightingales; pipits; redstarts; thrushes; and wheatears!"

"Is that ALL" queried Gold, thoroughly enjoying himself. He could see that I had difficulty not to stumble. It had been a real tongue-twister.

"Oh, no, that's not all. We have left out the birds of prey: buzzards; eagles; falcons; harriers; hawks; kestrels; kites;

lammergeyers; owls; and vultures!"

I felt quite puffed out. Gold's merriment ceased and he settled down to make a serious comment:

"It must be wonderful to be so free and fly to foreign lands," he sighed. His romantic mood had returned, and did I detect a trace of envy?

"It is not all fun and games, you know, Gold. The annual migration is a tremendous achievement for those birds that reach their final destination. Following behind the smaller birds that fly from winter's cold to warmer lands, come those carnivorous birds – the powerful birds of prey."

"What do you mean 'carnivorous? Don't birds just eat insects and worms. I suppose worms are meat. . ."

"Well, no, Gold, apart from water birds and the raptors (that is the term for birds of prey) birds are basically divided into seed-eaters and insect-eaters. Seed-eaters have thick bills, or beaks, and insect-eaters have thin, pointed bills. The carnivorous birds not only eat other birds; they hunt and eat small animals, too, such as hares – and rabbits," I teased.

"Hmmm!" said Gold, as he shot me a knowing glance. He knew that there were no wild rabbits in Arabia. He looked expectantly for me to continue.

"Among the carnivorous birds, certain ones kill in order to eat, while others habitually feed off carcasses. Such birds are referred to as 'carrion-eaters'.

"The owl is a nocturnal carnivorous bird with a big head and enormous eyes, and there are several species in Arabia. They have exceptionally keen eyesight and excellent hearing.

"Owls cruise the desert at night, in search of small nocturnal creatures that are active in the cool dark hours."

"It doesn't seem fair. If they take the trouble to stay up at night, and then have owls after them," observed Gold.

"The laws of nature do seem harsh sometimes, Gold; and no creature seems to have a more difficult time of it than a small bird. A bird's life can be full of trials and danger. For some, mankind has been the worst enemy – especially since the gun was invented. And, chemicals used in agriculture have also reduced the number of birds. Before the gun, the Arabian Bedouin hunted with a bird, the trained falcon. Falconry has been the favoured sport of Arab rulers for centuries. Now, it is a popular pastime for many people. It is sad that both the raptors, and game birds that they used to hunt, have decreased in number."

"What happened to them?" queried Gold.

"They were hunted too much, Gold. For example, there are two species of bustard in Arabia – they are birds that were hunted for their meat and eggs – and are now endangered. The Great Arabian Bustard, a huge magnificent bird known as LAWWAM, is found on the TIHAMA, the coastal plain parallel to the Red Sea coast; but, Macqueen's Bustard, called HUBARA, was hunted even more. It is often called the Lesser Bustard, being smaller than the Great Arabian Bustard. The HUBARA's habitat was north and central Arabia, as well as the eastern seaboard, from Kuwait in the north, down to Muscat

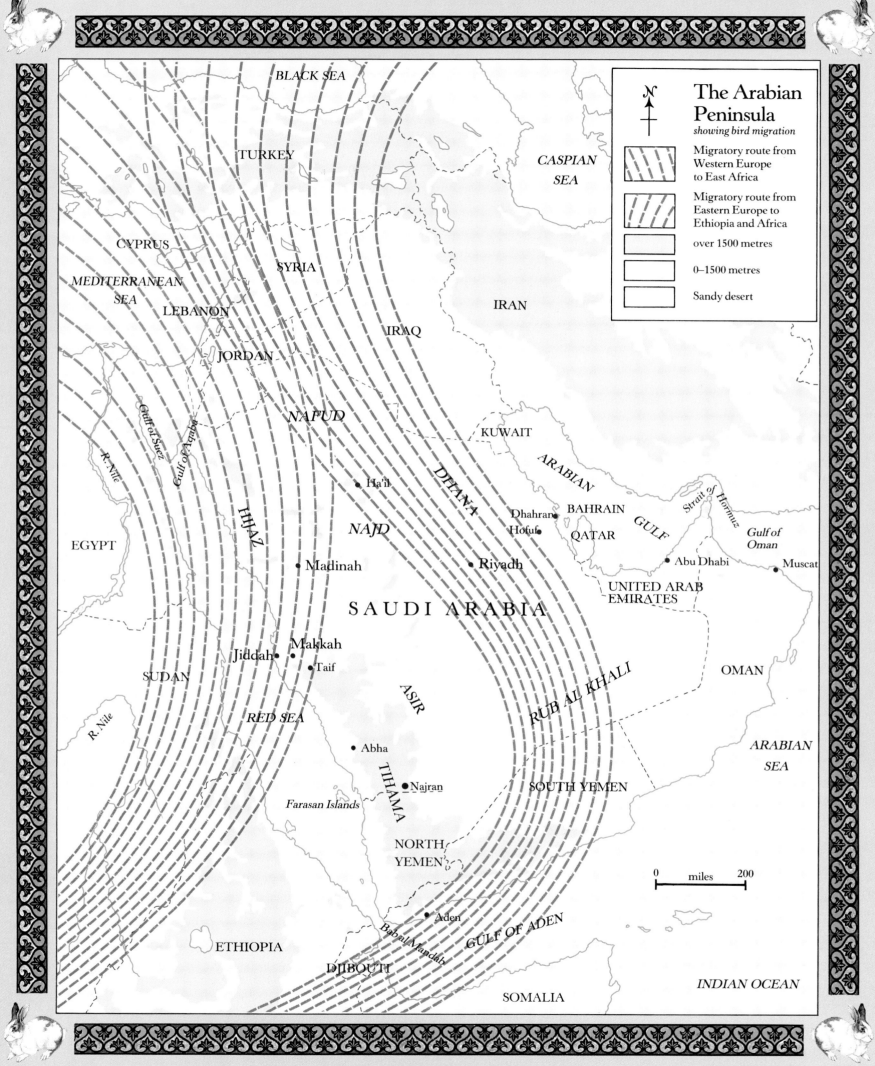

The Arabian Peninsula
showing bird migration

Migratory route from Western Europe to East Africa

Migratory route from Eastern Europe to Ethiopia and Africa

over 1500 metres

0–1500 metres

Sandy desert

BLACK SEA

CASPIAN SEA

TURKEY

CYPRUS

MEDITERRANEAN SEA

SYRIA

LEBANON

IRAQ

IRAN

JORDAN

Gulf of Suez

Gulf of Aqaba

R. Nile

NAFUD

KUWAIT

Ha'il

DHANA

NAJD

Dhahran

BAHRAIN

ARABIAN GULF

Strait of Hormuz

Hofuf

QATAR

Gulf of Oman

EGYPT

HIJAZ

Madinah

Riyadh

Abu Dhabi

Muscat

UNITED ARAB EMIRATES

SAUDI ARABIA

OMAN

Makkah

Jiddah

Taif

SUDAN

ASIR

RUB AL KHALI

RED SEA

R. Nile

Abha

TIHAMA

Najran

ARABIAN SEA

Farasan Islands

SOUTH YEMEN

NORTH YEMEN

0 miles 200

Aden

Bab al Mandab

GULF OF ADEN

ETHIOPIA

DJIBOUTI

INDIAN OCEAN

SOMALIA

in the south – and inland to Gassim.

"In the valleys near the sea, the land is covered with perennials. These plants reappear year after year, and the HUBARA like to hide in them. They frequent any undisturbed and open place where they can feed on plant shoots, grubs, beetles and other insects. HUBARA also eat small lizards and locusts. Although their natural habitat is harsh and arid, they have been known to venture onto cultivated land to feed, usually in groups."

"I imagine the HUBARA as a scared and skinny bird, Susan. Is it?"

"Oh, no, Gold. The female is about the size of a plump hen, the male slightly larger. The HUBARA is an unwieldy-looking bird – not at all elegant or 'well-designed'. It has astonishingly good camouflage, and seems to be well aware of this advantage. The feet and legs are pale creamy-grey and the bill is olive-grey. The underbody, neck and head are a mottled grey with a black cap, and the back and wings are a mottle beige with white patches on the wings. Huntsmen and falcon bearers often have eyes almost as sharp as their birds, but, unless the HUBARA moves, its camouflage is so perfect that even the falcon's keen eyes cannot see it. However, in flight, the flashes of white on the slow-beating wings make it an easy target for a falcon – even at great distances.

"The HUBARA is a strong flier, so it is strange that it usually walks. It might trot or walk for several kilometres; yet, once airborne, HUBARA can fly out of sight before landing. Sometimes, when a bustard is startled, it just lies flat on the ground with the neck outstretched, hoping not to be seen. Usually, it will crouch behind a low bush or rock, hiding as the enemy approaches. It does not come out until danger is very close by. Then it panics. Such a bird might fly out, close to the ground, settling every one or two hundred paces, in a continuous effort to escape.

"Some people have claimed that the HUBARA flies clumsily. Others tell stories of how it takes off very fast, flying straight up to a height of 17 metres (50 feet). HUBARA have been claimed to fly at 100 kilometres (60 miles per hour) an hour for five kilometres (3 miles) before being caught by a falcon. When pursued, HUBARA have been known to go up into the air, circling higher and higher, and dodging every attempt at capture. It might reach a height of just over 300 metres (1000 feet), but is usually caught if the falcon gets above it. The falcon usually wins, but the chase might last 10 or 15 minutes. If there is a strong wind, the HUBARA flies into it, often escaping because it is the heavier of the two. It can plough through the wind faster than the falcon, which has thinner wings.

"I have heard that some HUBARA sneak off low to the ground. It is also recounted that King Khaled always refused to release a hunting falcon until the HUBARA was well into the air, giving the quarry a sporting chance. But, it is doubtful that a hungry Bedouin could afford to let ANY kind of HUBARA have a chance to escape. Of course, a rider on horseback could weary it. I have been told that Bedouin tribesmen are fascinated by the HUBARA, and enjoy tales of its cunning and courage. Apparently, these birds defend themselves valiantly until the last moment of their lives.

"The Stone Curlew, known as KAIROWAN in Arabic, is hunted, too. It has similar habits to the HUBARA, and shares the same habitat. It is a timid bird, smaller than the HUBARA, and can hide very well under clusters of bushes. This bird emerges at dawn, dusk and during the night. The Bedouin say it is easy to track and catch, because it does not care to travel far, and does not fly at all well.

"Migrating birds arrive about the end of October each year, and depart in April. The hunting season begins in late November."

I could see that Gold had something that he was anxious to say, because his interest had suddenly turned to fidgets.

"So, these carnivorous birds actually help humans to catch animals. It's disgusting! They are traitors! I'm glad I'm a pet rabbit, and the worst I have to face is an ugly stray tomcat coming over the wall. I think carnivorous birds are perfectly rotten!"

I could appreciate how Gold felt, but he looked so funny when he was indignant. He sat up, with his small front paws at full length and apart, his fur all fluffed out. His ears went straight up, and there was a look in his eyes that said he would like to give a falcon a piece of his mind.

"Whatever you may feel about falcons, Gold, you have to admit that they are fantastic birds. They can dive at enormous speed, hurtling out of the sky to snatch their quarry with incredible accuracy. You may not agree with falconry, but, just think: for the Arabian Bedouin, the falcon was a valuable procurer of meat in the desert; and until the arrival of firearms at the end of the last century, the hunting bird was his only means of catching food that flew. I've told you how important poems and stories are to the Bedouin, Gold. Do you know, thousands of Arabian poems are about falconry. That's because it was vital to them."

"Hmmm. I suppose that's so. I must say falcons do sound exciting. I just hope they never come around here troubling us. I feel safe here, and, right now, the only thing bothering me is a question."

"And what's that, Gold?"

"Well, what EXACTLY do you mean by falconry?"

Gold was clever enough to know that he could now count on more of his favourite pastime. Already, he had nestled into his familiar egg-shape and fixed me with an expectant look. Where to begin. . .

"Well, Gold, falconry means keeping and training falcons for the purpose of hunting wild quarry. Hawks (which are a different species to the falcon) are also used for hunting in Arabia's neighbouring countries. Nobody knows exactly when and how falconry began, but it is believed that it started with the Central Asian nomads, about four thousand years ago. It did not enter written records until it caught the attention of

city dwellers; but since then, falconry has become the amusement of aristocrats and royalty worldwide.

"Falconry is an important part of the Arabian Peninsula tradition, and it is mentioned in the Holy Koran. To hunt with trained birds and the Arabian game dog, the SALUKI, is now considered a national Saudi Arabian sport."

"The falcon hunts with the saluki, Susan? What sort of creature is this fierce bird – the falcon?"

"It is not really fierce, Gold. In the wild, the falcon kills only to eat, just as other carnivorous creatures do. Falcons can become quite tame, although not as tame as the dog. It will however, accept humans as hunting partners, or food suppliers. Falcons are usually caring towards their own bird family. The male in the wild, will catch small birds, rats, mice and jerboas for his mate to feed to their young. These small creatures are excellent food for young falcons – much better than hares. If the male falcon is killed, the female will hunt for the food; and if the female dies, leaving the nest undefended, the male has been known to do his best to bring up the young ones alone."

"Sounds like a sissy to me!" Gold snorted. No doubt, he based his opinion on the fact that it would be unheard of for a male rabbit to behave thus.

"Do not be deceived, Gold. The falcon is a bird with a strong, firm body and huge, long, beautiful wings. It appears larger when relaxed, because the front feathers fluff out. When it is ready to fly, the falcon looks long and sleek. The shoulders are broad, and the wings powerful. They give the bird strength and speed. And, the tougher the wing and tail feathers, the faster the bird can cut through the wind. These are known as 'speed' feathers. In contrast, a falcon's chest and belly feathers are soft, to keep it from freezing in cold weather.

"In the past, there were mostly two types of falcons used in Arabia: the Peregrine and the Saker. A third kind, the Lanner, was rarely used. The peregrine is said to be the 'aristocrat' because it is more sensitive – although this quality makes it a difficult bird to cope with. Arabians prefer the saker because it is tough and practical. And, it is easier to tame. A saker will eat without being fussy, and it does not mind rough treatment. SAQR, the Arabic word used for falcon, is obviously derived from this favoured species. TAEIR is the general word for bird."

"Susan, I thought you said before that falcons catch hares, but you also said that they don't like to eat them; so why do they do it?"

"These birds attack the creatures that they are trained to hunt; even though the hare can be the falcon's most dangerous quarry, being able to deliver a powerful kick with its hind legs. The bird can also damage feathers on the hard ground during a struggle, while it rides the hare's frantic somersaults. When the Arabian Peninsula menfolk hunt hares, their falcons are sometimes assisted by a saluki. This dog can flush out the quarry, and even keep the hare on the run, tiring it until the falcon attempts to 'bind' to it, and hold it until their master arrives to take over."

Gold muttered an almost inaudible 'Meanies!' under his breath. As a rabbit, he had the right to share a hare's point of view, I suppose.

"A perfect falcon is called HURR in Arabic, meaning 'noble', 'free' or 'a bird of fine breeding'. It is the equivalent of the English word 'debonair', which comes from falconry. In French, the three words 'de bonne eyre' mean: 'from a good nest', which the English adapted to 'debonair', to describe a fine gentleman.

"True falcons are long-winged predators with a short tail and dark eyes. They live in open country, hunting by flying above their quarry and diving on it from a great height. This is called a 'stoop' attack. It can spot a bustard up to three kilometres (2 miles) away, the falcon usually attacking after a long, fast, level flight.

"At the moment of capture, the falcon forcefully digs its vice-like talons into the victim, killing it instantly with a quick bite on the neck. The powerful beak is specially shaped for this task. Then, after a short break to overcome its exhaustion, the falcon will start to pluck and eat the prey. When the falconer arrives, he cunningly removes the victim by covering it, but rewards the falcon with a small piece of its flesh."

"Eeek!" squealed Gold. "How do men get these birds to catch food for them?"

"It is not easy, for it takes great patience and a good knowledge of falcons to catch and train them. To begin with, a wild falcon is one of the most unapproachable of creatures; yet, it can be trained within a few weeks to be tolerant. Sometimes, the bird will become an affectionate companion for a devoted master. These birds often make their nests at the highest points in inaccessible gorges and difficult mountainous reaches – but, the falconer is not seeking young ones from the nest. He is looking for the youthful migrating falcons that have left the family band, having learnt how to hunt and fend for themselves. All sorts of tricks must be used to catch these clever creatures.

"It is odd that in falconry, only the females are called falcons. The male is referred to as 'tiercel' meaning 'one-third'. That's because they are approximately one-third smaller than the females. The females are not only larger, they generally have more stamina, so, traditionally, the Bedouin trained only the females. However, occasionally, a powerful male was recognized as exceptional. It was once believed that the larger birds were male, so females were given masculine names. Furthermore, when a Bedouin recounted a story about a bird of great power, size and ability, he claimed it was a male, even if he knew it to be female. In recent years, Saudi Arabians have called males MATHLÛTH, which also means one-third, or medium-sized. Smaller ones are GARMUSH. Arabs always give personal names to their birds, and teach them to respond, unlike falconers from most other cultures.

"Bedouin folklore tells us that falcons were fertilized by the

*A falcon
dressed to kill*

Suki – a short-haired
male saluki

Charlie – a long-haired
female saluki

Falcon

wind. And, it was a tribal belief that the palest-coloured falcons were best. Certain tribesmen would keep a trapped bird only if it was broad, strong and healthy – with shiny feathers. They say a good falcon must also have a defiant eye – such as you have, Gold, when Chipolatta tries to take your food . . . docility in an untrained hunting bird is not a good sign. The perfect bird should measure – from head to tip of tail – the length of a man's arm, from fingertip to elbow. The best are fabulous and quite majestic-looking. I shall find a picture of one to show you.

"When a falcon is caught, a leather hood, (known as a BURQA in Arabic) is placed over the bird's head to cover its eyes. Sometimes the eyelids were carefully stitched with fine thread instead, and kept like that for about three days. Afterwards, the bird was hooded. The darkness does not harm the eyesight at all, and it is remarkable how it calms the bird in seconds. Falcons do not like to be touched, but they will accept it after a while, just as they accept the hood. Arabian falconers usually soothe their birds with stroking, using downward sweeps of the hand. These birds seldom drink, and very few bathe. The peregrine is the exception because it loves to bathe. Even so, a desert falconer may find the need to cool his bird down, so taking a mouthful of water, will gently spray it through his lips.

"Training can take from 10 to 30 days. Apart from the bird and its BURQA, the falconer needs several pieces of equipment. He must have a DASS or KAFF (Arabic for the padded glove) which must be worn on the left hand to protect it and the wrist from the falcon's powerful talons. Some hunters prefer the MANQALAH, a padded leather sleeve; and, the bird must have a WAKR, a pedestal, shaped like a giant golfing 'tee' or drawing-pin. The bird can rest on this between flights. Short thongs, or jesses, (known as SBUQ in Arabic) are attached to the bird's legs. They connect to the MURSIL, or leash that is fastened to the pedestal. A hawking bag, the MIKHLA, holds spare items; and, hopefully, also the day's 'kill', which would be the Bedouin's supper. The MIKHLA is often thrown over the dead animal, to remove it from the falcon's view. In this way, a falconer can draw his bird away, and stop it from eating too much. The last and most vital item for training, is the TILWAH, a bundle of dried hubara wings, which the trainer uses as a 'lure'.

"A newly-captured bird is placed to rest until it is hungry. The falconer knows it will trade its natural fear of humans for food. Because he feeds the captive every time he picks it up, the bird begins to associate being handled with being fed. A falcon is very intelligent: in the wild, it must adapt quickly to any change in hunting situations in order to survive. In captivity, it sees that cooperation with humans is successful, because they provide food. Traditionally, hunting birds are housed indoors, shuttered from daylight; and, during this first period of training, the falcons are kept awake at night. From time to time, morsels of bird flesh are offered.

"At first the falcon has only to become used to humans and being handled, so, to begin, the bird is trained to come to the person's fist for food. Afterwards it is taught to hunt the lure. This is swung on a short line, held by the falconer's one hand, while the bird is flying free, trying to catch the lure. Once the falcon can do this, it can be freed to catch and eat birds which are shown to it before being released. These should be the same species as those that the falcon is expected to hunt later. After a few kills, the master and his trained bird can begin to hunt in the wild.

"When the time comes to see how well falconer and bird have done, the master speaks gently to his falcon before they set out. It is then hooded and left undisturbed, until the moment that hunting starts.

"Imagine, now, Gold, that you are a hungry Bedouin, walking with your falcon in the desert, hoping to provide your equally hungry family with food that night. You might see HUBARA tracks in the sand, so you unhood your hunter, and hold it up high on your wrist. At this time, a traditional Arabian falconer makes a loud cry, and his bird peers eagerly in all directions, bobbing its head and craning its neck. Perhaps it sees nothing. In that case, the falconer hoods his bird again, and continues to follow the tracks. The unhooding, shouting and searching are repeated until the falcon bobs its head sharply, peers intently far into the distance, and takes off in a rush, flying low with increasing speed. The quarry also 'takes off'.

"The pursuer and the pursued 'fly' as fast as they can. If the falcon happens to lose its quarry, it returns to the master's outstretched arm. Ultimately and inevitably, the terrible moment comes when the hunter flies off, and dives. It might miss, then turn and dive again. It may knock out some feathers. Then, twisting for advantage to catch its prey by the neck, and providing it is not too large, the falcon renders it lifeless. After a Bedouin's bird has been victorious, it is a tradition to give it a small piece of the victim's left breast as a reward.

"A good hunter may kill as many as six of its quarry in one day. Such falcons become valuable, and sell for enormous prices today. These fine birds have also become very expensive because they are rare. This is partly due to the nomad's lessening need to hunt with this bird, but mostly because nowadays, no one wants to release the falcons to breed at the end of the season. The result is that the number of falcons has decreased very rapidly.

"Before firearms arrived in Arabia, falcons were a necessity for the Bedouins. Even though guns proved an efficient substitute, however, falconry has continued in the Middle East because people find it to be an enjoyable sport. In olden times, although Bedouin braves hunted game primarily for the family cooking pots, there is little doubt that they, too, enjoyed working with these marvellous birds.

"In times past, at the end of the hunting season (Season: January–February) when the quarry had mostly departed, it was the custom for a Bedouin falconer to release his bird to

the sky. It could then breed in the wild and provide falcons for the future. Some Bedouin say that it is practical for them to let the birds go so they don't have to feed them during the summer when food is scarce.

"In the south west, or the ASIR region, on JEBEL SOODAH, the highest point in Saudi Arabia (3,190 metres 10,500 feet) an Englishman, Peter Whitehead, now breeds falcons in captivity. This challenging experiment, established in 1982 by Prince Khaled Al Faisal, has become a successful venture.

"The breeding season is between January and July. Six days before the eggs were due to hatch in the third year of breeding, I visited this wild place and saw Peter speaking 'falcon' with several of his birds. I was amazed to see them react to him as he had previously explained they would. Each had its own personality, building up a unique relationship with him at this Al Faisal Falcon Breeding Centre, where the falcon gets another chance to survive."

I glanced at Gold who was now dozing, and caught a glimmer of gratitude in his sleepy eyes. I was feeling like dozing myself . . .

Some days passed before I had a chance to say more than "Hello". How are you, Gold?" Then, inevitably, we found ourselves sitting together by the swimming pool. A little earlier, I had looked out of the window to see Gold and Chipolatta squabbling. The argument was not about food, so I assumed it must have had something to do with one of their lady-friends. Gold's son, Chipolatta, had grown into a fine-looking buck, whose size and temperament were becoming a threat to his father's authority. It was only a matter of time before Chipolatta won a challenge and took over some of the does in our warren. I decided not to refer to their fight, but instead, to tell Gold a little story. This would cheer him up and take his mind off the bickering.

"Do you remember, Gold, a few days ago, we were trying to decide which pretty bird you had seen on our wall? We then digressed and I told you about Arabia's most majestic bird, the falcon?"

"Yes, Susan, I wondered if you'd remember to look for the book of Arabian birds?"

"I have it, and we shall look at it. But, first, I think I should tell you a little about the Peninsula's most aristocratic bird – the Arabian Ostrich."

"Ostrich! I've heard something about the ostrich . . . but I forget what it is. Perhaps an ostrich is the bird I saw sitting on our wall last week."

"That's not possible, Gold. This bird cannot fly, and, besides, an ostrich is so huge, it would break our wall. It is the largest species of bird in the world. With its long legs and long neck, an ostrich stands over two metres (7 feet) tall. In any case, the ARABIAN Ostrich is now extinct in the wild."

"What's 'extinct' again? I forget what that means."

"It means that there are none alive any longer in the wild state. It is believed that the last Arabian Ostrich was drowned by a flash flood, or instant deluge in a gorge in southern Jordan. Jordan lies to the north of Saudi Arabia, and it is part of Greater Arabia. Sometimes, in the Arabian deserts, a year's rainfall or more, will pour down in one cloudburst, lasting a few dramatic hours. It can create a destructive torrent that sweeps away all in its path. People and animals are sometimes drowned. The dead bird was found in the debris after one such flood. Sadly, no ostrich has been sighted since."

"But, Susan, how could they just disappear from the desert? How could THAT have been the very last one?"

"Oh, Gold, it can happen all too quickly. The Arabian Ostrich (which is known as NA'AME in Arabic) was hunted for its fat and feathers – and its meat was considered delicious. The fat was used as a remedy for many diseases, and also rubbed into the skin to insulate the body against heat and cold.

"All of the ostrich was precious to humans. Even the skin sold for a lot of money. The magnificent tail and wing plumes were especially valuable. Fine ladies wore them in their hats; and, as if that wasn't enough, sometimes there was that special item on the dinner table of desert folk: ostrich eggs! Whenever they could, the Bedouin enjoyed eating ostrich eggs. Western art collectors also exhibited them on precious metal mounts, often set with semi-precious stones."

"Oh, so no eggs, no babies, eh, Susan, huh?"

"That was an important factor, Gold. Desert birds do not always have a tree in which to make a nest. Trees are rare in many parts of Arabia. They have to make do with whatever there is. This often means the eggs and babies are easily accessible to predators. The sandgrouse places its eggs near stones, hoping the greedy birds will not notice them. Crows, ravens and vultures eat birds' eggs whenever they can. The bustard lays two or three eggs in a crude nest on the ground, so these are easily taken. Some birds collect polished stones and pebbles to make their nests. This is probably a partial disguise for their eggs.

"Of course, the ostrich and its eggs are far too large for any tree – being the largest laid by any bird. Fortunately, as the hot sun does not harm these heavy-shelled eggs, trees are not required to shade them. They are laid in shallow scrapes in the ground, so are not too difficult to steal, despite the adult birds standing guard, prepared to attack a thief.

"It is claimed that the Arabian female ostrich has laid as many as 30 eggs at one time. However, at breeding time, a male sometimes collected a harem of 2–5 females, so several females may have shared a nest. It is the male who does most of the incubation, or sitting on the eggs to warm and hatch them. He is a most protective father and takes his turn guarding the eggs, too.

Ostrich

"During the day they may be left for a time, partly covered by warm sand, while the adults feed.

"Ostriches eat practically anything – even lizards. They usually pasture as camels do, though. Their natural habitat was northern Arabia, but they would go even further north in the dry season where there is more vegetation. It is a great pity if the Arabian ostrich has been lost forever."

Gold had begun fidgeting and darting looks at me. He was getting anxious about something.

"What is it, Gold?"

"I remember now, Susan. An ostrich is that silly bird which buries its head in the sand and thinks it is hiding. How could it do that if it is so big?"

"Well, to begin with, Gold, the story is not quite true. Ostriches do hold their head – and as much of their neck as possible – close to the ground when they want to hide. Naturally, this does not work in open desert areas because of their huge bodies. Furthermore, the male is a stark black and white, and can usually be seen from far off. It would be easier for the female to hide, because the hen is a drab and spotty greyish-fawn. An ostrich can run from danger at tremendous speed, in any case. There is no need for an ostrich to hide unless his enemy has a gun. This bird can deliver a powerful kick should it need to defend itself. Incidentally, each foot has only two toes.

"There are several Arabian birds that are endangered because they are good to eat – and their numbers are further diminished because their eggs are eaten, too. In the southwest, one seriously endangered species is the Arabian Tufted Guineafowl, a stoutly-built bird with bluish-grey feathers that are speckled with white. It's really odd-looking, with no feathers on its head – and, there are two bright blue flaps hanging down beneath its eyes. Can you imagine?

"This bird lays up to 14 eggs. It tends to live near human habitation where there are crops, because it likes to eat seeds, bulbs, grain, and lots of insects that can be found there. Since the increase in human population in Arabia, creating more garbage, there has been an increase in feral cats, foxes and ravens that steal the guineafowl's eggs and babies.

"Talking about eggs, let me tell you about a rare 'character' of a bird in Arabia – one of the few creatures to use a tool. It is the Egyptian Vulture, and its habitat is open country. This bird feeds on flamingo's eggs, and those of the ostrich, too, once upon a time. It cracks them by dropping rocks. Being somewhat smaller than other vultures, it stands back at mealtimes, allowing the larger species to eat first, contenting itself with the scraps that are left. It is a known scavenger, but it also eats insects.

"The adult has a pure white body, tail and wings, with a black patch on the wing bend at the front, and black feathers edging the wings at the back. The unfeathered face, the untidy ruff around its neck, and the unusually long and pointed bill, are yellow. When seen in flight, this bird also has a fairly long, wedged tail and long, pointed head which help to identify it. Vultures are notable for being scruffy-looking on the ground, and for their ability to soar to great heights, yet see for miles as they scan for food and enemies.

"The partridge is another game bird endangered through hunting. On the other hand, with the development of agriculture and water resources, some birds are increasing in numbers and even widening their original range. Among these are the lovely Namaqua Dove; the beautiful but noisy Rose-ringed Parakeet; and two species of bulbul.

"Now, Gold, let us have a look at the prettiest birds in this book." I turned to the pages I had marked, but Gold kept shaking his head and muttering: "No . . . no . . . no . . ."

Then he spotted a tiny picture on the bottom of page 93, and he was instantly up on my lap with his paws all over the pages. "There it is. There it is. Susan, that's the bird. Oh, isn't it beautiful."

"Well, yes, it is quite pretty, Gold, but I thought it would be much more colourful. It is the Woodchat Shrike. It says here: a small bird with a pale creamy front; a bright chestnut head and nape; black wings with white bars and shoulder-patches. The broad black eyestrip extends across the forehead over the bill. The tail is partially black on the underside. The book also says that it has a white rump, and this, together with the prominent wing bars and shoulder patches, make it easy to identify in flight. The Woodchat Shrike has a habit of visiting town gardens, and it likes to perch on telegraph wires more often than other shrikes." So THIS was Gold's beautiful bird! I waited while he stared silently at its picture.

"Now, Gold, would you mind if we stop here for today? I have rather a lot to do. We have dinner guests tonight."

"Oh, that's all right, Susan, but will you leave the book here? I'll make sure nobody nibbles it. There's Askalu coming with our tea 'grins', in any case. Gold hopped off happily – and with an eagerness that only food could induce. The other rabbits noticed and dashed after him. He called over his shoulder to me: "Thanks for the story, Susan – and thanks for finding my bird."

"Bye, Gold."

16
Tiny Creatures

It was the morning after a severe sand storm, and the air was still and oppressive. Fine sand covered everything, inside and out. Askalu busily dusted down the outdoor furniture and flicked sand from crevices around the windows. She is always so energetic, I mused, as I stood near the doorway, watching. Moving to sit on the terrace, I was soon surrounded by pets. We watched listlessly as she made small piles of sand to be swept into a large central heap. It was amazing to see how much the storm had delivered to us.

The end of summer had come at last and the weather was already changeable. In the centre of Arabia, the worst sandstorms are expected somewhat later, in the cooler months from October to March; but, even then, we rarely experience one so violent as this had been.

It had been unusually dark the previous morning when we arose, and there was an ominous stillness. The sky was a reddish colour. Later, someone arrived to say the airport had been closed because of an impending storm. Shortly afterwards, whipping sand began to lash and blind the land. Visibility was reduced to a few paces, and we could see our trees reacting like demented prisoners anchored to the earth. Surely some would be uprooted, I thought. Our rabbits dashed for cover and not one dared emerge from hole or house until the storm had abated. Aeroplanes, due to land, had been diverted to the Dhahran airport on the east coast.

Gold, who had never before seen the fury of a truly raging sand storm, became quite excited at first. He had made me promise to tell him about it later on. He now lay peaceably among the rabbits, cat and dog at my feet, and our eyes followed Askalu as she piled up the bright orange sand.

"Where did it all come from, Susan?" Gold's curiosity moved him to break the silence.

"It may have come from the Rub al Khali desert, Gold, – to the south of the Peninsula. You may remember, it is the largest Arabian desert, and known as the Empty Quarter because it is so barren that few humans live there – and only certain creatures. The dunes are mostly a bright coppery red, especially in some light. But the sand may be local. There are some red dunes in the Dhana desert, in central Arabia, not far outside Riyadh. Arabia has three great deserts. The third is the Nafud, located in the north."

"I think sand is comfortable and pretty. It does hurt, though, when it gets in your eye, and it is a bit of a nuisance when it ruins a whole day. I got so bored yesterday," frowned Gold. "What is sand, Susan?" he added, as a curious afterthought.

"Sand is a wonderful substance, Gold. It is made up of tiny grains of polished quartz crystals that were once part of harder rocks – particularly lava, sandstone and limestone. Askalu could be holding in her hand, all at once, grains from widely separated areas and ages. Some might be many millions of years old. As you saw, wind can be powerful – and strong wind polishes each grain, sometimes shifting it over vast distances.

"Mobile sand can seem almost fluid, and the spherical shape of the grains helps to keep it constantly flowing. Because it moves, sand dunes have drifted and revealed remains of long-gone villages, vast dried lakes with fossils, and skeletons of ancient life forms. Prehistoric relics have sometimes been delivered up to the surface, too. After storms, John, Christopher and I, have found ancient beads, and once, a rusty spearhead. They were lying on the sand, as if someone had just placed them there. These relics of bygone ages had lain buried for centuries. Yet, strangely, we did not find anything just beneath the surface when we scooped about. The sand saves its secrets for the wind to reveal, and shallow scrapes generally yield nothing – except, perhaps in certain areas where nature creates her own incredible treasures. I have shown you one – the sandrose – a beautiful crystal formation, shaped like an opening rose which forms in sand.

"On a gusty day, way out in the desert, you can see the wind lift and hurl veils of sand, falling in continuous showers from the uppermost edge of dunes. Bit by bit, in this way, the great sand mountains march slowly across the desert. On still nights, sand faithfully records the tracks and adventures of even very light creatures. A lot can be learnt about shy desert animals, Gold, without ever seeing one; especially in the early morning, when the dew still holds the sand firm. Tracks are clearly registered. The drama and drudgery of these creatures' lives, and the outcome of savage or harmless nightly encounters are unfolded in crisp outlines."

"What creatures?" Gold demanded quite loudly.

Meanwhile, he wiggled and shuffled into a more comfortable position. It seemed that a story was expected. Mamapuss lashed her tail once for some reason, and Samantha raised her doggy eyebrows sleepily, while a few rabbits startled a little. They soon settled again, and I continued:

"As barren as a desert might seem, Gold, it is actually teeming with tiny life, and each species has found ways in which to make a home."

"How could you make a home out of sand? It would all fall down and get in your eyes," Gold said in disbelief.

"Nevertheless, Gold, tiny creatures cope. Plants help a great deal. For many desert creatures, stones are also vital to survival. Many rocks support thriving micro-forests of lichen, the tiny plants that have adapted to the desert conditions. They are able to draw their nutriments directly from the minerals present in the rock, as well as from rain. In turn, these plants become food for certain creatures that live in rocky terrain.

"Even in the driest times, plants exist in areas classified as 'barren'. There are some desert shrubs, and euphorbias (hardy perennials) that are quite large. Also, there are various sparse, tough grasses, and tenacious trees such as the acacia – and juniper, too, at the higher altitudes, as in the southwest. Just like the animals that feed upon them, plants and trees are adapted in various ways in order to sustain no permanent injury from too much sun and inadequate water."

"That is very interesting, Susan, but how can the animals make homes in sand?" enquired Gold, trying to be polite but unable to mask his impatience.

"I'm coming to that, Gold. In their search for moisture, and to give them a grip on the sand, most plants have developed extensive root systems. Many have a mass of fine roots which spread out just beneath the surface. Some have roots that reach down to the lower, damper regions. For others, they extend outwards for many metres. Yet, above ground, there may be only a few stalks or tufts, or an isolated plant or shrub that is visible. It is these root systems that provide excellent foundations for all kinds of holes and burrows.

"Many desert creatures spend their daytime hours at home to avoid the glare of the hot sun. But, even without any root structure, certain tiny animals are able to make houses in the sandy desert.

"Above ground, when the sun bakes the land and the desert shimmers with heat, annual plants dry up. It is then that the perennial plants, bushes and evergreen trees become a haven for many plant bugs and insects. Some lay their eggs in sand, and their hatched larvae live there. Springtime provides a variety of desert blossoms for insects to visit, and the sweet scent of the flowers attracts all sorts of creatures for miles around.

"In winter months, sudden torrential storms or occasional rain make dormant seeds spring to life. For months afterwards, the desert remains busy with multitudes of tiny creatures that come to feed. There is a dizzy array of whirring wings and jumping things. There are lacewings, grasshoppers, praying mantids and crickets flying or hopping about. Ants scurry purposefully up and down stems, branches and trunks, seeking and bearing food for their nests; bugs explore while the bees and wasps buzz around; beautiful winged insects mate and lay eggs; and dragonflies contemplate pools, while caterpillars grow as they chomp on the fresh green leaves. Then, as the sun goes down, certain blooming evergreens open their flowers to welcome the night-flying insects."

"It sounds exhausting; not peaceful like here," commented Gold, as he stretched, yawned and settled again. "Tell me about a tiny creature that lives in the sand and can fly in the sky," he added, in a tone that was filled with doubt.

"Alright, Gold. Let me tell you about an insect: the ant-lion. There are at least 90 species of ant-lion, and many of them are indigenous, or unique to Arabia. As an adult, the ant-lion resembles a graceful dragonfly because of its long, large, lacy wings. It has four wings, folded back over the body when not in flight. Ant-lions generally fly at night, and like moths, they are attracted to lights. Their feelers, or antennae, are short with club-shaped ends. Both adults and larvae live on small insects.

"Of the ant-lion's four life stages, as egg, larva, pupa, and adult, the most fascinating is the larva – the creature sometimes called a 'doodlebug'. It lives in sand. The adult female lays her eggs near fine sand, and, once hatched, the larvae immediately build conical sand pits, and set about hunting and eating in a remarkable way. They are round-bodied creatures with large appetites. The head is small, although powerful, and armed with sickle-shaped mandibles, or jaws. An ant-lion larva is said to be as ferocious as any lion, and it traps other insects. You will be pleased to hear, Gold, it dines on ants, and it has an extremely clever way of catching them."

"Marvellous!" said Gold with glee. "How?" he asked.

"First, the larva selects a spot with loose and sandy soil in which to dig its remarkable steep-sided, funnel-shaped pit. Then, buried at the bottom, concealed by sand, the ant-lion awaits a victim. Every now and again an unwary creature topples over the edge and is unable to climb the loose sides. As it attempts to clamber out, grains of sand are dislodged and roll down, alerting the larva. With its strong head and jaws, the ant-lion bombards the unlucky insect with a stream of sand particles. They knock the prey off balance and send it sliding to the bottom, into the waiting jaws. The ant-lion then drags his victim under the sand to suck it dry of juice before hurling the remains skilfully clear of the pit."

"Yeough!" said Gold as he pulled a face.

"As the larva grows larger, it moults, or sheds its tight skin several times before becoming an immobile pupa, buried beneath the sand. The pupa is a kind of house – sometimes described as a laboratory in which the larva transforms itself into a winged adult. In time, it emerges to stretch its wings and fly in search of a mate, thus completing its life cycle.

"This creature is well-adapted to living in a dry desert. Certainly, heavy rainfall would destroy its sand-trap dwelling. And, it shares with some other Arabian insects the incredible ability to develop according to conditions. For example, when food is plentiful, the larva grows rapidly, and the insect goes from egg to adult in a month or so. In adverse conditions, it remains larval for much longer, awaiting suitable weather before proceeding to the pupal stage and onward to breed."

"That's clever" said Gold grudgingly. He had been listening carefully, probably expecting the ant-lion to be something like a very large ant. When his little fur face had been screwed up with distaste, it reminded me of yesterday, when I had heard a commotion coming from our rabbitry. I had run over to find out what was happening, and found Gold in great discomfort.

"Bleaah! Yeuouch!" spat Gold as he sat up hurriedly and repeatedly wiped his mouth with both paws, in an effort to rid himself of the tiny, clinging ants. How he hated them. Just sometimes, when he picked up his food, there would be ants concealed underneath, and they got in his mouth and clung to the fur on his face. Gold had looked so comical; but I really felt sorry for him, knowing how much he detested these tiny creatures. To make him laugh, I asked him a Bedouin riddle:

"Gold, what do you think this is?

'It devours barley and is not a camel;

it devours straw and is not an ass;

it pulls down a dwelling and is not a mouse;

it is black as night and yet is not night.'"

"I can't imagine," he said, somewhat curtly.

"It is the ant, my precious little Gold."

Gold suddenly regained his sense of humour, and we laughed at his attitude to ants.

"The riddle is about the Arabian Large Ant, called KAEJSI or SEJH AN-NAML in Arabic. Ants vary greatly in size, shape and colour, but, usually, they can be recognized as ants, with their slim segmented bodies and six long legs and long feelers. I hope it doesn't distress you, Gold, to learn that ants are more numerous than any other land animal.

"They are known as 'social' insects because they live in communities called colonies. Some colonies contain only a few dozen inhabitants, but others support several thousands. They are the world's greatest diggers and they keep busy running their underground nests. Ants scurry about during the daytime and go home at nights. Their tunnels are clean, round tubes, built to last for years, and they connect with many halls and rooms. Ants can chew wood and some live in timber nests.

"The Bedouin of Arabia recognize three varieties of ordinary ant, or NAML. They are called TAJJAR, FARSI, and DARR in Arabic. All of these ant species have three basic castes in each colony: the 'queens', 'males' and 'workers'. Most species also have a soldier caste which is usually stronger, and capable of defending the nest. Queens are much larger than the other ants and they have wings for part of their lifetime.

Males also have wings but the workers do not. Workers are the smallest, although by far, the most abundant members of the colony.

"For months on end, there may be few or no ants to be seen running about; then suddenly, they can be swarming all over the place. As you know, Gold, whatever you do, nothing seems to stop them. It is so interesting to watch them gather food: sometimes, they take it away from a much larger creature. Ants are very determined, and they can become quite fierce.

"New ant colonies are often formed when a male and queen mate. They pair during a marriage flight when the weather is suitable. Afterwards, the queen selects a place to begin a new colony. Then she tears off her wings, makes a nest, and lays eggs. From that single mating, this new queen can continue to lay fertilized eggs throughout her lifetime. She takes good care of the first hatched larvae, which eventually transform to become her worker ants. Thereafter, she lays many batches of 'worker' eggs before creating some which hatch into males and queens. There can be several queens in one nest and their families will live happily side by side."

"It's very interesting, Susan, but I would prefer a story about another animal now."

"Certainly, Gold, but I would like to add something first, which you might find interesting. Ants are said to be good fighters. They kick with their legs, and stab, cut, bite and tear with their jaws. Some ant species fight in armies, and appear to use strategy – and with great precision like the military. One famous naturalist said that while most creatures are far too sensible for warfare, ants are 'unpleasantly human' when they fight."

"Humpf!" commented Gold. "I suppose you think I am silly to get so upset about ants. But you must agree, they cause a lot of work when they attack our food. Sometimes I wonder why you keep us pets when we take up so much of your time," he added, fishing for some comforting.

"Of course I don't think you are 'silly', Gold. I don't like ants to get on me either. You can be sure, too, that it is a joy and a privilege for me to take care of you. You know, a lot of people feel as I do about animals. Many foreigners living in Arabia keep pets, in spite of the trying quarantine period that their animals must often submit to on returning to their home country. It is easy to understand that life might not seem complete or satisfying without an animal to share it – and to care for. For this reason, many people take in a stray, or take over an unwanted pet. My friends, Ruth and Jim, saved several animals from a sad fate.

"Some ex-patriates bring their pets with them. My friend, Malin, brought two giant poodles, Black Jack and Poker, from London. These enormous and comical characters delighted in their desert runs, bounding effortlessly out-of-sight whenever they were released. Poker, who was a rich milk-chocolate-brown colour, was remarkably compassionate, as well as intelligent. One day, he tore out a telephone and

"We look alike, we think alike, we eat alike . . ."

*"All the tomcats
find me irresistable"*

"I spy an intruder . . ."

"Let's discuss this man to man"

161

smashed it to pieces after seeing Malin weeping because of an upsetting call. Black Jack was very protective. He once lunged and almost knocked me to the floor when I raised my hand to greet his mistress. He thought I meant her harm.

"Animals can be purchased from pet shops in Arabia, Gold, and many Arabs enjoy keeping a variety of exotic creatures. Beautiful private gardens become homes for peacocks and other animals. A neighbouring princess keeps a gazelle, and one Saudi Army officer began a zoo with Bactrian camels, Caracal cats, lions and wolves. My friend, Betty, likes unusual pets. She kept two dhabbs called Donald and Dudley, and a pair of hedgehogs called Henrietta and Humphrey. One of their four babies was named 'Houdini' because he would regularly disappear and reappear without anyone discovering how he did it. He was named after the famous human 'escape' artist – no bonds could hold him.

"Betty also kept foxes and various 'creepy-crawlies'. She habitually searched the desert for anything that moved, and usually brought some creature home. One was Sammy the scorpion, and she kept him in a terrarium on the living-room coffee table. Sammy's favourite food was the large variety of cockroach that we call 'golden delicious' because they are plump, and a rich, shiny golden-brown colour, resembling ripe dates. I was not fond of Sammy."

"Why not, Susan? You love animals," said Gold, puzzled.

"The scorpion is one desert creature that casts fear into most minds, because of its venomous and painful sting.

However, this is its defence, to be used when cornered – and for hunting.

"Fortunately, this tiny creature can be recognized easily by its pincer-like pedipalps, or claws, and a tail that is usually held high and curved over its back. The claws are either very large or finely-pointed. They are for seizing and holding prey, and for digging. The tail is carried poised to strike, the scorpion flicking it further over its back to deliver the sting's needle-like point. It is many times finer than a doctor's hypodermic, the injected venom subduing the scorpion's prey. The pedipalps hold the victim, and the jointed jaws outside its mouth tear and chew, while the juices are sucked inside. Scorpions can survive on the liquid in their food, and can go without eating for months. This is not an insect like the ant-lion and ant, but a relative of spiders, and therefore it is classified as an Arachnid.

"Many birds and animals ignore the scorpion because of its sting, whereas the baboon has learnt to break off and discard the tail before eating the body."

"I hope I never meet a scorpion," Gold sounded equally frightened and fascinated.

"I don't think you will, Gold. Scorpions are nocturnal and lead secret, solitary lives. They are rarely seen moving about and often burrow to escape the heat.

Scorpion

"Hunting is normally done in the late evening and at night. Scorpions live in holes and beneath rocks, squeezing themselves into very narrow hiding places, to lie in wait for insects and small lizards.

"When hunting, this creature may even approach a camp fire so it is unwise for campers to sleep on the ground. And, shoes should be shaken out in the morning, in case a scorpion is resting inside. Occasionally, they do venture forth in daytime, so it is never wise to walk barefoot in the desert. And, naturally, care should be taken when turning over stones and other objects."

"Scorpions won't come into our garden, will they, Susan?" Gold asked, looking up at me anxiously with eyes that now widened with fear.

"I haven't seen a scorpion in years, Gold. They avoid humans as a rule. But, now and again we did have one in our garden when Riyadh was less developed. Once, we caught a blackish one. There are many species of scorpion in Arabia, their colours ranging from black to an almost transparent pale-yellow. The yellowish *Leiurus quinquestria* is considered the most dangerous, and small children and babies can die from its sting. The young tan-coloured species has a comparatively mild sting.

"Healthy people usually survive being stung, but children, and adults weakened by illness, are at great risk. Some animals are said to be immune to scorpion venom. And, human death from its sting is rare, partly because one that has been hunting, does not usually have a full dose of venom to inject. It takes time for it to build up a new supply after wounding prey. In any case, to be fatal, the sting would have to be injected at a point on the human body where the circulation of blood is fast, such as close to a large vein or main artery.

"Once, when Christopher was small, we found a little scorpion sleeping in his jacket which had been lying on the ground. The smallest are just over one centimetre (2/5th of an inch) long when fully-grown, and the largest in Arabia are about 10 centimetres (4 inches) from tip to end of tail.

"It is unwise to toy with these creatures because they are extremely agile. Despite a clumsy appearance, they can move speedily on four pairs of legs to escape an enemy or catch prey. The famed agility can be seen when performing their courting dance. The male grasps the female by the pedipalps; and then, their claws locked, they dance intricately and with great precision for hours before mating. The male eventually deposits his sperm in a shallow scrape in the earth. He then draws the female over it to fertilize her eggs. A big surprise awaits a female scorpion's lover after mating – when she grabs and devours him. Just sometimes, he is quick enough to escape."

"What a mean thing to do!" exclaimed Gold, glancing up with an indignant frown.

"That's how it seems, Gold. Such gratitude, after a romantic evening, and having been taken out dancing, too; but experts say that the mother scorpion needs a good protein-rich meal in order to produce healthy babies. In any case, it is one sure way to get the father involved in the children's welfare."

Gold snickered but said nothing. I continued:

"Shortly thereafter, the eggs hatch. This often occurs within the mother's body, and at intervals over a period of weeks, tiny scorpions emerge, a few at a time. The mother carries her babies around on her back, feeding and protecting them for about ten to twenty days, until they can hunt for themselves."

"Then she is a good mother." Gold said grudgingly.

"We should have some respect for the scorpion, as one of the oldest land animals. It is an ancient creature, and sometimes called a 'living fossil', because it has existed for more than 300 million years in almost the same form. Just as a very old human has seen the invention of the motor car, the aeroplane, and the spaceship within one lifetime, the scorpion's ancestors witnessed the arrival of the earliest small dinosaur, its growing to be gigantic, and its ultimate disappearance from the earth. Being tiny, does not mean a creature is less important or uninteresting.

"As you know, Gold, vertebrates are those animals which have a true backbone, such as fish, amphibians, reptiles, birds and mammals, and, they form a group that includes humans. Besides these creatures, and the invertebrates you already know about, there are millions of fascinating tiny creatures that inhabit our world. The ant-lion, ant, and the scorpion are just three of many that live in Arabia."

"Will you tell me about some of the others, Susan?" asked Gold, but his tone suggested he was only half convinced that they could be interesting.

"With pleasure, Gold. Let me tell you about some other Arthropods. They are the invertebrates with segmented bodies, a hard supporting external skeleton, and limbs with many joints. Arthropods include insects and spiders – and the scorpion. They form the largest group of all living creatures. Insects are the only flying Arthropods, but they are the largest class in this group, comprising about three-quarters of all known creatures."

"The ant-lion is an insect, isn't it, Susan?"

"Yes, Gold, and ants, bees, and wasps are other examples. The body of an insect has three main segments: the head, thorax, and abdomen. The thorax of an adult insect has two or three pairs of legs and one or two pairs of wings; although, a few species are wingless. Insects hatch from eggs into worm-like grubs or adult-like immature creatures. They then undergo the transformation known as metamorphosis before becoming adults.

"Ants, bees, and wasps – and termites – are the 'social' insects, living in colonies founded by a single female, known as the 'queen'; and, she lays all the eggs. Termites (sometimes called 'white ants') are as much as 250 million years old, and notable for being very destructive to timber.

"The unattractive earwig is a scavenging relative of the

termite. This tiny creature has large rear pincers which are strong. They can be raised threateningly if the animal is alarmed. Earwigs eat other insects, but despite their formidable appearance, they are harmless. And, the female is a devoted mother.

"Arabia has beetles as well, inhabiting all kinds of terrain. They are insects, too, but their fore-wings have evolved to become horny covers. They can fly, albeit rather clumsily. After completing metamorphosis, beetles have hard backs of various colours and shapes, the legs of each species varying in length. The black gum-drop beetles have rippled backs and very long legs. They eat plants. The female of the large, metallic-looking boring beetles lay their eggs on trees, the larvae boring deep into the wood.

"Pretty ladybird beetles (sometimes called ladybugs) are not always the familiar red and black. They can be yellow, orange and brown, too, with spots that differ in number. Some species have spots that merge to become stripes. Although most ladybirds do not eat vegetation, they have excellent appetites, and are popular because they feed on plant-eating insects. It can be a big surprise to come across large groups of ladybirds hibernating in winter.

"The domino beetle is black with 12 white spots on its back, as you might expect. It eats ants. The stainer bug beetle is bright red, black and white, and can be spotted easily when it is eating a farmer's crop. Herbivorous beetles with huge appetites can be formidable pests because they breed rapidly and lay a large number of eggs.

"One of the most fascinating beetles in Arabia is the ungainly, but sturdily-built black scarab. It was revered as a symbol of eternal life by the ancient Egyptians. In drab contrast, it is usually called the dung beetle today, because of its habit of making balls from animal dung which it feeds upon. The scarab scurries along backwards, using the hind legs to roll the ball. The female lays its eggs in little tunnels in the ground and leaving a ball of dung nearby for the larvae to eat."

"Do beetles live in sand?" queried Gold, screwing up his eyes, with that endearing puzzled expression he sometimes wears.

"Beetles are especially adapted for burrowing, Gold, and some have flat brushes of bristle on their legs to help them move about in sand and construct a home in all sorts of soil. It is not uncommon to see a beetle far out in the desert, lumbering by or bustling uphill. Just keep watching and eventually you will see it disappear down the neat round hole that is home.

"Arthropods have been called the 'master architects' of the Animal World because they build astonishing homes from a vast array of materials. Widely varying designs are constructed with sand, silk, mud, paper, wax and wood. Some species even manufacture the materials they use, such as silk and wax.

"Insects need a secure home, especially in times of drought, when the pupae might have to lie dormant for quite a while in the state of 'aestivation'. This is similar to hibernation. Many can remain thus, until conditions are suitable for them to proceed and transform into adults and breed. Their homes must be well-disguised to keep them safe from hungry birds and lizards, and also from Arthropod predators such as beetles, ladybirds, mantids, spiders, robber flies and wasps. Some of these do not kill the victim, but lay their eggs on it. Their larvae feed upon the live creature, and eventually cause its death.

"As adults, insects need camouflage to help them avoid detection. They often blend perfectly with their surroundings. Arabia's bush crickets (also known as long-horned grasshoppers and katydids) are generally common among lush vegetation within their range. They can be bright green. Those that live on small shrubs and bushes found on stony hillsides and in rocky gullies, blend with bark or foliage. They can fly and jump but prefer to walk.

"Some insects play tricks like dropping into leaves and twigs, where they remain perfectly still to appear as part of the pile. Slow-moving stick-insects are especially good at this disguise. Many stick-insects are wingless, which helps them to resemble twigs. This disguise is also helped by their habitual immobility – as if hypnotically tranced. They are ravenous plant-eaters. Another defence is advertising. Poisonous arthropods usually display bright colours that say: BEWARE! The ladybird is brightly-coloured to advertise its bad taste and it emits an unpleasant odour to discourage predators.

"Many Arabian Arthropods breed throughout the year, while others hibernate in the cold months. Some migrate to other parts of the world. Certain rare species are unique to Arabia, and new ones are still being discovered on the Peninsula, to be introduced to the wider World of Science.

"Wherever there is vegetation, Gold, you will find insects feeding upon it, and carnivorous Arthropods and other creatures feeding upon them. As you might expect, the greatest variety in Arabia is found in the mountainous regions of the southwest, where the higher rainfall creates more suitable habitats."

"Susan, if you don't like the scorpion, and farmers don't like insects, and I don't like ants, is there any tiny creature that none of us like?" Gold sat up, and delivered his long question very seriously. With his head turned and on one side, one ear erect and the other flopped over, Gold regarded me carefully with his gold eye. I could not see his blue eye, but it was a challenging stare. I contemplated the light shining through the little hole in his right ear, as I thought for a moment.

"The fly and the mosquito are two unpopular insects, Gold. Nevertheless, they are remarkable creatures in their way. They both fly with only one set of their wings, because the second pair of wing-like protrusions work only as sense-of-balance organs. Mosquitoes, and certain species of fly, can pass on disease to vertebrates when feeding off their blood. Flies can spread disease by carrying germs to wherever they

land, after feeding or laying eggs in dirty places. Yet, many of their species are important to the ecological chain because they assist in the disposal of carrion, dung and rotting materials.

"Flies and mosquitoes have many enemies. Humans, for a start, wish to control them, because some species cause extensive damage to root crops, and others are parasites, and a hazard to sheep, cattle and horses. In the Animal World, their enemies are in the air, on the land, and in the water.

"The mosquito is a tiny, slender, dainty-looking creature with narrow wings and long legs. The female has string-like antennae, and on the male, they are feathered. Females bite but the males do not. The proboscis, or long tubular mouth, is sharp as a needle in the female, and draws up blood and juice, which sometimes transfers disease from one victim to another. It is interesting that the female Common Mosquito requires a meal of blood before she can lay fertile eggs. Mosquitoes are usually found wherever there is water that contains a high proportion of organic matter upon which their larvae can feed. In Arabia, they often lay their eggs inside desert coolers – a type of air-conditioner where a shallow pool collects in the bottom tray.

"The male mosquito dies after mating, and the female lays her floating eggs in water, where the larvae live and feed for about a week – if they are not devoured by frogs, fish, birds or some other predator. Mosquito larvae are extremely active, wriggling and coming to the surface regularly to breathe. When their metamorphosis is complete, the adult flies off to seek a mate.

"As for the fly, Gold, there are several different species in Arabia. They often lay their eggs in decaying matter or animal droppings, because their larvae can feed there. Fly eggs hatch quickly, and the larvae (commonly called maggots) grow to full-size within weeks, in the right conditions. Then, after the pupal stage, the winged adults mate, and the female lays hundreds of eggs in several batches. In very cold weather, flies seek secluded places to hibernate, but, otherwise, they breed all year round. Their populations can be controlled to some extent by depriving them of breeding places.

"Flies have a short, sucking proboscis with a sponge-like organ at the end of it, to extract juice from food. If the food is too dry, the fly sends a drop of regurgitated fluid down the proboscis to moisten it, and then sucks up the result."

"Yeouch!" winced Gold, and he shuddered delicately, sending a ripple down his fur.

"Humans and animals also have reason to dislike ticks because they spread disease, too. 'Tick' is a common name for several kinds of insect that infest hair and fur. Such creatures have a stiff proboscis, known as a rostrum. It acts like a syringe to pierce the skin of the host animal to withdraw liquids. They attach themselves to skin as temporary blood sucking parasites.

"Lice are just as irritating. A louse is a tiny, pale, wingless insect with a tough, leathery skin, short legs, and tiny antennae. The legs have claws which permit it to retain a firm grip on the hairs of the victim. There are lice that bite, and lice that suck blood from birds and mammals. The mouth of the sucking louse is adapted to pierce, and can be retracted into the body when not in use.

"Another wingless parasite, with short antennae, is the flea, and it bites. Fleas have specially designed legs for rapid movement and powerful jumping. This tiny creature can jump 100 times the length of its own body. However, its reputation is far greater than its ability. In 17th century Europe, the flea caused the deaths of 30 million people, by transmitting the dreaded plague from rats to humans. I must say, Gold, I have always been pleasantly surprised not to find a flea on any of our pets in Arabia, although I know that some of our friends' pets have been infested from time to time, due to contact with a host animal.

"It makes me uncomfortable just to think about them." Gold said, as he wriggled in distaste.

"Talking about jumping, Gold, let me tell you about the herbivorous grasshopper. They have three pairs of legs and the hind pair are very strong. Aided by these greatly-enlarged hindlegs, a grasshopper can leap suddenly and powerfully. It goes farther than any other insect. The leaps can measure well over half a metre (20 inches), which is almost forty times its body length. This creature also crawls by means of the two other pairs of legs – but slowly. Grasshoppers are mainly ground-living insects, generally coloured greenish or brownish.

"Grasshoppers have shorter antennae than their cousins, the bush-crickets. Both have leathery forewings, which serve as coverings for the flight-organ hindwings – although, Gold, not all grasshoppers fly. Stridulation is another of their talents. It is the ability to make 'music' with the aid of a row of evenly-spaced, minute pegs resembling a file on the largest joint of the hindlegs. These are rubbed over the prominent veins or ribs of the forewings. The males lend more volume to their 'singing', and each species has its own 'song'.

"The desert locust is one of several species of grasshopper, notable for the formation of migrating swarms that have devastated arable regions. They sometimes occur in western Saudi Arabia and northern Oman. Becoming over-crowded, this type of grasshopper will suddenly change behaviour and become migratory. When this situation arises, these little creatures darken in colour and alter shape within a few brief generations. The wings become longer and stronger in readiness for day-long flights to wherever there is adequate vegetation. Farmers fear the sight of the approaching cloud that they recognize as a plague of locusts. Meanwhile, humans plot to rid the earth of this scourge.

"Moist conditions are necessary to hatch locust eggs and allow the larvae to develop. The eggs can lie dormant for many decades, or hatch in 10–14 days in suitable conditions. A new generation of locusts can be ready to breed in two months, each female laying over four hundred eggs within her lifetime. She lays them deep in the sand, sealing the hole with

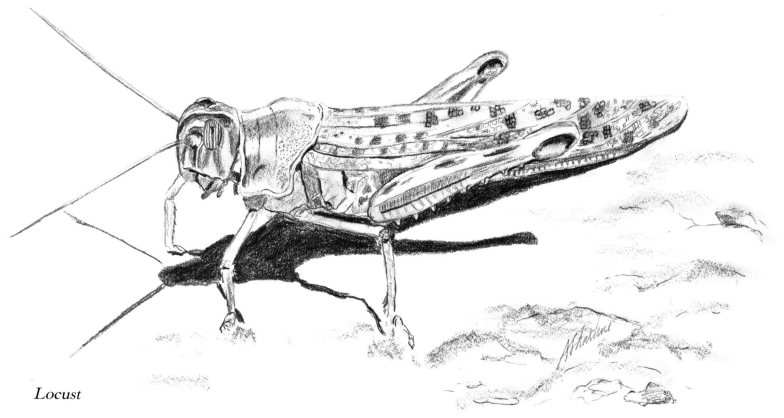

Locust

a secreted foamy substance which surrounds and protects the eggs, later becoming a pathway for the hatchlings.

"These grasshoppers are voracious eaters. When numerous, food becomes scarce, and this creates a need for them to change their usual solitary, hoppy habits. At such times, they band together and migrate in search of food.

"As locusts grow larger, they moult from time to time as their skin tightens. Flightless, immature locusts are called 'hoppers'. Their wings form in the last two moults. In the final moult, they emerge as mature adults that can take to the air. In flight, they resemble a great column that spreads out, blocking the sun from view. Like a black cloud, they cruise along at an airspeed of between 15–20 kilometres an hour (10–12 mph) for as much as twenty hours or more.

"In plague proportions like this, the wings of the locusts grow longer and stronger, enabling them to travel for distances up to 4,800 kilometres (3,000 miles) over several weeks – including stops to eat along the way. The hoard noisily wipes out all vegetation in its path, advancing upon green places and leaving behind brown stubble.

"The only chance mankind has of combatting these pests, protecting crops, and maintaining nature, is to attack them before they become adults. In Saudi Arabia, where locusts have been known to breed before migrating to attack other lands, there is an active anti-locust programme. It is a problem that must be shared, because, it is said: if locusts, forming a swarm of only two square miles, were to breed successfully, they could cause a severe infestation of the entire earth's 196 million square mile surface within just four generations. Fortunately, there are many natural hazards

facing the locust: wind that fails to carry the adults to a suitable breeding area; soil not moist enough to hatch the eggs; insufficient food or plant growth to protect hatchlings from heat and sun; predators; and disease.

"In complete contrast, locusts are welcomed by the nomad who calls them GERAD. The Bedouin consider these creatures a great delicacy. Locusts are either cooked and eaten immediately – or ground up, after roasting and drying in the sun, for storing away to add flavour and nutrition to future meals.

"The praying mantis looks a bit like a thin grasshopper, but it is totally carnivorous. And, although most species of mantises can fly, they rarely go far. They are extremely slow moving on the ground, so they depend on their camouflage and the ability to remain perfectly still to avoid detection by birds, lizards and wasps. Their name is said to come from the pious stance: you may have seen them sitting motionless on four hindlegs with the forelegs raised, together, as if in prayer. Yet, it could also be derived from the fact that they are poised this way in order to 'prey', the mantis waiting in this position for an insect to come within reach. It can then be swiftly seized and held with the jagged-edged forelegs that snap shut like a closing penknife."

"Eeeek!" screeched Gold. "How big are they?"

"Don't worry, Gold. They are only about thirteen centimetres long (5 inches). The only one who should be concerned is the male mantis, because it is the female's habit to gnaw off his head and munch up his body during the act of mating."

"Good grief! Don't you think insects are barbaric, Susan?

Do you mind if I hop off and grab some 'grins' before we continue? I can hear Askalu coming around the corner with our tray."

"Not at all, Gold. I'll make myself a cup of tea, and we can meet back here in fifteen minutes. John is collecting Christopher from school, and they are going directly to horse-riding, so we can continue then. I want to tell you about the cockroach; another of your 'unfavourite' creatures. It is interesting, and it happens to be related to Mantids and stick-insects."

Before going inside, I spent a moment watching Gold spring to life, and dash with the other rabbits to where Askalu had left the tray of salad. I never ceased to marvel at a rabbit's appetite – no locust could do better.

I had been longer than the planned fifteen minutes, and when I returned to the terrace, Gold was already waiting, nestled in his familiar 'egg-shape', with ears laid back and front paws placed neatly in front.

"Well, there, Gold, ready for 'cockroaches'?" I asked with a laugh. Cockroaches occasionally approached his food, and he disliked them almost as much as ants.

"Perhaps they are interesting," he said, grudgingly, not wanting to miss the opportunity of hearing the story. "I do like to hear about these creatures. I just don't like them touching me."

"You are not alone in finding cockroaches unpleasant, Gold. Yet, in the wild, they are useful. They clean up by eating waste and decaying vegetation, where their various patterned colours serve as camouflage. But, the domestic varieties (which can be as much as five centimetres long (1½ inches) can become a kitchen nightmare. And they are very difficult to get rid of. Fossils tell us that the cockroach has existed for 300 million years, so I suppose they are here to stay. Most of their species are nocturnal and omnivorous and this has contributed to their success. Cochroaches are naturally denizens of warm climates, and have spread throughout the world by inhabiting artificially warm places such as kitchens. These pests scavenge food and will eat almost anything. By day, they hide away, and their flattened bodies allow them to creep into cracks and crevices.

"Compared with most insects, cockroaches breed slowly and lay few eggs. These are laid in a purse called an 'oothecae' which some females carry about with them. Otherwise, it is left in a crack or crevice. One species of cockroach lays 16 eggs, which take 2–3 months to hatch into wingless copies of the adult. These larvae moult, or shed their skin as much as 6–12 times within one year before becoming a fully-grown, winged adult. Most species have two pairs of wings. The front, leathery pair are folded flat over the body when not in use. Although they can fly, cockroaches usually depart very quickly by running.

"Now, centipedes and millipedes are incredible-looking Arthropods. They dwell in gardens among stones and in the earth. Both are long creatures with many-segmented bodies and lots of pairs of legs. Centipedes have one pair to each segment, and millipedes have two pairs on most segments. The total number of legs varies according to their species. As you can probably imagine, centipedes can run with remarkable speed and agility, and they are active predators, feeding on other Arthropods and small lizards which they subdue with venom. Their bite is painful for a human, but the mouth is not the cause. Centipede venom is inflicted by the front pair of legs, which are modified hollow fangs connected to special glands.

"Baby centipedes and millipedes hatch from eggs. The young do not have as many legs as an adult, bu develop more each time they moult. Millipedes are shy creatures that dislike the light, and they behave differently to centipedes, if disturbed. They do not run, but push powerfully into earth or vegetation until they are out of sight. Millipedes are mainly herbivorous, and not all species are venomous. Like centipedes, THEY often fall victim to birds and reptiles.

"The earwig is another tiny creature that is found in Arabian gardens. Despite its fierce appearance, it is timid and harmless. The strong pair of curved pincers at its end can be raised threateningly, however, and it resembles the scorpion. It is nocturnal and feeds on small insects, plant material, carrion and fungi. The females are known to be good mothers.

"I think it is time for another riddle, Gold. Are you ready? This is an Arabian Bedouin riddle about a POPULAR insect. Can you guess what it is?

'It feeds in the waterless region;
no man tastes its flesh;
but its offspring is eaten by every passer-by.'"

"Let me see . . .," said Gold, putting his little head on one side, and staring at nothing. "It must be the larva of something," he added thoughtfully, after some moments.

"That's clever, Gold, but it's not right. It is the honey bee. In Arabic, it is called NAHAL. The bee is liked, although the female can sting if it becomes angry or afraid. It is a pity if a honey bee stings, because it will die afterwards. The sting is barbed, and in pulling away from the victim, this tiny creature tears its own body fatally.

"Many species of bees inhabit the rocky regions of Arabia, but the honey bee can be found throughout the Peninsula.

"Some are 'solitary' or living independently and others are 'social', and inhabit a hive which they construct to house one female queen, female workers, and male drones.

"You cannot help noticing a honey bee, Gold. It is bigger than most insects, and it stands out because it never seems to stop buzzing or working.

"I do believe they thought
the refrigerator was purring"

"My sleeping
partners"

"Don't you think I'm beautiful?"

"I like to
sit here for
a little while
every night"

Potted cat

"Are there any rabbits in there?"

"Bees are great 'talkers'. A scientist named Karl von Frisch, studied bee language and spent years translating. He says bees give each other lots of information and good advice. They are good listeners, too, and when a bee 'scout' returns to announce its findings for the day's harvest, the colony listens attentively. Apparently they 'dance' as they talk, and convey the exact location of their discovery.

"Some farmers in Arabia keep bees, not only for their honey, but also to pollinate their crops. Pollen is needed to fertilize female flowers, so that a seed will form to reproduce its species. Wind carries pollen, but plants, shrubs and trees that bloom cannot always depend on the wind. They need the help of insects, and bees are especially good at transporting pollen. Of course, the bee needs nectar and pollen as food for the hive's inhabitants. Flowers for this tiny creature, are like bright posters outside a store. Once inside, the bee can suck up nectar through its tube-shaped mouth, or proboscis, sipping from the deep well in the heart of the flower. When a bee first enters, it capers about, splashing and rolling around, so sticky pollen clings to its hairy face, body and legs. After a while, the bee cleans itself up and stashes away the pollen.

"A bee is built to carry huge cargoes, and has lots of storage space, plus astonishing lifting power. It can lift almost its own body weight. It is an incredible flier, equipped with high-speed, short, wide wings that can weave a figure-eight motion of several variations. They can propel it straight up, forward, back, down, or hold in neutral for hovering. And, they fold in an instant for a sleek dive into the depths of a narrow flower, or a tight-fitting cell back home in the hive. A row of hooks link the wings for flying. These can be unhooked to fan the inside of the hive to make it cooler.

"The bee packs pollen (and sometimes varnish scraped from sticky vegetation) in the two baskets, one on each hind leg. The varnish is used to fill cracks and crevices in the hive. Nectar is carried in a tank inside the bee's body. Water can also be stored to take home when the colony is thirsty. Roving bees are kept especially busy, making visits to several flowers to gather just one load. At home, the workers manufacture the nectar into honey – that delicious and nutritious product enjoyed by many animals, as well as humans. When a hive or nest is discovered inside a hollow tree, there is almost always somebody trying to rob it despite the risk of being stung by its irate occupants.

"Wasps are similar and live in much the same fashion, although their mud and 'chewed-up wood mash' dwellings are often beneath ground. But the main difference between bees and wasps is their diet. Bees prefer nectar and pollen where wasps generally feed on other insects. Female wasps, most bees, and certain ant species, have an egg-laying organ, or ovipositor, modified into a sting and connected to a venom sac. Wasps can be aggressive, Gold, and their sting is painful, with no known antidote. Fortunately, they usually attack only when annoyed, or if their nest is approached. Apart from enjoying to banquet on fruit, tree sap and nectar, wasps suck the juice out of their arthropod victims. So, it seems strange that they permit certain tiny flies and moths to enter their nests and lay eggs; except, perhaps the wasps appreciate them as housemaids, as these insects are scavengers that clean up."

"Wasps are not as nice as bees, are they, Susan?"

"It is true that most people do fear the wasp, but hold an affection for the bee. Although their life patterns are similar, they are not identical. The queen honey bee and her attendant workers survive winter by living on food stored in the cells of their hives; whereas, in the case of other social insects, such as bumble bees and wasps, only the newly-fertilized queen survives the onset of winter. She hibernates until spring, when she searches for suitable nesting quarters. Having started the nest, she lays the first eggs. When they hatch, she feeds the larvae. Then, when they develop into workers, the queen can spend the rest of the summer laying many more eggs secure in the knowledge that they will be tended by these workers.

"Soon after the young honey bees are able to feed themselves from the pantry of honey and pollen, they can build and repair cells in the hive with their newly-developed wax glands. Then, they begin taking short flights outside the hive. Young bees also have indoor tasks such as cleaning and tidying, and converting nectar into honey – and storing it away with pollen that they take from returning worker bees. When three weeks old, THEY are ready to bring home nectar, pollen, water and resin.

"A worker bee's life is so hard that it dies within two to three weeks. To keep pace with this continual loss, the queen must keep laying. But, when she feels there are sufficient workers, the queen produces 'male' eggs which hatch into idle 'drones'. Drones have nothing to do, other than fertilize females when the queen lays 'fertile female' eggs. These are for founding new colonies as only one queen is tolerated in each hive. If it should occur, the two queens fight to the death or divide the colony. When this happens, one queen leaves with her followers in search of a new site. Such a congregation of bees is called a swarm. By mid-summer, a hive may contain 50 thousand workers and few hundred drones. The queen rules by exuding a special substance from her body, which controls the behaviour of the colony,"

"I wish I could do that," Gold said, under his breath – no doubt thinking about controlling (with this wonderful substance) some of the rascally young rabbits in the warren.

"Many other Arabian insects use their sense of smell and sight to find nectar, too. Nectar is a clever device plants have to lure creatures, so they can be cross-pollinated and produce seeds. Certain Arabian plants have stinking flowers and depend on the fly to help them. Other desert plants open sticky flowers only at night, giving off their enticing sweet scent to attract the night fliers. Both the butterfly and the moth have an excellent sense of smell to help them find food or a mate. Their antennae are receptive to touch, smell and perhaps noise."

"Butterfly?" queried Gold, in surprise. "Do they eat butter?"

"No, Gold, butterflies feed on the nectar of flowers."

"Do they bite or sting?" he asked cautiously.

"No, Gold. Butterflies are gentle creatures – elegant and beautiful. They are like lovely flowers, and they make the world a prettier place."

"Good! I'd like to hear about a gentle insect for a change," approved Gold.

"You know Gold, the first insects, that existed in the earliest times, were very small and wingless. Some wingless ones still exist today, with a way-of-life for which wings are not needed, or where they may even be a disadvantage. Butterflies rank among the more advanced winged insects. Despite butterflies and moths being delicate-looking insects they have survived for more than 50 million years, so they are remarkably successful. Some of their species migrate for thousands of miles, and this confirms that they are strong.

"These creatures have four wings, and the front wings are the large ones. They are covered with coloured scales whose formation resembles slates on a roof. To the naked eye, these scales just look like pretty dust. In other flying insects the colours are inside the wing membrane.

"The proboscis of most butterflies and moths is coiled, and it can be unrolled to suck up liquid food which is often nectar and water. The difference between the butterfly and moth is usually apparent because butterflies fly by day, and in bright sunshine, as a rule. Yet a few do fly in the evening and some moth species are active during the day, although usually nocturnal.

"Closer observation will show that a butterfly sleeps and rests with its wings folded over the back. Moths hold their wings flat against the surface upon which they are resting, or tuck them around the abdomen. The Arabian Orange Flat is an exception. This butterfly's wings are held flat when resting. Butterflies also have long feelers, or antennae, with knobs on the end while moths have antennae with various ends, thinner towards the tip. Both have the usual six legs of the insect, but the front pair are sometimes very small and not obvious.

"The butterfly is not only pretty, Gold, it is important to the world of science, just as you are. Torben Larsen, a noted authority on butterflies (and especially Arabian ones) writes that they are useful in many aspects of scientific research, among which is the study of insect 'intelligence', and in an understanding of chemical warfare. By studying the butterfly, scientists have made some important discoveries that have helped mankind and the environment. They have helped, too, in producing some of the best-documented studies of evolution.

"Butterflies carry out important work all by themselves, too, by cross-pollinating flowering plants, shrubs and trees, as bees do. Butterfly larvae do eat plants, although rarely are they as seriously destructive as certain kinds of moth. The Small Cabbage White Butterfly is an exception, and it can make a pest of itself in gardens, sometimes destroying crops.

"Nearly all butterfly larvae feed on plants and grasses. Arabia's exceptions are some of the Blues, Coppers, and Hairstreaks, which are carnivorous, feeding on ant eggs, grubs and pupae. Arabia's Leopard Butterfly is suspected of feeding only on ants. Those butterflies that do not migrate from the desert in summer, can feast from wild daisies and lilies. The pretty yellow flowers of the acacia tree provide nectar in June, and the Sodom Apple shrub produces its purple blooms in August.

"The desert is never long without flowers of some kind. Soon after rain, the annual flowering plants quickly bloom and produce seeds, before they can be dried out by summer's scorching heat. Even as the heat increases, there might be late flowers found among the rocks and stones of slopes and plains. They may also appear on the sandy floor of wadis – the dry river beds where the silty sand sometimes covers damp soil.

"There are about 150 species of butterfly recorded so far in Arabia, and it is believed that more await discovery. Some are exclusively Arabian, as a result of the land being situated at a unique bio-geographical crossroad, and within a zone where plants and animals have been isolated long enough to develop differently."

"I've seen a butterfly," Gold boasted. His tone suggested he enjoyed the reflected glory, just as Christopher did when he returned from school to tell us that he had seen the King pass by.

"I'm sure you must have done so at some time, Gold. There are so many in Arabia. The variety of both butterflies and moths is enormous. They exist in a wide range of sizes and colours. Yet, people in some other parts of the world are surprised to learn that such delicate-looking creatures exist here at all. They do not expect them to cope with Arabia's extreme and harsh climate and barren places. Of course, butterflies and moths do very well in the highlands where the higher rainfall provides plenty of foliage. The astonishing part, is that they are also seen in the most arid regions, and even the great Rub al Khali desert. They survive through their peculiar ability to postpone metamorphosis until conditions are suitable for breeding. This immobile state of aestivation may last as long as six years in some species.

"Butterflies and moths have four distinct stages in their life cycle: ovum (egg), larva (caterpillar), pupa (crysalis), and imagio (adult). The most important function of the adult is to mate and for the female to lay eggs. The adult female can lay a couple of hundred, and sometimes a thousand eggs. The large number is necessary for survival of a species, because so many eggs and larvae get eaten by predators.

"It is amazing, Gold, that the female butterfly selects only the most, suitable specimen of plant upon which to lay eggs. And it must be only a healthy one. She knows her hungry caterpillars must feed there. She therefore inspects the plants very carefully, using sense organs of smell and taste located in the legs and antennae. The Arabian Swallowtails lay a single

egg in one place. Some species leave only a few to each plant, whereas others lay their tiny eggs in neat clusters of 20 to 50, or in untidy clumps. Most butterflies carefully glue each egg to the leaf with a secretion from a special gland.

"The egg stage is brief. The caterpillar emerges after four to ten days, varying from species to species, and subject to weather conditions. Caterpillars can be many shapes and colours, and some are very pretty with stripes, spots, hairs or spines. They are crawling creatures that obtain their nourishment by eating enormous quantities of foliage with their powerful jaws. They begin by eating their own egg shells.

"The larva has been described as an 'eating machine' and, while feeding, it expands until it must moult. This process of shedding the old, tight skin occurs five or six times before the caterpillar is fully grown. Some desert species develop from egg to pupa in less than a week, but it may take as much as a month in adverse conditions when the quantity and quality of food, and the temperature are not suitable. The nourishment consumed by the larva sustains it through the pupal stage, and sometimes as an adult. It is remarkable that many adult butterflies do not take time to feed, although, those that do, appear to live longer.

"The body of a caterpillar is made up of a head plus thirteen body segments, the first three having a pair of true legs which serve as hands when feeding. The remaining ten segments have five pairs of false legs or pro-legs with tiny hooked fringes which assist them to move about. The last segment has a pair of claspers for holding on. Some moth larvae have only two pairs of pro-legs."

"Incredible!" whispered Gold.

"Caterpillars have a special organ at the mouth, the spinneret, which spins silken threads made of a substance secreted from a special gland. The silk is used to make a secure platform at moulting time, and a safety girdle, leaf-case or cocoon to live in as a pupa. Some species will even escape a predator by departing swiftly on a silken strand."

"Amazing!" Gold whispered.

"Once it is fully grown, the larva becomes a crysalis, or pupa. Certain species spin a complete cocoon for this stage. It is from this hardened shell, or crysalis, that the adult butterfly or moth emerges after about ten to sixteen days, hanging itself out to dry before flying. Some adult females do not fly, and depend on the caterpillar crawling to new places and spreading their species.

"Many butterflies are not only capable of flying vast distances, they cross seas, mountains and continents. Others can make only short flights. For certain species, migration is an essential part of their life-cycle and survival strategies. In many parts of Arabia, one-third of the butterfly population departs when conditions seem impossible, and in the most arid places, more than half the species migrate to greener pastures. There are Arabia: the African Caper White; the African Emigrant; the Bath White; the Blue Pansy; the

Caper White; the Clouded Yellow; the Leopard Fritillary; the Painted Lady; the Pea Blue; the Plain Tiger; and the Salmon Arab."

"Oooo, they do have marvellous names," said Gold, shivering his little fur coat and squirming in appreciation.

"There are sixteen species that undertake long-distance flying, only now and again. They are the African Babul Blue; the African Clouded Yellow; the African Joker; the Blue Spotted Arab; the Common Zebra White; the Desert Babul Blue; the Diadem; the Giant Eggfly; the Grass Yellow; the Lime Butterfly; the Millet Skipper; the Pale Clouded Yellow; the Pomegranate Playboy; the Small Cabbage White; the Small Salmon Arab; and the Yellow Pansy."

"I do like their names, Susan. Are there any more?"

"There are lots more, Gold. The twelve species that do migrate but not often and not far, are: the African Lime Butterfly; the Brown Playboy; the Encedon Acraea; the Eponina Acraea; the Golden Arab; the Leaden Ciliate Blue; the Lesser Millet Skipper; the Mediterranean Skipper; the Olive Swift; the Small Copper; the Small Grass Yellow; and the Tiny Orange Tip.

"Of all the butterfly species represented in Arabia, the swallowtail is perhaps the largest and most beautiful. It is named for the tails that are often present on the hind wings. The swallowtail is fast and powerful in flight. And while most butterflies sit quite still to sip nectar, the swallowtail normally hovers with quivering wings. It is a very beautiful creature with wings of yellow or deeper tones patterned with black, and a band of blue spots on the hind ones. There are four Arabian species but only two have tails.

"Arora's Ciliate Blue and Pittaway's Giant Cupid are amongst the few species of butterflies exclusive to Arabia, being the only members of their kind found anywhere in the world. My friend, Tony Pittaway, an entomologist and co-author of a fascinating book about eastern Arabian insects, was first to discover the Giant Cupid. He had just emerged from having lunch at an hotel in Taif, on the western side of Arabia. Enjoying the refreshing mountain air, he stopped to observe some flowers by a stone wall, when an unknown butterfly landed there. Tony, who rarely goes anywhere without his net, captured it. Later, he was able to discover its host plant and learn of its lifecycle. Named after its discoverer, Pittaway's Giant Cupid is brown, enhanced with a bluish sheen.

"I could go on describing their gorgeous colours endlessly, Gold. I will show you pictures later, and we can watch out for them from now on. Often, the rear wings have spectacular eye-like markings which serve as a warning to predators, since the bright colours are usually an indication that the butterfly is poisonous. It is remarkable that the poison digested from plants by the larva, still exists in the adult. I am told, there is sufficient poison in the Plain Tiger Butterfly to kill a small rabbit."

"Just when I was beginning to think butterflies were

harmless." Gold puffed in exasperation. "Perhaps moths are better."

"Not all moths are plain creatures, as many people think, which means: they may not be all that good to eat, either. I think the Oleander Hawkmoth is very pretty. With its three greens and two beiges and white markings it looks as though it has been cut out of 'camouflage' cloth. Hawkmoths are known for their wonderful colours, and for being strong fliers that migrate long distances. The African Crimson Speckled Footman, seen in central Arabia at various times of the year, is a day-flier with attractive colours. It has been described as one of the most beautiful moths in the world.

"Dragonflies are pretty, too, and resemble the butterfly and moth in many ways, although they are a less-advanced winged insect. They have chewing mouthparts like the ant-lion, ant, termite, earwig, beetles, crickets, stick-insects, grasshoppers, mantids, cockroach, bee and wasp, while the butterfly, moth, fly, mosquito, bugs, lice, and fleas have sucking mouthparts."

"Why is it called a 'dragon'? Does it behave like a dragon?"

"Dragonflies may have been named after their very large ancestors that lived around 300 million years ago, or it may be just because they are carnivorous, Gold. They are day-fliers, and prey on butterflies as well as 'mankind's best enemy': the mosquito. Some species are most aggressive hunters. They are among the fastest fliers of all insects.

"The dragonfly larva has a modified, folding lower-lip that can be flicked out to hook its underwater prey. Dragonflies

are one of those unusual species of insect whose larvae (sometimes referred to as 'nymphs') are aquatic, breathing through gills like fish. This stage lasts from 1–4 years and there is no pupal stage. When it is ready to become an adult, the larva climbs out of the water and begins to breathe the air. Very slowly, a beautiful lacey-winged adult breaks out of the unattractive larval casing. The wings do not have scales.

"Dragonflies are often found in the desert far from the water in which the female must place her fertilized eggs. They are strong fliers, though, and many species migrate vast distances between oases and other sources of water. I am sure you will be happy to know, Gold, dragonflies have no sting and, they have few enemies. But let me tell you about some tiny creatures that will give you a good bite."

"I am not sure I want to know about any more 'bitey' creepy-crawlies, Susan, unless they are VERY interesting. . . ." Gold's voice trailed off, as he did not want to miss out on the story.

"Oh, these ones are very interesting indeed, Gold. They are Arachnida, another class of Arthropoda, which includes scorpions, spiders, and mites. While insects have six legs, Arachnids have eight. Furthermore, they are wingless and have no antennae. Let me tell you about the spiders and similar tiny creatures.

"Most true spiders spin a web of silk in which they catch their prey. Some do not spin, and hunt on the ground instead. Certain related species with similar habits are often called 'spiders'. One such creature is Arabia's 'camel spider',

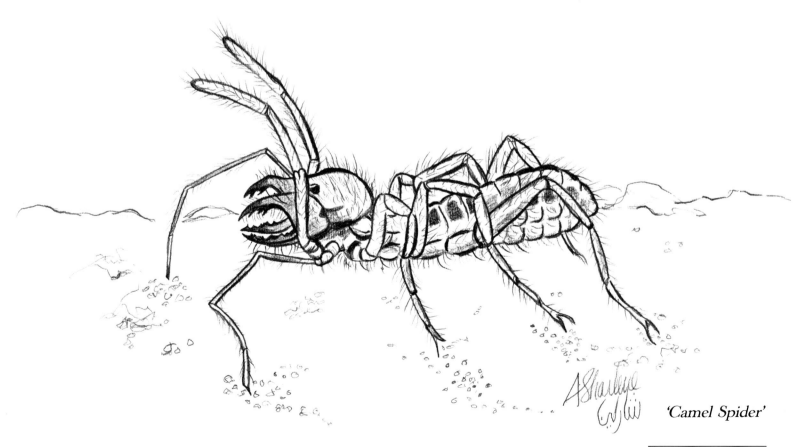

'Camel Spider'

sometimes referred to as the 'sun spider'. In Arabic, it is called SHEBETH. Although an Arachnid, it belongs to a separate order, known as Solifugid, meaning 'run from the sun' – apparently, because it is nocturnal. By day, it hides under rocks or in sandy burrows.

"The 'camel spider', or Solifugid, is aggressive, and will eat its own kind as well as spiders and small lizards. Sometimes, it can win a battle with the scorpion. It is normal for the female to try to devour her mate after mating.

"The stomach of the Solifugid is elastic, stretching to cope with huge meals, and to carry eggs in the case of the female. She digs a burrow in which to lay about 200 eggs. When hatched, she feeds and cares for her young until they can hunt for themselves."

"Have you noticed, Susan, lots of tiny creature females are 'man-eaters'; yet they are awfully good mothers. It's peculiar," Gold added thoughtfully.

"It is one of Nature's stranger ways, Gold, but there is probably a good reason. It could be that the mother benefits from a special meal. Certainly, she does not have to worry about having an unfaithful mate. Spiders usually have eight eyes, and the 'camel spider' has two or more – but she cannot be watching him all the time, can she?

"The spinneret of silk-spinning true spiders is at the end of their abdomen. Their venom is injected from openings at the tip of their claw-like fangs. All true spiders are venomous, and venom is used to subdue and digest prey. Some species wrap up the victim in silk before eating it. The 'camel spider' has no poison or sting; yet, it is dreaded by the Bedouin, for it

enters their tents, and children have died from its bite. The danger seems to result from the bacteria around the 'camel spider's' hairy mouth, and the deepness of its bite.

"Compared to true spiders, the 'camel spider' is very large, very hairy, and has enormous jaws in relation to its size. These huge and powerful jaws can tear up prey, while the juice is sucked out until only the bones or shell remain. The female of the species is larger than the male, and the biggest can measure about 15 centimetres (six inches) including pedipalps and legs. The pedipalps or pair of feelers resembling extra legs at the front of the creature, are held up high when running around searching for prey. The sensory hairs on the pedipalps are an aid to hunting, the suckers on the tips helping to hold a captive, and assist when climbing smooth surfaces."

"Eeek," shrieked Gold. "Are there any 'camel spiders' around here, Susan?"

"Oh no, Gold; they are mostly in the open desert where their colours blend with the terrain. It is yet another creature that survives the year round in Arabia's arid places. There are quite a few true spiders in Arabia, too, and some are new to science. But, most are rare in the arid regions."

"I won't even ask, Susan, if that means there are spiders around here. I don't want to know."

"Alright, Gold, I won't tell you; except, I will say that Askalu can be seen quite often swiping down their webs."

For once, Gold was speechless. As he pondered my remark while casting nervous glances at his surroundings, I left him with a wink and a smile.

Epilogue

My story of Precious Gold, the talking rabbit in Saudi Arabia, has come to an end. I hope you will think fondly of Gold. He is a fellow creature that has shared our daily life for many years, and he has become very precious to us. We admire him tremendously. Whatever has befallen Gold, he has remained cheerful and confident when others might have become mean and miserable; and, we have enjoyed his needing us. Everyone likes to be needed, and pets fulfil one of the most important roles in the world, in allowing humans to take care of them.

Since Gold became a celebrity, we have tried to shield him from stress and fatigue, and this has often meant that we have found ourselves exhausted at the end of the day. Yet, we still feel it has been a privilege to know and care for him. We believe that humans must accept total responsibility for their animals. Keeping a pet is a very serious commitment not to be undertaken lightly. It should be made for the entire lifespan of the animal, whether the pet is special (as Gold is) or one that is quite unremarkable.

Gold is a most important animal in the World of Science because he can talk. Many offers still come to us with promises of luxury for Gold – and for us – but we have turned them down. Rabbits are not as robust as most animals,

living very short lives compared to humans, or, say, a tortoise, an elephant, a whale or a dolphin. Domesticated rabbits are middle-aged around four years, and at nine years, they are old. After that age, they may suffer from mental deterioration (a state that is commonly known as senility). Soon, it will be very important for us to take especially good care of Gold.

If Gold had a longer lifespan, we may have permitted scientists to work with him more; but, as it is, he is far too precious for us to allow it. He is happy living with us and does not wish to change his lifestyle. Moreover, we are not prepared to take chances with his happiness and the rest of his short life.

It has been a wonderful experience preparing this book to share Precious Gold with you, but it is time for us to part. From now on, Gold will live a rabbit's normal existence in our Arabian garden. Don't you think it marvellous that he is the Chief High Buck of our warren at last?

Best wishes
from
Susan, John and Christopher Blake.

Bibliography

ALI, ABDULLA YUSUF (English translator). *The Holy Koran* Kutab Khana Ishaat-ul-Islam Delhi, (1979).

ALLEN, MARK. *Falconry in Arabia.* Orbis Publishing Ltd., London, 1980.

BASSON, P.W., BURCHARD, J.E., HARDY, J.T., AND PRICE, A.R.G. *Biotopes of the Western Arabian Gulf: Marine Life and Environments of Saudi Arabia.* Aramco, Dhahran, Saudi Arabia, 1977.

BEMERT, GUNNAR AND ORMOND, RUPERT. *Red Sea Coral Reefs.* Kegan Paul International Ltd., London, 1981.

BLUNT, ANNE. *Pilgrimage to Nejd.* John Murray, London, 1881.

BOURLIÈRE, FRANÇOIS. *The Natural History of Mammals.* Alfred A. Knopf, New York, 1954.

BREASTED, JAMES HENRY. *A History of the Ancient Egyptians.* John Murray, London, 1935.

BRITISH HORSE SOCIETY AND THE PONY CLUB. *The Manual of Horsemanship.* The British Horse Society 1972.

BURTON, MAURICE AND ROBERT *Encyclopaedia of the Animal Kingdom.* Octopus Books Ltd, London, 1977.

BURTON, MAURICE AND ROBERT (editors). *Wildlife Encyclopaedia, Funk & Wagnalls'.* Vol. 15 pp 1846, 1848, 1979/1970 Funk & Wagnalls, New York.

COLLIE, KEITH AND PESCE, ANGELO. *Spirit of the Wind – the horse in Saudi Arabia.* Immel Publishing, London, 1982.

CRANDALL, LEE S. *Management of Wild Mammals in Captivity.* pp 202–206. 1964 University of Chicago Press, Chicago.

DICKSON, H.R.P. *The Arab of the Desert.* George Allen and Unwin Ltd., London, 1951.

GREEN, FRANCES AND KEECH, RICHARD. *The Coral Seas of Muscat.* Middle East Economic Digest Ltd., London, 1986.

HARRISON, DAVID L. *The Journal of Oman Studies, Scientific Results of the Oman Flora and Fauna Survey, 1975, Special Report.* Ministry of Information and Culture, Sultanate of Oman, Muscat.

HARRISON, DAVID L. *The Journal of Oman Studies, Scientific Results of the Oman Flora and Fauna Survey, 1975, Special Report No. 2.* Ministry of Information and Culture, Sultanate of Oman, Muscat.

HARRISON, DAVID L. *The Mammals of Arabia.* Ernest Benn Ltd., London, Vol. I, 1964, Vol. II, 1968, Vol. III, 1972.

HASS, HANS. *Under the Red Sea.* Jarrolds Publishers (London) Ltd., London, 1952.

HIGGINS, ANDREW J. *Arabian Camel – Exciting scope for improvement.* Arab World Agribusiness, 1985.

HIGGINS, ANDREW J. (editor). *The Camel in Health and Disease.* Baillière Tindall, London, 1986.

HVASS, HANS. *Reptiles and Amphibians.* Blandford Press Ltd., London, 1975.

KATAKURA, MOTOKO. *Bedouin Village.* University of Tokyo Press, Tokyo, 1977.

KAY, SHIRLEY. *The Bedouin.* David and Charles, London, 1978.

KUMMER, H. *Social Organization of Hamadryas Baboons – A Field Study, Bibliotheca primatologica 6:1–189.* (S. Karger, Basle) and University of Chicago Press, Chicago, 1968.

KUMMER, H., GOETZ, W., AND ANGST, W. *Triadic Differentation: An Inhibitory Process Protecting Pair Bonds in Baboons Behaviour 49: 62–87.* Brill, Leiden, 1974.

KUMMER, H., JAY, Ph. (editor). *Two Variations in the Social Organization of Baboons 293–312 in: Primates: Studies in Adaptation and Variability.* Holt, Rinehart and Winston, New York, 1968.

LAMBERT, MARK. *Prehistoric Life – Encyclopedia.* Rand McNally of Company, Chicago, New York, San Francisco, 1985.

LARSEN, TORBEN B. *Butterflies of Oman.* Bartholomew Books, London, 1980.

LARSEN, TORBEN B. *Butterflies of Saudi Arabia and its neighbours.* Stacey International, London, 1984.

LOCKLEY, R.M. *The Private Life of the Rabbit.* Corgi Books, Transworld Publishers Ltd., London, 1954.

MANDAVILLE, J. JNR. *Wild Flowers of Northern Oman.* Bartholomew Books, London, 1978.

MILES S.B. *The Countries and Tribes of the Persian Gulf – 2 vols.* Harrison and Sons, London, 1919.

MORRIS, PAT. *Hedgehogs.* Whittet Books Ltd., Surrey, England, 1984.

MUSIL, ALOIS. *The Manners and Customs of The Rwalla Bedouins.* American Geographical Society, Oriental Explorations and Studies No. 6, 1928.

PESCE, ANGELO AND PESCE, ALVIRA GARBATO. *The Camel in Saudi Arabia – Marvel of the Desert.* Immel Publishing, Jeddah, 1984.

PITTAWAY, A.R. *Lepidoptera: Rhopalocera of Western Saudi Arabia. Reprint from Fauna of Saudi Arabia, Vol. 7.* Pro Entomologia, Natural History Museum, Basle, Switzerland, 1985.

PLATT, RUTHERFORD, AND THE STAFF OF WALT DISNEY STUDIO. *Worlds of Nature.* Golden Press, New York, 1974.

POND, GRACE. *The Observer's Book of Cats.* Frederick Warne & Co., Ltd., London, New York, 1959.

PRINCE, ANDREW R.G. *The Important of the Fraser Island Region to Dugongs (Paper).* Zoology Department, James Cook University, Townsville, Australia, 1976.

RHODES, FRANK H.T. *Fossils – A Guide to Prehistoric Life.* Golden Press, New York, 1962.

SCOTT, PETER (FOREWORD) BÜTTIKER, WILHELM (INTRODUCTION). *The Wildlife of Arabia.* Stacey International, London, 1981.

SHARABATI, DOREEN. *Saudi Arabian Seashells.* VBI Publishing, Weert, The Netherlands, 1981.

SHARABATI, DOREEN. *Red Sea Shells.* Kegan Paul International, London, 1984.

SILSBY, JILL. *Inland Birds of Saudi Arabia.* Immel Publishing, London, 1980.

STEPHEN, DAVID (editor). *Encyclopedia of Animals.* Collins, Glasgow, London, 1973.

SUMMERHAYS, REGINALD S. *The Arabian Horse.* A. S. Barnes and Company, New York, 1972.

SUTTON, CATHERINE G. *The Observer's Book of Dogs.* Frederick Warne & Co., Ltd., London, New York, 1945.

SVENDSEN, ELISABETH. *Down Among the Donkeys.* Pan Books Ltd., London, Sydney, 1981.

THESIGER, WILFRED. *Arabian Sands.* Dutton, New York, 1959.

THOMAS, BERTRAM. *Arabia Felix.* Jonathan Cape, London, Toronto, 1932.

TOWNSEND, F.W. AND OTHERS. *On some Deep Sea Fishes (Article) Bombay Natural History Society Journal. Vol. XIV.* G.A. Boulanger, 1901.

TURNER, DENNIS C. AND BATESON, PATRICK (editors). *The Domestic Cat: the Biology of its Behaviour.* Cambridge University Press, Cambridge, England, 1988.

TURNER, DENNIS C. *Das Sind Katzen: Informationen Für Eine Verständnissvolle Partnerschaft.* Albert Müller Verlag, Rüschlikon-Zürich (Müller Rüschlikon), 1989.

VINCETT, BETTY A. LIPSCOMBE. *Wild Flowers of Central Saudi Arabia.* Nebbiuno (Novara) Italy, 1977.

VINCETT, BETTY A. LIPSCOMBE. *Animal Life in Saudi Arabia.* Nebbiuno (Novara) Italy. 1982.

VINCETT, BETTY A. LIPSCOMBE. *Golden Days in the Desert – Wild Flowers of Saudi Arabia.* Immel Publishing, London, 1984.

VINE, PETER. *The Red Sea.* Immel Publishing, London, 1985.

VINE, PETER. *Pearls in Arabian Waters.* Immel Publishing, London, 1986.

VINE, PETER. *Red Sea Invertebrates.* Immel Publishing, London, 1986.

VINE, PETER AND SCHMID, HAGEN. *Red Sea Explorers.* Immel Publishing, London, 1987.

WALKER, D.H. AND PITTAWAY, A.R. *Insects of Eastern Arabia.* Macmillan Publishers, London, 1987.

WAR OFFICE, VETERINARY DEPARTMENT. *Animal Management. Chapter 2: The Points of the horse, colours, markings, and age.* HMSO, London, 1956.

WENTWORTH, LADY. *The Authentic Arabian Horse.* George Allen and Unwin, London, 3rd edition. 1980.

WHITFIELD, PHILIP (editor). *Macmillan Illustrated Animal Encyclopedia.* Macmillan Publishing Company, New York, 1984.

WITTMER, h.c.W., BÜTTIKER, W. AND KRUPP F. *Fauna of Saudi Arabia Volumes 1–9.* Pro Entomologia, Natural History Museum, Basle, Switzerland, 1979–1988.

ZEUNER, FREDERICK E. *A History of Domesticated Animals.* Harper and Row New York and Evanston, 1963.

Index